TOOL STEEL SIMPLIFIED

REVISED EDITION

The Carpenter Steel Company, Reading, Pa.

TOOL STEEL
SIMPLIFIED

*A handbook of modern practice for
the man who makes tools*

BY

FRANK R. PALMER
President

and

GEORGE V. LUERSSEN
Vice President
THE CARPENTER STEEL COMPANY

REVISED EDITION

Published by
THE CARPENTER STEEL COMPANY
READING, PENNSYLVANIA

ATLANTA	DAYTON	NEW YORK
BRIDGEPORT	DETROIT	PHILADELPHIA
BUFFALO	HARTFORD	PROVIDENCE
CHICAGO	HOUSTON	SAN FRANCISCO
CINCINNATI	INDIANAPOLIS	ST. LOUIS
CLEVELAND	LOS ANGELES	SYRACUSE
	MILWAUKEE	

1948

ACKNOWLEDGMENT

The authors desire to express their appreciation and gratitude to the many builders of equipment through whose courtesy illustrations of their products have been used; to the editors of *Steel* for photographs of steel mill equipment; to the American Society for Metals for extensive quotations from their publications; and finally, to the members of the Metallurgical Staff of The Carpenter Steel Company for their many technical contributions.

READING, PA.,
February, 1948.

PREFACE TO THE SECOND EDITION

Presentation of this revised edition of "Tool Steel Simplified" provides an occasion on which we might well take "stock account" of the past performance of this book, and possibly forecast something of its possibilities for the future.

The decade since the book first appeared embraces a period of advancement in the manufacture and heat treatment of tools without precedent in our history. The pressure of war has made necessary more and better tools than were previously thought possible. The greater latitude required in tool design has imposed tremendous burdens on the tool maker, the tool hardener and the tool steel manufacturer as well. In the accomplishment of many hitherto impossible jobs there have appeared new and improved types of heat treating equipment, new and improved steels, and new and improved methods. Such conditions provided the best possible test of the practicability of the Matched Set Method first published in these pages ten years ago. The tide of progress in tool design, tool making and treating, and in steel making, has been so swift and strong, that any method not based on firm foundations certainly must have been swept into oblivion.

Actual experience, however, has demonstrated the ability of the Matched Set Method to more than meet this test. The Matched Set Method was so sensible, so usable and so practical that it proved actually to be one of the forces motivating our vast improvement in tool technique. In fact the method has been so practicable that not only has it become firmly fixed as a dependable implement in the hands of the tool maker, but it has pointed out avenues of improvement in the steels themselves. The first statement is attested to by the fact that the demand for "Tool Steel Simplified" was quite heavy during the war, not only in tool rooms, but in schools throughout the country engaged in training tool designers, tool makers and heat treaters. The second is attested to by the fact that two improved steels have been introduced in the Red-Hard Matched Set, and a complete

Air-Hardening Set has been added and described in this Second Edition. The Matched Set Method was never intended to be static and fixed. Like the tools it mothers, it is itself a tool, subject to resharpening, and, if necessary, realignment to meet the new needs of industry. In its improved form, we hope it will continue to fulfill this responsibility.

Throughout the present book, many additions will be found beyond those just mentioned. The newer conceptions of hardenability are discussed in Chapter 4. Chapters 10, 11 and 12 have been revised and enlarged to cover the latest advances in heat treating equipment, heat treating methods and testing. In Part IV, the latest hardenability tests have been added to Chapter 16. Chapters 18 and 20 have been revised and enlarged to cover best present knowledge of atmosphere control and quenching methods. Three new chapters have been added—Chapter 9 presenting the Tool Steel Selector, Chapter 19 on the important subject of "Time Required to Heat Tool Steel" and Chapter 13 devoted to High Speed and Hot Work Steels. These additions are designed to provide both the tool maker and the hardener with the latest information on tool steels, and to present this in the most concise, accurate and understandable form.

Frank R. Palmer
George V. Luerssen

Reading, Pa.
February, 1948.

TABLE OF CONTENTS

TOOL STEEL SIMPLIFIED

This book is addressed to the men in industry who are responsible for the design, making, or heat treating of tools. In this group has been included not only tool supervisors, foremen and the men actually engaged in the work, but apprentices and the students in trade and engineering schools—the men who will some day inherit the responsibilities of the tool room. Its purpose is to present simplified methods for *selecting* and *heat treating* the proper tool steel to make any kind of tool.

Fig. 1.—Here is a punch and die that must blank out millions of pieces of sheet mica.

Fig. 2.—Here is a stud bolt setter that will be used in continuous daily production.

1

FIG. 3.—Here is a set of embossing dies that will be used to make brass emblems.

FIG. 4.—Here are the tools to be used for hot forging manganese copper pins, and must finish them so accurately and smoothly that no final machine work will be required.

These are photographs of real tools that some tool maker has already made, but the reader is asked to imagine that, instead of being photographs, they are merely sketches of tools that have never existed and he is required to make them. Or, if it will make it easier, assume that the tools have actually been made— they are approved for design and workmanship—*but* their production has been very poor—and the reader is now required to deliver duplicate tools that will really produce.

If a tool is to give maximum production with the least trouble and maintenance, it is necessary that the following four things be done correctly:

1. *Design.—The blueprint or sketch must lay out a tool of the right size and shape to do its work efficiently.*

2. *Tool Making.—The tool maker must make the tool accurately according to the blueprint design.*

3. *Tool Steel.—The proper kind of tool steel must be selected.*

4. *Heat Treatment.—Finally, the correct heat treating procedure must be developed.*

A tool cannot be successful unless *all four* of the above requirements are fulfilled. If the tool is incorrectly designed, nothing can save it. If it is inaccurately made, it goes into the scrap box. Good design and accurate tool making are of no use if the wrong steel has been selected. And everyone knows that poor heat treatment can ruin an otherwise perfect tool. These statements are so important and so fundamental that it will be time well spent at this point to discuss them further, and show their full significance.

It would be natural to think that the four requisites mentioned in our formula *add up* to a good tool. They do not; they actually multiply. If a good tool is rated at 10,000 points, and each of the separate items were rated 2,500 points, they would add up to 10,000. If the heat treatment were only half a job, the tool would add up like this:

$$2,500 + 2,500 + 2,500 + 1,250 = 8,750$$

or $87\frac{1}{2}\%$ perfect—but this certainly would not be so. Each of the items is really worth 10 points, and they *multiply* like this:

$$10 \times 10 \times 10 \times 10 = 10,000.$$

Now with half a job of heat treatment we get

$$10 \times 10 \times 10 \times 5 = 5,000$$

or only a 50% tool—which is correct. If any *one* of the four things is entirely wrong, the answer is:

$$10 \times 10 \times 10 \times 0 = 0.$$

For example, suppose a tool made of an oil-hardening steel has correct design, good workmanship, and the right steel, but some one tells the hardener it is made of a water-hardening steel and, when hardened, it goes to pieces in the water tank. The value of the tool is zero—not 75%. These examples should serve to show that each of the four factors are vital to a good tool, and that no one can be neglected. Unlike the individual strands of a cable, where if any one strand fails, its strength is simply subtracted from the whole, they are rather like the links of a chain, in which the failure of one link would result in complete failure.

The first two items in our formula are taught tool makers from the very beginning of their apprenticeship. Neither of these phases of tool making fall within the scope of this book—although both will be considered insofar as they may affect the selection of the proper tool steel, and its heat treatment. Tool makers, however, have had less opportunity to learn about the last two. Tools will never approach maximum efficiency as long as the knowledge of design and tool making is in one head, and tool steel and heat treatment in another; and one purpose of this book is to place in the hands of the tool maker the necessary information on the selection and heat treatment of tool steels so that he can effectively apply all four ingredients to the building of better tools.

Most of the tool maker's difficulties arise in operation No. 3— selecting the proper tool steel. There is less known about this subject than about any of the other three. Tool makers look in vain in textbooks for the type of information that they need on the subject of tool steel. Dozens of metallurgical books dealing with constitutional diagrams, microstructure and other fundamental data are available, but this is not what the tool maker wants to know. A much more useful type of literature is found in the catalogs and publications of the tool steel manufacturers. These catalogs describe each of the various brands of tool steel that the manufacturer makes, setting forth its properties, its uses, and its heat treatment. It is necessary for the tool maker to translate these descriptions into the requirements of his tool, and then try to decide which one seems to best fit the problem. His decision is made doubly difficult by the fact that there are offered in America today hundreds of different brands of tool steel—made and sold by dozens of different manufacturers and jobbers. While it is true that many of these different brands could be grouped according to their analysis, yet this is no guarantee that they are strictly "interchangeable." When faced with a tooling problem, what chance has a tool maker of reading the description of a great many steels and selecting the one which will prove best and most economical for his purpose?

Experience over many years shows that there is tremendous need for simplification in this phase of tool making.

In the heat treatment of tools there is again need for simplification. Treating instructions given in catalogs—or even by letter —must necessarily be very general. A typical instruction would read somewhat as follows:

"In heat treating tools made from our . . . brand of tool steel, proceed as follows. Heat slowly and uniformly to 1500/1550°F. and quench in oil. Draw the tool to suit requirements. A good average drawing temperature would be 400°F. but either higher or lower temperatures may be used, depending upon the nature of the tool and the work it must do. The hardness values to be expected at various drawing temperatures are given in the following table . . . "

It would seem that heat treating instructions could be more specific than this, but considering the fact that the steel maker is generally hundreds of miles from the tool room where his steel is being applied, and usually knows nothing whatever about the job, it will be appreciated that only the most general instructions can be given. However, looking at the subject from the tool maker's standpoint, what is he supposed to do? Is he supposed to make up a number of tools and heat treat them in different ways in order to find out which heat treatment will work best? This might be a practical procedure on a simple tool like a boiler punch, but think what it would mean on a complicated and expensive tool which might easily cost several hundred dollars to make. Unfailing accuracy in selecting the ideal heat treatment for all tools is not to be expected—however, a simplified procedure that would even reduce by half the amount of cutting-and-trying would represent a great saving to tool steel users.

As it is, the difficulty in arriving at exact heat treatment recoils upon the selection of the tool steel. Suppose the first tool made does not perform satisfactorily—has the wrong steel been selected, or has the wrong heat treatment been used? More often than not, the tool maker is so disgusted by the failure that he decides the tool steel is no good and proceeds to try something else. Since this involves reading more catalogs, picking another steel, and deciding upon another heat treatment, it is small wonder that many tool makers finally get into a frame of mind where they refuse to try anything.

Tool steel manufacturers have done everything possible to

avoid these difficulties by training their salesmen in the proper use of their various brands of tool steel and by sending tool steel experts from the mill to recommend the proper steels and supervise their heat treatment. Even this, however, is not the perfect solution of the difficulty. Not only is it impossible for these men to be everywhere at once but, while they know a lot about tool steel, they are seldom expert tool makers. No one can understand a tooling problem like the men who must work with it daily, and it is highly desirable that these men should have a simplified and workable method for selecting and treating tool steels so that they can accurately solve their own problems with a minimum of outside help.

Since it is the purpose of this book to present such simplified methods, it is desirable here at the beginning to take a bird's-eye view of the chapters that are to follow.

Part I covers two things the reader should acquire by way of background. He should have a speaking familiarity with the words and terms that he is likely to encounter in his reading or conversation on tool steel. This is contained in Chapter 1. Also, he should know what tool steel is. This is largely a matter of "getting acquainted" and is covered by Chapters 2 to 5.

Part II describes a simplified method for selecting the right tool steel for making all sorts of tools. Chapter 6 describes the method, Chapter 7 gives the analyses of twelve steels that will do the job, Chapter 8 discusses a number of examples to show how the method works out in actual practice, and Chapter 9 concludes with a very practical means of implementing the method in the form of a simple tool steel selector.

Part III deals with simplified methods for heat treatment. Chapter 10 is devoted to general considerations of methods and equipment; Chapter 11 discusses hardness and toughness; Chapter 12 gives specific information on the group of twelve steels; and Chapter 13 completes the section with a comprehensive discussion of the specialized subject of High Speed and Hot Work Steels.

Part IV presents a group of "things worth knowing." Although the first three parts of the book tell "how to do it," the reader will find that he can do it more easily and more accurately after he has read the chapters in Part IV. Chapter 14 puts an interesting angle on tool design. Chapters 15 and 16 give rules for hot acid etching and timbre and hardenability testing. Chapter 17 tells how to identify steels by their emery sparks. Chapters 18, 19 and 20 discuss three of the most interesting and important phases of heat treating—furnace atmosphere, heating time and quenching. Finally, Chapter 21 contains some practical tips on "trouble shooting."

Part V concludes with a few tables that will be helpful to the user of tool steel.

PART I

GETTING ACQUAINTED WITH TOOL STEEL

CHAPTER 1

TOOL STEEL TERMS

It is not necessary to have detailed knowledge of all the technicalities of tool steel manufacture in order to be a good tool maker. On the other hand, ignorance of the significance of certain common terms that are likely to be encountered—both in reading and in conversation—is likely to prove embarrassing to a man who is responsible for the selection, purchasing, or working of tool steel. These men are continually exposed to a barrage of *words*—perhaps from advertising, or in personal contact with outside salesmen, metallurgists and engineers; it may come second-hand through the purchasing department, or it may originate in some other department of his own plant. These things press for an answer.

The tool maker must realize that his purchasing department is involved in the buying of many products, and cannot hope to be expert in all of them. Under the pressure of lower prices, or perhaps some "wild" claim, the buyer depends upon the tool room to give him the other side of the story. If the tool man does not even understand the significance of the new "claim"—if he does not know enough about the tool steel he is now using to adequately defend it—changes may be made that will plunge both the tool room and the production department into expensive trouble. On the other hand—and just as often—new and valuable ideas will be rejected by the tool maker, simply because he cannot recognize their merit.

The whole purpose of this Part I is to fortify the tool maker, and others who may be concerned in the selection of tool steel, with sufficient general knowledge so that they will be able to avoid costly and foolish experiments on the one hand, and the rut of obsolete practice on the other. The present chapter will briefly explain the meaning and significance of certain important terms that the tool maker is likely to encounter.

11

Steel.—As defined by *Tiemann*, steel is

1. That form of iron produced in a fluid condition and hence practically free from slag (difference from wrought iron), which contains less than 2.20% carbon—as a rule less than 1.50% (difference from cast iron). It is produced by the crucible, the Bessemer, and the open hearth process and also in the electric furnace.

2. The product obtained by carburizing wrought iron (more rarely, low-carbon steel) by the cementation process and generally known as *cement steel.*[1]

3. Formerly steel was defined on the basis of its malleability as produced and its capability of being hardened (usefully) by quenching, while iron could not.

Fig. 5.—Open pit on Mesabi ore range.   (*Courtesy of Steel.*)

In daily conversation, practically everything made in a "steel mill" will be referred to as "steel"—regardless of analysis.

Tool Steel.—Without attempting an exact definition, any steel that is used for the working parts of tools may be called a "tool steel." Since this book limits its attention to those types of tools that are made in the tool rooms of the metal working industry,

[1] Authors' note: Cement steel is practically obsolete in America.

our immediate conception of tool steel involves the steels that are used for making these particular tools.

Tool steel is almost always hardened and must therefore contain, alloyed with the iron, some elements that will give it the ability to harden. The most important of these is carbon. In a general way, tool steels seldom contain less than .50%, or more than 1.30% carbon. Other alloying elements are frequently

FIG. 6.—Blast furnace plant. (*Courtesy of Steel.*)

used to supplement the carbon as will be discussed in greater detail later.

Iron Ore.—Iron is derived from iron ore. American ores consist chiefly of natural iron oxides containing minor percentages of nonmetallic impurities known as **gangue.** About 80% of our iron ore comes from the vicinity of Lake Superior (Fig. 5). This is a heavy reddish, stone-like mineral called **hematite.** Its chemical formula is Fe_2O_3. The symbol "Fe" stands for iron and the symbol "O" stands for oxygen. Thus, hematite is an oxide of iron containing two parts (theoretically by weight 70%) of iron and three parts (30%) of oxygen. A black, magnetic oxide known as **magnetite** (Fe_3O_4) is also of considerable commercial importance in this country.

Blast Furnace.—A blast furnace is used for converting iron ore into pig iron. A typical installation is illustrated in Figs. 6 and 7.

The furnace is charged with a mixture of iron ore, coke and lime-stone. The coke has three jobs to do. First, it supplies the heat for the process. Second, it combines with the oxygen in the iron ore and liberates the metallic iron. Third, the melted iron has a great affinity for carbon and it absorbs from the coke about 3% to 4% of carbon as it drains to the bottom of the furnace.

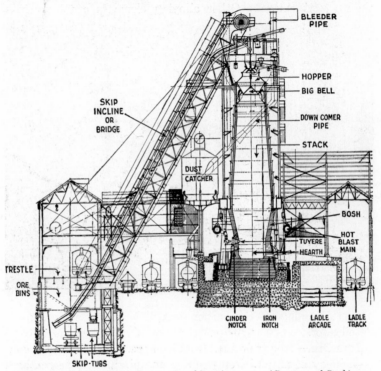

Fig. 7.—Section through a modern blast furnace.   (*Courtesy of Steel.*)

The limestone is used as a flux to carry off the gangue which occurs in the ore.

The pig iron and slag are tapped from the furnace periodically —a large blast furnace yielding from 1000 to 1500 tons of pig iron every 24 hours.

Pig Iron.—Pig iron contains about 92% iron, and about 3.50% to 4.00% carbon. The balance is largely silicon and manga-nese, with small percentages of phosphorus, sulphur and other impurities.

As the molten pig iron comes from the blast furnace, it is run

into molds that hold about 100 pounds each and is allowed to
solidify for shipment and further use. A large pile of these
"pigs" is shown in Fig. 8. Sometimes the liquid iron is caught
in a ladle-like receptacle called a **mixer** and is transferred
directly to a nearby steel making furnace.

FIG. 8.—Pig iron. (*Courtesy of Steel.*)

When pig iron is remelted in a **cupola** (with various analysis
modifications) and cast into useful shapes, it is called **cast iron.**

Wrought Iron.—Wrought iron is the product of the **puddling
furnace** as illustrated in Figs. 9 and 10. Pig iron is charged on a
heated hearth which has been covered with iron oxide (usually
scale). As the pig iron melts, its manganese, silicon, phosphorus
and carbon are oxidized out by the action of the scale. As the
carbon is exhausted, the metallic mass becomes pasty and the
puddler works it into balls which are removed through the furnace
door. Much liquid slag is entrapped with the metal and this is
promptly squeezed out under a press. The final product is
substantially pure iron containing a considerable percentage of
residual slag, and is known as wrought iron. The old hand-
puddling process has now been largely supplanted by more

FIG. 9.—Removing iron ball from puddling furnace.   (*Courtesy of Steel.*)

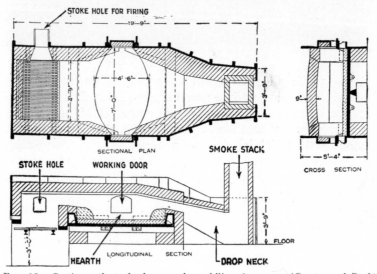

FIG. 10.—Sections through drop neck puddling furnace.   (*Courtesy of Steel.*)

modern methods, notably the Aston Process, which consists in mixing blown Bessemer metal with slag of proper composition and temperature, the result being a mass much like the puddle ball obtained by the older processes.

The Bessemer Converter.—This is one of the oldest types of steel making equipment that is still in extensive use. Figs. 11

FIG. 11.—Bessemer converter blowing. (*Courtesy of Steel.*)

and 12 show it to be a huge brick-lined steel retort provided with vents or tuyéres near the bottom through which compressed air can be blown. Molten pig iron is brought from the blast furnace and poured into the Bessemer converter. The compressed air is turned on and allowed to blow through the metal. This air burns out the manganese, silicon and carbon, and reduces the charge to a low carbon steel. After the blowing is stopped, the metal is full of oxygen and is very "wild." Certain alloying

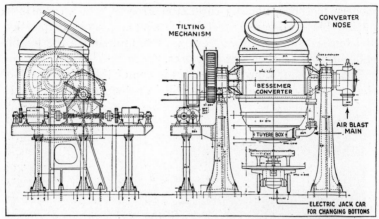

Fig. 12.—Diagram of Bessemer converter.   (*Courtesy of Steel.*)

elements (principally manganese and silicon) are then added to deoxidize the charge and improve its quality. The Bessemer converter is not used for making tool steel, but is used for such soft steel products as wire, screw stock, sheets, plate, skelp, etc.

The Open Hearth Furnace.—The open hearth is a large brick unit used for making steel in large quantities. A typical installation and section of the furnace are shown in Figs. 13 and 14. This furnace converts pig iron into steel by oxidizing out the surplus carbon, but instead of using air like the Bessemer converter, the oxygen is supplied by throwing raw iron ore into the furnace. The oxygen from the iron ore combines with the carbon, silicon and manganese of the bath, thus lowering the carbon in the pig iron and, at the same time, reducing the iron ore to metallic iron. The resulting products mix to form an average composition.

In practical operation, the open hearth is seldom charged entirely with pig iron. A considerable percentage of the charge is usually made up of scrap steel. This lowers the average carbon content of the mix and greatly decreases the amount of "oreing down" that is necessary. The oil or gas fuel used to heat the furnace burns directly in contact with the slag which covers the molten metal. Thus the atmosphere of the furnace is oxidizing and will gradually burn out the carbon, manganese, silicon, etc., even without the use of ore. The basic open hearth furnace likewise has capacity to largely eliminate phosphorus and partially eliminate sulphur.

Fig. 13.—Battery of 100 ton basic open hearth furnaces. (*Courtesy of Steel.*)

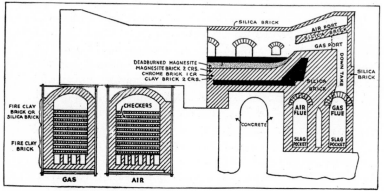

Fig. 14.—Diagrammatic section of open hearth furnace.

When the open hearth charge has arrived at the proper carbon, the bath is not as highly oxidized as the blown Bessemer metal, but it is still too highly oxidized and "wild" to be cast into sound ingots. When **killed steel** (free from blow holes) is desired from the open hearth furnace, final additions of manganese, silicon, aluminum or other deoxidizers are used.

Although the bulk of the steel made in the open hearth furnace is low in carbon and without special alloys, quite a large tonnage will contain higher carbon—with or without special alloy additions (such as nickel, chromium, vanadium, etc.). The simple low carbon steels go into plates, sheets, wire, structural shapes, etc., and the alloy steels are used for heat treated gears, shafts, and other highly stressed machine parts. Quite a little open hearth steel containing from .50% to 1.00% carbon (with or without alloys) is used as an inexpensive steel for springs, mechanic's tools, quarry tools, etc., but very little ever finds its way into the tool room for expensive production tools.

The Crucible Furnace.—The crucible process, although now practically obsolete, was the first method in existence for melting tool steel, and as such still deserves a place in this book. Before the crucible process was invented by Benjamin Huntsman in 1740, tool steel was made by carburizing wrought iron and then welding and hammering the carburized pieces into bars. This was known as **shear steel.** Huntsman's invention consisted in placing the carburized pieces in a crucible and melting them to a uniform composition. The liquid steel was then cast from the crucible into molds. For this reason, it was known as **cast steel.** Since all steel today is *cast* from the liquid condition into molds, this expression has largely lost its significance—although it will still be seen stamped on some hatchets and other forms of hand tools.

The crucible furnace does not start with pig iron and oxidize it in the manner of a Bessemer or open hearth. The crucible practice is really a "mixing" operation. The pots may be charged with pure bar iron and a certain amount of refined pig iron which, when melted together, will average to give the percentage of carbon finally desired. If alloys are required, they are added along with the rest of the charge and allowed to soak and mix together until the composition is uniform. A 36 pot crucible furnace is illustrated in Figs. 15 and 16.

Excellent quality tool steel was made in crucible furnaces but since each crucible held only about 100 pounds of metal, the process was expensive and for this reason has given way to the electric furnace which is now our principal process for making tool steel.

Scrap.—At this point, it is necessary to say something about scrap. To the layman, scrap is almost synonymous with junk. This is a wrong conception. Junk consists of a miscellaneous

Fig. 15.—Crucible melting furnace. (The Carpenter Steel Co., furnaces dismantled about 1925.)

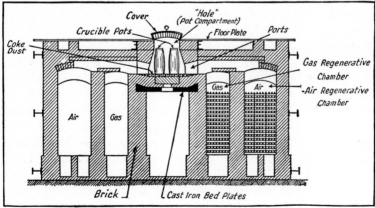

Fig. 16.—Diagrammatic section of crucible furnace. (*Courtesy of American Society for Metals.*)

assortment of scrap metal having unknown analysis and would be absolutely worthless to the steel maker. Scrap is perfectly good clean steel of known analysis which, because of its physical size and shape, cannot be used for anything but remelting purposes. For example, if a circle is cut from a square plate, there will remain four corners, which may be useless for further manu-

Fig. 17.—Ten ton top charge electric arc furnaces and melting plant, showing charging of furnace and pouring of ingots. (*The Carpenter Steel Company.*)

facture. However, the metal in these corners is exactly the same quality as the center which was used, and when a sufficient quantity of this plate scrap—all of the same analysis—has been accumulated, it becomes valuable melting stock for the steel maker. Actually, steel which has been twice melted has opportunity to become even better than steel that is made entirely from raw materials. Scrap is purchased by the steel maker to definite analysis specification and is carefully stocked according to its analysis. Some highly alloyed tool steel scrap is extremely valuable because the alloy can be salvaged in the remelting process. Thus, a worn out high speed tool is still a perfectly good piece of steel, having a definitely known analysis, and it can be remelted to make new high speed steel at a considerable saving. Entirely aside from the economic features, better high speed steel will result if a portion of the charge is made up of scrap, rather than entirely of raw materials.

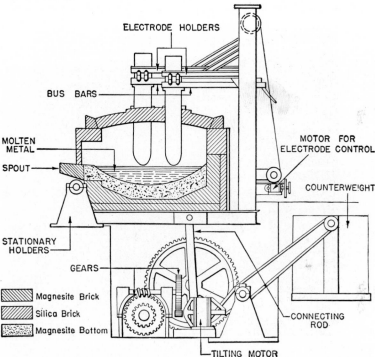

Fig. 18.—Diagram of electric arc furnace. (*Courtesy of American Society for Metals.*)

The Electric Arc Furnace.—This furnace today is our largest producer of high grade tool steel. The units used for making tool steel range from about 1 to 10 tons capacity and will tap a heat about every five or six hours. Fig. 17 shows a battery of 10-ton Heroult electric furnaces used for making tool steel. The mechanical details of this type of furnace vary somewhat, particularly in the appliances for charging and tapping. A diagrammatic view illustrating the essential parts of one of the simpler designs is given in Fig. 18.

Through snugly fitting holes in the roof there are projected large carbon or graphite electrodes—perhaps 17″ in diameter.

These electrodes reach to within a few inches of the charge and across this gap springs an electric arc. The principle is very similar to the ordinary street arc lamp, excepting that the carbons are infinitely larger and the heat of the arc is tremendous. This heat serves to melt the charge and keep it molten during refining.

Since there is no fuel being burned in the electric furnace, there need be no oxygen to support combustion. Thus, the atmosphere of the furnace can be reducing and the metal is not con-

Fig. 19.—Half-ton high frequency coreless induction furnaces. (*The Carpenter Steel Company.*)

tinually being oxidized as it is in the open hearth furnace. Under this reducing atmosphere, the metal can be highly refined and large quantities of alloy can be added if desired without danger of their burning up through oxidization. The basic electric arc furnace can remove both phosphorus and sulphur to extremely low values.

These furnaces are charged almost entirely with carefully selected steel scrap or pure iron of known analysis. They never start out with a charge of pig iron. If the charge consists of cold materials, it is spoken of as **cold melt** electric furnace steel to distinguish from the big production practice of charging the electric furnace with molten steel previously melted in an open hearth furnace. The slower and more expensive cold melt practice is almost universally used for making fine tool steels.

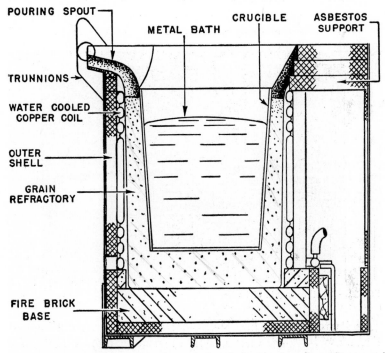

FIG. 20.—Section of high frequency coreless induction furnace. (*Courtesy of American Society for Metals.*)

The Coreless Electric Induction Furnace.—This is the newest type of furnace used for making high grade tool steel, and is illustrated in Figs. 19 and 20. It operates on the principle of an electric transformer. The primary is a high frequency alternating current, and this is passed through a water cooled copper coil which surrounds the melting crucible. The crucible is filled with carefully selected steel scrap which acts as the secondary of the transformer. When the high frequency current passes through the copper coil, currents are generated in the pieces of scrap causing them to become very hot so that in a comparatively few minutes the entire charge is melted.

This furnace does something that no other tool steel melting furnace can do—it stirs and mixes the steel continuously by the action of the induced electric currents.

The capacity of induction furnaces ranges from a few hundred pounds to five or six tons and when properly powered they are capable of pouring a heat about once every hour. There is, of course, no oxidizing condition present so that high quality dead-killed steel can be made just the same as in the electric arc furnace. The induction furnace, as used today, has little if any

Fig. 21.—Casting ingots of tool steel from bottom pour ladle. (*The Carpenter Steel Company.*)

capacity to eliminate phosphorus or sulphur so that these impurities must be kept very low in the charge of raw materials. Except for the method of heating, the induction furnace makes steel by much the same principle as the old-fashioned crucible furnace.

Ingots.—Regardless of the melting procedure used, the finished steel is tapped from the furnace and poured into cast iron molds. After the steel has solidified, it is removed from the mold and this steel casting is called an ingot. Each batch of ingots from the furnace is called a "heat" and for convenience is put through subsequent operations as a unit whenever possible. Ingots may be of all sizes and a variety of shapes. Tool steel is usually cast in square or octagon ingots ranging from 6″ to perhaps 20″ in section. An assortment of typical tool steel ingots has been assembled in Fig. 22.

Pipe.—When molten steel solidifies in the ingot it shrinks. Thus, although the ingot mold may be poured full of molten steel, due to this shrinkage there will not be enough metal to completely fill the ingot. Of course, the metal freezes first in contact with the cold walls of the mold and the last metal to freeze is at the center of the ingot. Thus, unless something is done to prevent it, there will be a shrinkage cavity down through the middle of the ingot almost its entire length. This cavity is

Fig. 22.—Typical tool steel ingots. 1. 18″ octagon. 2. 10″ octagon. 3. 10″ square. 4. 7″ square. (*The Carpenter Steel Company*.)

called a "pipe" and insofar as it is present in tool steel ingots they must be scrapped and remelted because this pipe will persist through forging and rolling and will appear as a defect in the center of a finished bar.   Fig. 23 shows the upper part of an ingot that was cast without any precaution to prevent piping.   The ingot has been partially slotted on a planer and then broken longitudinally through the axis to reveal the shrinkage cavity.

To avoid pipe, the steel maker sets on top of the ingot mold a hollow fire clay sleeve having high insulating qualities.   (See Fig. 21.)   A variety of such "hot tops" or "hats" are shown in Fig. 24. When the ingot is poured, this hot top is also filled with metal. The ingot itself naturally freezes much faster than the metal inside the insulating brick, and this pool of liquid steel is therefore available to feed down into the ingot as it solidifies and fill up the pipe.   When the ingot is finally cold, the space within the hot top brick has largely emptied itself—but the ingot is sound. Later on, at the time the ingot is forged or rolled, this upper portion is cut off and scrapped. From 10% to 25% of every ingot must be sacrificed in this way in order that the remaining portion may be sound and usable. Fig. 25 shows a longitudinal fracture through the axis of an ingot that was cast with a suitable hot top. Note how the top has been partially emptied in feeding the pipe— also the soundness of this ingot compared to the one in Fig. 23.

Fig. 23   Fig. 24   Fig. 25

Fig. 23.—Piped ingot poured without hot top.
Fig. 24.—Typical assortment of refractory hot top bricks.
Fig. 25.—Sound ingot poured with hot top.

Cogging.—The first operation on a tool steel ingot is to convert it into a **billet** by a process known as cogging. This may be done by hammering, rolling or pressing. At The Carpenter Steel Co., ingots are roll cogged up to about 9″ square—providing the analysis of the steel lends itself readily to rolling. This operation is illustrated in Fig. 26 where a 9″ square ingot is being cogged to a round billet. Some of the highly alloyed steels, like high speed steel, cannot be cogged very satisfactorily on a rolling mill and these analyses are therefore hammered—whatever the ingot size may be. At this plant all ingots larger than 9″ square are hammered, regardless of analysis. Fig. 27 shows a 14,000 pound hammer cogging a tool steel ingot into a billet. It is of passing interest that this hammer is operated by compressed air instead of steam.

In cogging, the ingot is carefully heated to a pre-determined temperature and the cross section is reduced with a corresponding

FIG. 26.—Roll cogging 10″ square ingots into round billets on 22″ mill. (*The Carpenter Steel Company.*)

FIG. 27.—Hammer cogging tool steel ingot on 7 ton hammer. (*The Carpenter Steel Company.*)

amount of elongation. Thus, a 9″ square ingot would yield a 4″ square billet which would be about six times as long as the original ingot. As the hot billet comes from the mill or hammer, the top is "cropped" to remove the pipe. This crop goes back to the melting department as scrap for future heats. At the Carpenter mill it is common practice on some grades of tool steel to roll cog the ingot into a round billet instead of a square billet. The reason for this will develop in the next paragraph. Billets are hot cut to convenient and suitable lengths before they are allowed to cool.

Billet Preparation.—It may readily be imagined that when liquid steel is cast into a mold, the surface of the ingot does not freeze as smooth as glass. There is a certain amount of splashing and motion with the result that the surface of the ingot is rather rough. By the time the ingot has been cogged into a billet, these surface imperfections have been stretched out along the length of the billet into defects that are known as **seams.** These must be removed before the billet is further processed. Four methods are employed for doing this, as follows:

Chipping.—The billets are pickled to remove the scale and make the seams easy to see. Chippers using pneumatic hammers and gouge chisels then chip out all surface defects, as shown in Fig. 30.

Grinding.—On hard steels like high speed steel, it is sometimes preferable to grind out the defects. Billet grinding is done with swing-frame grinders, as illustrated in Fig. 29, using very free cutting wheels. They obviously cannot be as selective in their action as a chipping chisel and such billets are usually ground all over.

Rough Turning.—Sometimes it is desirable to completely remove the surface from the billets and for this purpose, the billet is rolled round instead of square. These are annealed and straightened and then put through rough turning machines that remove the entire surface of the billet. Fig. 28 shows a rough turned round billet issuing from a turning machine.

Billet Disc Inspection.—Just as the surface of billets can be inspected and insured against surface defects by the operations just described, so can the interior be insured against defects by means of a disc inspection. In the Carpenter mill as each billet is cogged, its ends are marked to identify them with their

FIGS. 28–31.—Various operations in preparation and inspection of billets. (*The Carpenter Steel Company.*)

location in the original ingot. Discs are cut, deep-etched, inspected, hardened and fractured and again inspected. (See Figs. 31 and 73.) Where recutting is necessary to clean up "end defects," a final disc is cut for verification. Each heat of steel is inspected and handled as a unit, and this not only assists the inspector, but also provides the melting department with valuable information for correcting and guiding future practice. A further discussion of the details of this method will be found in Chapter 5.

Fig. 32.—Billet storage preparatory to final rolling. (*The Carpenter Steel Company.*)

Prepared Billets.—Billets which have been prepared by the procedures just mentioned are stocked in a billet yard (Fig. 32) to await orders from the finishing mills.

Finish Rolling.—Practically all tool steel bars at the Carpenter mill are brought to their final size and shape on rolling mills. Even those grades which did not lend themselves readily to rolling in ingot form, can now be rolled from prepared billets with very little difficulty.

A tool steel rolling mill, as shown in Fig. 33, is entirely different from a rolling mill used for rolling merchant bar and mild steel. A tool steel mill reduces the cross section of the billet very slowly and about twice as many passes through the mill are required to reach a given size.

The prepared billets are heated to a pre-determined temperature and are then rolled to the desired size and shape. In many
cases, the finishing temperature as the bar comes off the mill is
almost as important as the original temperature to which the
billet was heated. If it is desired to finish a bar hot, the mill is
speeded up and if it is desired to finish it cold, the mill is slowed
down. In order to obtain this control, all of the rolling mills at

Fig. 33.—Finish rolling tool steel bars on 16″ mill. (*The Carpenter Steel
Company.*)

this plant are equipped with variable speed, direct current motors.
Heating furnaces are equipped with pyrometers and automatic
oxygen recorders to control both temperature and atmosphere.
Such an installation is shown in Fig. 34. In addition, starting
and finishing temperatures are measured by means of optical
pyrometers which can be sighted on the work and measure its
temperature by the incandescent color. In Fig. 33 a temperature
observer may be seen at the right of the roll stand.

Annealing.—This operation has been defined as follows:

A heating and cooling operation of a material in the solid state.
Annealing usually implies a relatively slow cooling. NOTE: Annealing
is a comprehensive term. The purpose of such heat treatment may be:

(*a*) To remove stresses

(*b*) To induce softness

(*c*) To alter ductility, toughness, electrical, magnetic or other physical properties

(*d*) To refine the crystalline structure

(*e*) To remove gases

(*f*) To produce a definite microstructure.

Fig. 34.—Pyrometer and oxygen recorder connected to reheating furnace.
(*The Carpenter Steel Company.*)

Practically all bars of tool steel must be annealed before they are sold. To avoid scaling, much of this work is done by packing the bars in large pipes or boxes with a non-oxidizing substance like cast iron borings. These containers are carefully sealed and charged into the annealing furnace, as shown in Fig. 35. They are uniformly heated to the proper annealing temperature and the charge is slowly cooled in the furnace. For extra slow cooling, a diminishing amount of fuel may be kept burning during the cooling cycle.

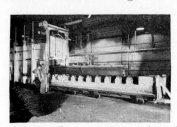

Fig. 35.—Box annealing tool steel bars. (*The Carpenter Steel Company.*)

Decarburization (or Bark).—During heating for cogging, rolling and annealing, it is virtually impossible to prevent a certain amount of carbon from being oxidized from the outside skin of the bar. A typical condition on a 1″ round bar might show that the extreme outside skin, to a depth of say .005″, would have lost practically all of its carbon. The next .005″ or .010″ would form a gradation zone with the carbon gradually increasing until it reaches the normal carbon analysis for the rest of the bar. This is known as surface decarburization (or "bark"), and it is very important for a tool maker to understand.

The degree to which a bar may be decarburized depends upon the analysis of the steel (some analyses decarburize much more easily than others) and also upon the practice used during the heating of the bar. Sometimes there will be no skin of total decarburization at all but there may be a zone on the surface which is simply somewhat lower in carbon than the balance of the bar. Decarburization is one of the reasons why steel manufacturers recommend removing a certain amount of metal from the surface of the bar in making a tool. The following machining allowances represent good practice.

TABLE I

Dimension of Bar	Minimum Amount to be Removed per Side
Up to $\frac{1}{2}''$	$\frac{1}{64}''$
Over $\frac{1}{2}''$ to $1\frac{1}{4}''$	$\frac{1}{32}''$
Over $1\frac{1}{4}''$ to $3''$	$\frac{1}{16}''$
Over $3''$ to $5''$	$\frac{1}{8}''$
Over $5''$	$\frac{3}{16}''$

Straightening and Inspecting.—The annealed bars are straightened on various types of mechanical straightening machines and are finally inspected for size and surface condition. Inspectors go all over the surface of the bar with files hunting for seams and other surface defects which may have escaped detection in billet preparation. The annealed softness is tested on a Brinell hardness testing machine which is shown in Fig. 36. (See page 264 for description of this machine.)

It is also uniform practice in tool steel mills to nick each end of every bar and break off a short piece so that the inspector can examine the fracture. Any pipe or other gross defect that might have been missed in the earlier inspection can readily be seen on this clean fractured surface. Experienced mill inspectors can in this way frequently spot a bar of the wrong analysis accidentally included, and they also recognize certain structural irregularities.

At the Carpenter mill is employed an additional—and more

positive—method of inspecting the inside of the steel, the hot acid etch disc test.   This is more fully described on page 397.

Hot Rolled Bars.—The bars just described are known as "hot rolled" bars and the bulk of tool steel bars are sold in this form.

Fig. 36.—Brinell hardness inspection.   (*The Carpenter Steel Company.*)

Fig. 37.—Interior of typical Tool Steel Warehouse. (*The Carpenter Steel Company.*)

They go directly from inspection to the warehouse racks to be shipped out on orders.

Cold Drawn Bars.—A considerable quantity of tool steel is purchased in cold drawn bars for the manufacture of drills, taps and similar tools. For this purpose, hot rolled, annealed bars (or coils) are pickled to remove all scale and are then drawn (Fig. 38) through a die which is perhaps $\frac{1}{16}''$ smaller than the diameter of the bar. Cold drawing does not "iron" down the surface as is frequently supposed; it is a stretching operation just like taffy candy is stretched. The grains of the steel are stretched and elongated clear through to the center, and the

Fig. 38.—Cold drawing tool steel bars. (*The Carpenter Steel Company.*)

outside of the bar is rendered smooth and accurate to size. Cold drawn bars are normally furnished within a few thousandths of nominal size and are thus ideal for use in the collets of automatic screw machines.

Contrary to general opinion, cold drawn bars will show just about as much decarburized surface as hot rolled bars. This is perfectly obvious in view of the fact that no metal is actually removed from the surface excepting the small amount that might be eaten away by the pickling acid. If tool steel is required free from surface decarburization, it should be ground.

Centerless Grinding.—Some forms of tool steel—notably drill rod—are put through centerless grinders to remove the entire surface and produce an accurately ground finish. Rough-ground bars may be no more accurate to size than a cold drawn bar, but finish-ground bars can be furnished within plus or minus .001''—

or even .0005″. Grinding makes possible the complete removal of all surface defects—including decarburization. Centerless grinders working on small drill rod sizes are shown in Fig. 39.

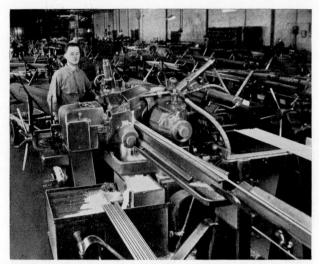

Fig. 39.—Centerless grinding drill rod. (*The Carpenter Steel Company.*)

Tool Steel Forgings.—Although the vast majority of tools are made from pieces cut from bars, the tool maker has frequent need for large discs or rectangular pieces of odd dimensions such as are illustrated in Fig. 40. These are generally hammered. A

Fig. 40.—Hammered tool steel forgings. (*The Carpenter Steel Company.*)

prepared billet of sufficient size is carefully heated in a hammer furnace and is then forged to the dimensions required. Hammered ring forgings are extremely useful in many cases as they save the time and expense of removing all of the metal from the center of the disc. There are a great many job forge shops throughout the country which carry tool steel billets on hand and furnish tool steel forgings. All such forgings are, of course, annealed to make them machinable.

Macrostructure.—This word means "large structure," and as applied to tool steel it refers to the structure which can be seen with the unaided eye. The most convenient way to reveal the macrostructure of tool steel is to cut a section through the portion to be examined, and etch in some reagent which will dissolve the various constituents in the steel at different rates, in this way developing a pattern. The section etched may be simply a saw cut surface, although a ground surface is usually preferred. The reagent most frequently used is hot dilute hydrochloric (muriatic) acid.

The patterns developed by macro etching largely result from the original ingot structure, distorted to an extent which will depend upon how much hot work the ingot received in hammering or rolling to the finished bar.

Microstructure.—This term refers to the more detailed structure of steel as revealed by the microscope. As we have already seen, macrostructure is dependent almost entirely upon the original ingot structure, and the amount of hot work. In contrast to this, microstructure depends primarily upon the *heat treatment* to which the steel has been subjected.

The specimen to be examined is prepared by cutting a section and polishing the cut face, by special methods, to a perfect mirror surface. This is then lightly etched in a suitable reagent to bring out in relief the various constituents which make up the structure. When this specimen is placed on the stage of a special type microscope sometimes known as a "metalloscope," a beam of light reflected from the polished surface throws an image into the eyepiece, or upon a photographic plate, much like the picture one sees from a high altitude over mountainous country, where the sunlight falling on the hills casts shadows which throw the high points in bas-relief in contrast to the dark valleys.

As a matter of convenience the various constituents in steel have been given special names. The carbon in steel usually occurs as a compound of iron and carbon known as carbide. This constituent is called **cementite.** The soft iron constituent is called **ferrite.** When the cementite and the ferrite occur in a laminated structure such as shown in Fig. 41, the composite structure is called **pearlite.** If the cementite occurs in little balls or spheroids embedded in the iron, the structure is referred to as "spheroidized" as shown in Fig. 42.

Both Figs. 41 and 42 illustrate steel in the soft condition, Fig.

FIG. 41.—**Lamellar pearlite** in 1.00% Carbon Tool Steel— ×1000.

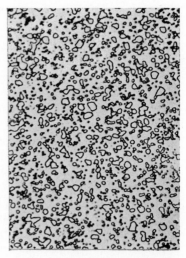

FIG. 42.—Spheroídized structure in 1.00% Carbon Tool Steel— ×1000. The small circles are **cementite.** The white background is **ferrite.**

FIG. 43.—**Martensite** in 1.00% Carbon Tool Steel— ×1000. The white circles are **excess cementite.**

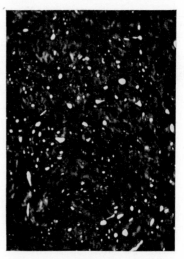

FIG. 44.—**Troostite** in 1.00% Carbon Tool Steel— ×1000. The white circles are **excess cementite.**

42 being typical of properly annealed carbon tool steel. When tool steel is heated above the critical temperature, some of the cementite is dissolved in the iron, and at the same time the iron becomes nonmagnetic. The resulting structure is known as **austenite.** If the steel is now quenched rapidly, the austenite changes to a hard needle-like structure known as **martensite** as illustrated in Fig. 43. Sometimes during quenching not all of the austenite changes to martensite, and the part which does not change is then referred to as **retained austenite.** This structure is not easily seen under the microscope, and the amount of retained austenite is usually detected by either the hardness of the quenched steel, or by the fact that the steel in this condition is partly nonmagnetic.

The portion of the carbide which remains out of solution after hardening is referred to as **excess cementite.** (See Fig. 43.) When tool steel is drawn at a high temperature after hardening the martensite loses some of its needle-like appearance, and tends to darken when etched. This drawn structure is sometimes called **troostite.** (See Fig. 44.)

The photograph of a microstructure is referred to as a **microphotograph** or a **micrograph.** When microphotographs are shown, the number of times the structures were magnified should also be shown. Magnification is always expressed in the number of diameters. If the structure were magnified 100 diameters, the magnification would be shown as $\times 100$; if 500 diameters, $\times 500$, etc.

Machinability.—Every tool maker and mechanic should understand something about this property of tool steel—because it is so important to the economy of his work. It is common knowledge that tool steel is hard when it comes from the rolling mill or hammers, and that it must be softened by annealing in order to machine satisfactorily. It is, however, not so well known that machinability is not a definite property of tool steel—like hardness, for example. It is not something that can be measured with an instrument and definitely forecast in advance. A steel which is annealed to give best machining properties on the drill press will not necessarily have the best machining qualities for broaching or a delicate finishing operation like "backing off." A tap maker for example cannot buy tap steel extremely soft for rapid turning because when he mills the flutes he will throw up a burr on the threads which must be removed at considerable expense. Furthermore, one tap maker might find that a certain type of annealed structure, within a definite hardness range, would give him exactly the machining qualities that he desired. Another tap maker with a little different tooling set-up might want an entirely different structure with a different hardness range to suit the conditions of his machine shop.

When a tool steel mill places standard sizes of standard brands of tool steel in the warehouse racks, it is annealed for the best *average* machinability for most tool room conditions. About 95% of the time this is perfectly satisfactory, but the tool maker should always bear in mind, when tool steel is purchased in large quantity for production manufacture of tools, that the steel mill can work out for him a special annealing practice. He must also understand that the steel maker cannot prophesy in advance exactly *what* annealing procedure is going to suit *his* particular needs. This must be worked out by a cut-and-try process with considerable patience on both sides. Once the proper machinability has been established, however, subsequent shipments can be made to duplicate the satisfactory sample.

Critical Point (or Critical Range).—This is the temperature above which a tool steel must be heated in order that it will harden when quenched. The exact temperature of the "critical" will vary with the analysis.

Hardness Penetration (Hardening Penetration; Hardenability).—Throughout this book all three of these terms will be used. They all denote the same thing, and here is what they mean.

In order to harden a tool steel, it must be heated above the critical and then cooled rapidly. Some steels must be quenched in water to harden, others will harden when quenched more slowly in oil, and still others will harden if cooled in air. Let us think of a water-hardening steel for a moment.

It is quite evident that the outside surface of a tool cools most rapidly because it is in direct contact with the water, while the inside of the steel cools more slowly. If the steel must be quenched *very* rapidly in order to harden, it is easy to see that the inside may not cool fast enough, hence will not harden. This is exactly what happens in most water-hardening tool steels unless the tool is very small. In a 1.05% carbon, water-hardening tool steel, only a shell about $\frac{3}{32}''$ to $\frac{1}{8}''$ deep will harden and the "core" will merely be strengthened somewhat by the quench. The fracture in Fig. 45 shows a $\frac{3}{4}''$ round piece of this steel after hardening. The fine grained shell will be file hard and the core will be toughened. The "penetration of hardness" as seen on the fracture is the depth of the hardened surface.

It is known that many alloys, when added to tool steel, increase the penetration of hardness. The fracture of a silicon-molybdenum alloy steel in Fig. 46 shows a fine grained, hard case about $\frac{3}{16}''$ deep on the surface, and a coarser grained, toughened core underneath.

F I G . 4 5 .— Hardened fracture of 1.05% carbon tool steel.

High speed steel is said to be "deep hardening." The fracture of a $1\frac{1}{2}''$ round piece of this steel in Fig. 47 shows it to be fine grained and hard throughout.

Fig. 46.—Hardened fracture of silicon-molybdenum tool steel.

Fig. 47.—Hardened fracture of high speed steel.

With a little thought, it will be seen that a "deep hardening" steel is one which will harden on slower cooling—and a "shallow hardening" steel is one which requires rapid quenching. Hence oil-hardening steels average to show deeper hardness penetration (greater hardenability) than water-hardening steels; and the air-hardening steels have the greatest hardenability of all. It is worth noting here that the quenching speed needed to harden a steel is called its **critical quenching speed.** This subject is discussed more in detail in Chapter 4.

CHAPTER 2

TOOL STEEL—WHAT IT IS

To make a person "acquainted" with tool steel is not the easiest thing in the world—the subject is almost too big. Many people who have used tool steel all their lives do not feel very well acquainted, excepting perhaps with one or two brands that they have regularly used. In fact, it is not uncommon to find people who are actually *afraid* of tool steel—so much so that they lock themselves up with the few grades they already know, and refuse to investigate steels that may be new or different. This is not difficult to understand. As has been pointed out, the problem of selecting a new tool steel that will handle some troublesome job has been a difficult one, and the number of failures far exceeds the number of successes. If a tool maker has been unfortunate in having several expensive failures follow one upon another, he can hardly be blamed for being "afraid of strangers."

In marked contrast to this over-conservatism there is the other extreme—the man who is "too friendly to strangers." There is a type of tool maker who tries everything that comes along and buys tool steel from every salesman who sees him. This attitude arises perhaps from the fact that he never used any one steel long enough to really become well acquainted and therefore considers that one "stranger" is as good as another.

Neither of the above extremes is in the interest of best tool economy—and both of them cost their firms money. It is perfectly obvious that new steels and better steels are developed as time goes on. The fearful or ultra-conservative tool maker misses these improvements and his tool room becomes old-fashioned. On the other hand, the man who tries *everything* is certain to waste a lot of money too—because he will inevitably encounter more failures than successes. The safe course lies in between

44

these two extremes. If a tool maker knows and understands something about tool steel, he will be open-minded but cautious. He will have at least a rough idea as to whether a certain claim is likely to be true. He will tread new ground carefully, but will be persistent enough to dig out the right answer—knowing in advance that even the best of things do not always click the first time they are tried. In this way he will catch the important new developments, without forever running up blind alleys.

In order that the reader may more quickly acquire the acquaintanceship with tool steel that he needs, the subject will be presented in parallel with a subject he already understands—namely, getting acquainted with a human being.

Suppose a manufacturing firm had a responsible position vacant and wanted to hire a man to fill the job. Suppose Mr. John Doe applied for the position—what would it be necessary to know about Mr. Doe before hiring him?

First, his "specifications" would be asked for. This is the information that appears on practically all employment blanks—age, weight, height, nationality, education, etc.

The next thing to investigate would be his character. Is he honest, industrious, careful, competent, etc., and does he have an *aptitude* for the particular work in question?

Finally would come inquiry into his state of health. Is he physically sound or does he have some permanent weakness that might cause him to break down under the strain of his work?

After investigating a man from these three angles the employer would feel just about as well acquainted with him as possible—until he had actually lived with him and worked with him.

Likewise, there are three things that should be known about a tool steel and they can very well be described as "specifications," "character," and "physical soundness." If a steel measures up in these three particulars, it is a likely candidate for the job; it can be put to work and a personal acquaintance allowed to develop to a point where a final decision can be reached. Even in cases where such a steel is not an outstanding success, it will seldom cause any serious or expensive trouble.

To further emphasize the comparison which has been drawn between men and tool steel, they are presented in the following parallel columns.

JOHN DOE (Applicant)

Specification (General Information)

Age?
Height?
Weight?
Schooling?
Nationality?
Etc.

Character

Personality?
Honest?
Industrious?
Careful?
Aptitude?
Dependability—That is, under a given set of circumstances can he be *depended* upon to behave as expected?
Etc.

Physical Soundness

Hearing?
Sight?
Heart?
Operations?
Diseases?
Etc.

Comments

There are employers who hire applicants, knowing very little more about them than the general specifications given in the first paragraph above. They meet with many disappointments. Poor health, incompetence, or bad traits of character take a heavy toll of men hired in this way. The number of employers who follow this policy is certainly much smaller today than it used to be.

In employing men, much less is known about the second requirement —character and personality—than about the other two. This is a comparatively new study but one that is fast gaining ground. Modern methods of aptitude testing are beginning to teach much about the potentialities of different individuals.

TOOL STEEL (Applicant)

Specification (Analysis)

Carbon?
Manganese?
Silicon?
Chromium?
Tungsten?
Etc.

Character

Timbre (Personality)?
Hardenability?
Toughness?
Safety?
Uniformity?
Dependability—That is, under a given set of circumstances can it be *depended* upon to behave as expected?
Etc.

Physical Soundness

Pipe?
Slag?
Seams?
Surface decarburization?
Segregation?
Etc.

Comments

There are tool steel users who buy steel based entirely on the analysis specification as given in the first paragraph above. They meet with many disappointments. Unsound material containing hidden internal defects, or unexplainable variations in character take a heavy toll from the production of their tools. The number of people who are doing this is certainly growing less.

Much less is known about the second requirement—character or timbre, hardenability, etc.—than about the other two. This is a comparatively new study but one that is fast gaining ground. Modern methods of testing are beginning to teach much about the utility of different tool steels.

Still another analogy may be drawn between the hiring of an employee and the purchase of a tool steel. Competition is said to be "the life of trade" and a lively competition between different brands of tool steel in the market place is just as constructive and necessary as a competition between employees for a new job or for a promotion.

Some folks thoughtlessly think of competition only in terms of dollars; and the less they know about a product or its use, the more likely they are to adopt a "pigs is pigs" attitude and resolve everything to terms of purchase price. Even the most thoughtless of these would probably never hire employees by the pound, or award a promotion to the lowest bidder—but they may make this mistake in their consideration of tool steel. Would such folks say that Civil Service Employment is not competitive— just because all the applicants are willing to work for the same price? Tool steel competition is truly "economic competition," but economy involves more than purchase price; in the case of tool steel, *much* more.

Tool steel is not like ice—to be bought by the pound; it is much like a human being to be employed on the basis of expected service and general dependability. A piece of tool steel costing only one dollar may have one hundred dollars of labor expended on it to make an important tool or die; and this tool may be mounted in a machine tool involving extensive overhead cost and labor use. Still further, this operation may be only one on an integrated production line, where a single tool failure might cause financial loss and damage of considerable magnitude. What does it profit a buyer if he can save ten cents on the cost of that original piece of tool steel if he thereby disrupts the entire tool room, or even the factory production line?

Tool steel in America is made by a small group of specialty steel mills, many of whom have experience dating back into the last century. Among these mills there is the keenest of competition—not to whittle a penny off the price, but to add a dollar to the value. It is extremely important that tool steel buyers and users understand this, and it is worth their while to visit a few steel mills and observe the working of this phenomenon. Here is a mill employing the hot acid etch test as a routine inspection; here is another discarding an extra ten per cent from the top of every ingot; and still another making "winged ingots," or cutting his billets crosswise and expending hours of extra labor to subdue a potential trouble-maker—all to the end that their salesmen may be able to meet the *quality competition* of the other mill or perhaps out-do them.

This is the reason and the justification for tool steel brand names. Each manufacturer jealously guards the quality of the product that carries his brand—and backs it up with his guarantee. When science has advanced to a point where complete and trustworthy "engineering specifications" can be written for human beings and tool steels, then *both* can be bought on price competition—but not before.

The next three chapters will be devoted to a study of tool steel under the three headings already proposed. Chapter 3 will discuss the subject of analysis. Chapter 4 is devoted to the character of tool steel, and its effect on the utility of the steel. Chapter 5 describes a method for determining the internal soundness of tool steel.

CHAPTER 3

THE ANALYSIS OF TOOL STEEL

This chapter discusses analysis as the first step in getting acquainted with tool steel. It is not supposed that a tool maker would want to specify the exact analysis of his tool steel—or try to tell the steel manufacturer how the formula should be worked out. On the other hand, there is no reason why he should feel

FIG. 48.—Chemical laboratory. (*The Carpenter Steel Company.*)

embarrassed when somebody mentions manganese, or cobalt or chromium. Nearly all modern tool steel catalogs give the analysis of the various grades, and the tool maker should be interested in these specifications—just as he would be interested in knowing the age, nationality, etc. of John Doe if he were going to hire him.

Although iron is the predominating element in the analysis of any steel, it is never mentioned as a part of the analysis. After listing all of the alloying elements present, it would be perfectly

49

proper to say "The balance of the analysis is iron"—but this is never done.

In presenting the analysis of a steel, it is not uncommon to use the chemical symbols instead of the full names of the elements. A list of the usual elements with their chemical symbols is given in Table II.

TABLE II.—CHEMICAL SYMBOLS

Name of Element	Chemical Symbol
Iron	Fe
Carbon	C
Manganese	Mn
Silicon	Si
Phosphorus	P
Sulphur	S
Chromium	Cr
Nickel	Ni
Tungsten	W
Vanadium	V
Molybdenum	Mo
Cobalt	Co
Columbium	Cb

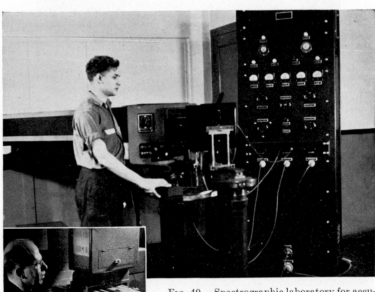

Fig. 49.—Spectrographic laboratory for accurately controlling analysis of tool steel. (*The Carpenter Steel Company.*)

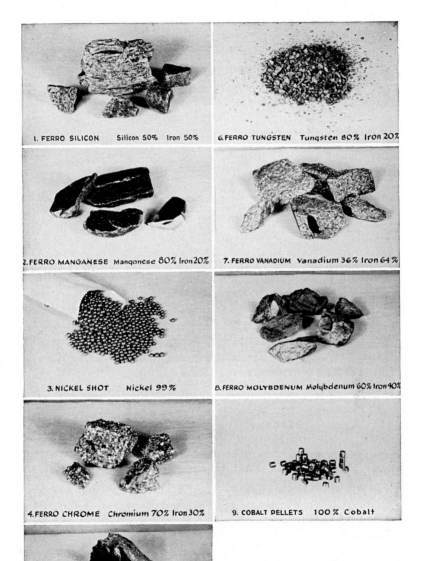

1. FERRO SILICON   Silicon 50%   Iron 50%

6. FERRO TUNGSTEN   Tungsten 80% Iron 20%

2. FERRO MANGANESE Manganese 80% Iron 20%

7. FERRO VANADIUM   Vanadium 36% Iron 64%

3. NICKEL SHOT   Nickel 99%

8. FERRO MOLYBDENUM Molybdenum 60% Iron 40%

4. FERRO CHROME   Chromium 70% Iron 30%

9. COBALT PELLETS   100% Cobalt

5. WASHED METAL   Carbon 3.5%

FIG. 50.—Alloying elements as added
in the melting of tool steel.

Alloying elements are added to tool steel during the process of melting. Sometimes suitable alloy steel scrap is used in the original charge so that only final adjustments need be made to secure the exact percentage of each element required. In either event the alloying elements are thoroughly and completely mixed throughout the bath. With a few exceptions, alloying elements used by the steel maker are in the form of **ferro-alloys**—that is, the alloying element is already combined with a certain percentage of iron by the maker of the ferro-alloy. For example, silicon is added to the steel in the form of ferro-silicon. This is illustrated in Fig. 50 and contains approximately 50% silicon and 50% iron. Other forms of alloying elements are also shown with their type analysis.

It might be well to inquire *why* alloys are put in tool steel. Carbon is, of course, necessary in order that the steel may harden. Plain carbon tool steel is as old as history itself—dating back no less than three or four thousand years. Alloys to augment carbon have been introduced during the past fifty years.

If plain carbon tool steel had been perfectly satisfactory for all tooling problems, there would have been no need for alloy steels. Alloys are put into steel to enable it to do things that a plain carbon steel cannot do. Strangely enough, these *extra* requirements can be assembled under four heads.

1. *To secure greater wear resistance for cutting or abrasion.*

2. *To secure greater toughness or strength.*

3. *To secure hardening accuracy and safety—and increased hardenability.*

4. *To give the steel "red hardness," or the ability to do its work when the tool is heated so hot that a plain carbon steel would soften.*

Alloys may produce many other minor effects, but the four just mentioned constitute the principal reasons for which they are added to the steel. The effect of each element will be briefly discussed.

Carbon.—The function of carbon is to make the steel harder and more wear resisting. Plain carbon tool steels must be quenched rapidly in water in order to harden and therefore they harden on the surface only. If the piece is about $3/4''$ round or larger, it will harden only about $3/32''$ or $1/8''$ deep and beneath this there will be an unhardened tough core.

The lowest carbon likely to be found in a plain carbon tool steel would be about .50% to .60% and this steel might be used for such things as blacksmith's tools, hammer dies, etc. As more carbon is added, the steel's capacity to harden is increased until about .80% carbon is reached, whereupon it will become file hard when quenched. Adding more carbon than this does not increase the measurable hardness—but it does increase the wear resistance. The highest carbon normally found in a plain carbon tool steel is about 1.30% and is used for razors, engraving tools, etc. A good average carbon content for use in the tool room is about 1.05%. This becomes very hard, has good wear resistance and yet the carbon is not high enough to make it fussy or sensitive to heat treat.

Before the discovery of timbre (see page 59) practically all troubles with plain carbon tool steel were blamed on the analysis. No inventory was complete that did not contain at least a half dozen different carbon ranges to take care of various types of tools—and to be prescribed in case of trouble. If a 1.00% carbon steel were used and the tool broke or chipped, a .90% carbon steel would be recommended. It is now known that most of these troubles were due to timbre, rather than analysis; and today, a good tough timbre steel containing 1.05% carbon is more universally applicable than all the old brittle timbre analyses put together. This is one important type of simplification made possible by modern research. As will be seen in later chapters, when a tough timbre 1.05% carbon tool steel will not solve a problem, the answer is usually to be found in an *alloy* tool steel— rather than by experimenting with different percentages of carbon.

Manganese.—Manganese helps to make the steel sound when it is first cast into the ingot. It also makes the steel easier to hot roll or forge. For these reasons, practically all tool steel will contain at least .20% manganese. Manganese can be present up to perhaps .50% before it would be regarded as a special "alloy" addition.

The effect of adding more manganese to a simple carbon steel is to increase the penetration of hardness. So powerful is its effect that the inclusion of about 1.50% manganese to a steel containing .90% carbon would cause it to harden clear through to the center of a 2″ cube—whereas without the extra manganese, this same cube would harden only about $\frac{3}{32}$″ deep on the surface.

Furthermore, the manganese causes the steel to harden so

rapidly and so deeply that it can no longer be safely quenched in water but must be quenched in oil.   This is one way of making an oil-hardening non-deforming tool steel—namely, by adding about 1.60% manganese to a .90% carbon tool steel.

A third effect of manganese is to slightly lower the critical point and hence the temperature to which the steel must be heated for hardening.

Silicon.—Practically all tool steel contains a small percentage of silicon (usually from .10% to .30%) which is added for much the same purpose as small quantities of manganese—namely, to facilitate the casting and hot working of the steel.

As an alloy, silicon is almost never used alone—or simply with carbon.   Some deep hardening element like manganese, molybdenum or chromium is usually added along with the silicon.   In combination with such elements, silicon possesses a tremendous power to add strength and toughness to tool steel.   It also cooperates somewhat in increasing the hardness penetration.   For alloying purposes, silicon may be found between .50% and 2.00% —but always in conjunction with something else.

A tool steel is more likely to decarburize in both forging and hardening when considerable silicon is present as an alloy.

Phosphorus and Sulphur.—These two elements are usually reported in the complete analysis of a tool steel.   They are both regarded as harmful impurities and are kept as low as possible. In open hearth tool steel they will be less than .05%.   In electric furnace tool steel, they will run under .03%—even in the cheapest grades.   In the better grades they are kept below .02% and it is not uncommon to find them below .015%.

In machinery steel, phosphorus and sulphur are sometimes deliberately added to make the steel more free machining.   However, in these products quality is not of such paramount importance—and besides, they do not have to be heat treated in the same sense as a tool steel.

Chromium.—Like manganese, chromium causes the hardness to penetrate deeper and when present in sufficient quantity will confer oil-hardening properties.   It is not as potent as manganese in this respect but, on the other hand, it contributes wear resistance and toughness to a greater degree.   The increased wear resistance is not necessarily accompanied by greater hardness.

The low and medium chromium steels do not hold size as

accurately as manganese steels, and those which are water-hardening will frequently change size more than even plain carbon tool steel. Again, chromium raises the temperature necessary for hardening whereas manganese lowers it.

Chromium will be found in tool steel in all sorts of percentages. Plain carbon-chromium steels may contain from .25% to 1.50% chromium and find their largest use in twist drills, reamers, machine knives, mandrels, etc. A steel containing 5% chromium together with 1% molybdenum has very deep-hardening properties, and constitutes a very valuable air-hardening die steel. Another interesting chromium tool steel is found in the so-called "high carbon high chromium" types. These contain from 1.50% to 2.20% carbon and about 11.00% to 14.00% chromium. Sometimes other alloys are added in small percentages. These steels possess remarkable wear resistance, and may be either oil-hardening or air-hardening. Their properties are so completely changed that they hold their size and shape accurately when hardened.

There is about 4.00% chromium in high speed steel in conjunction with tungsten and vanadium. It is a little difficult to separate the behavior of individual elements when the analysis is as complicated as this, but chromium continues to serve its normal purpose of increasing the hardenability and hardness penetration.

Nickel.—Nickel is a rather unusual element to be alloyed in tool steel, although it will be found in the two oil-hardening tool steels described on pages 303 and 306. It has very little effect on the hardenability of the steel but it does add to the toughness and wear resistance when used in conjunction with some hardening alloy like chromium. Nickel lowers the hardening temperature somewhat and tends to make the steel oil-hardening rather than water-hardening.

Tungsten.—Tungsten is the most dramatic alloy to be found in tool steel. It must be added in fairly large quantities to be effective. Tungsten to the extent of about 1.50%, when added to a high carbon tool steel, increases somewhat its wear resistance. If the tungsten is increased to about 4% with about 1.30% carbon, the steel will acquire such wear resistance upon being hardened as to be quite difficult to grind with an ordinary emery wheel. This is about as much tungsten as is ordinarily used in combination with carbon alone. These carbon-tungsten steels have no increased hardness penetration and they decarburize to a slightly greater extent than plain carbon tool steels—perhaps because their hardening temperature is higher.

When tungsten is added between 12% and 20% in conjunction with chromium, it gives the steel a new property—namely, red-hardness. Plain carbon tool steel may become very hard when quenched—but if the tool is put to work under some condition where it becomes quite hot, the heat will draw the temper out of the steel and soften it. For example, cutting tools are heated by the friction of cutting and if attempts are made to cut rapidly with carbon tool steel, the cutting edge will become so hot that it will soften. A steel containing 18% tungsten and 4% chromium can, however, continue cutting—even after the cutting edge has been heated to a dull red color (about 1000°F.). Steels of this character are known as **high speed tool steels** and represent what is undoubtedly the most important class of alloy tool steels. The best known standard type contains about .70% carbon, 18.00% tungsten, 4.00% chromium and 1.00% vanadium. The vanadium adds further to the red-hardness of the steel. Another standard type of high speed steel will be mentioned under "molybdenum."

Tungsten, when combined chemically with carbon, forms a carbide having extreme hardness and wear resistance, together with excellent red-hardness. On account of these properties, tungsten carbide has found application in tools cutting at extremely high speeds, and in those used to cut very hard materials. The carbide itself is quite brittle, and must be bonded together with some tough metal such as cobalt, and sintered to form an insert, which is usually brazed to an alloy steel shank to form the cutting edge of the tool.

Vanadium.—Vanadium is sometimes added in small quantities (about .15%) to an otherwise straight carbon steel. In such quantities, it does not affect the measured hardness or the hardness penetration. In some steels it has a toughening effect by keeping the grain size small—especially when it might tend to enlarge as a result of overheating. Thus, a vanadium tool steel might be accidentally overheated 100° in hardening without damage. This same effect can now be produced without vanadium by controlling the timbre of the steel (see page 59). Vanadium may also increase the red-hardness of a steel. It is used in quantities between .15% and 1.00% in conjunction with chromium, tungsten, etc., in hot working die steels, and about 1% to 3% of vanadium is put in high speed tool steel for the same purpose.

Molybdenum.—Molybdenum shares somewhat the properties of both chromium and tungsten. Like chromium, it increases the hardness penetration and inclines the steel toward oil or air-hardening. Like tungsten, it increases red-hardness and wear resistance. Molybdenum encourages greater decarburization in forging and heat treating.

When used in percentages of .80% to 1.25% along with high percentages of chromium, or with combinations of chromium and manganese, it greatly increases hardenability, and is therefore an important element in many air-hardening steels. When used with silicon, it makes a very tough, hard tool steel for battering purposes.

A very important application of molybdenum is in high speed steel. One of the standard types in which it is used contains about .80% carbon, 4.00% chromium, 5.00% molybdenum, 6.25% tungsten and 2.00% vanadium.

Cobalt.—Cobalt is seldom used in tool steels other than high speed. Here it is added to increase the red hardness so that the tools may be used at higher operating speeds. At the same time it raises somewhat the temperature necessary for hardening, increases the tendency toward surface decarburization and decreases the toughness.

Columbium.—Columbium has some potentialities as an alloying element in tool steels. Its outstanding property is that of forming extremely hard carbides which add greatly to wear resistance. On account of its affinity for carbon, it is necessary in steels containing columbium to allow sufficient carbon to completely satisfy the columbium, and in addition enough extra carbon to provide for the normal hardening processes. Columbium decreases the tendency for decarburization in hardening, and like vanadium raises the maximum allowable hardening temperature.

While a newcomer in the field, columbium has potentialities as an alloying element both in high speed steel, and in the die steels, primarily to increase their wear resistance.

In conclusion, it must not be assumed that the effects of the above alloys are all cut and dried—and that the steel maker can always tell in advance what the properties of a new formula will be. This is far from true. The steel maker *expects* certain *tendencies* when he adds an alloy—but he never knows what he has until he tries it out. Two or more alloys in combination will usually behave quite differently from the individual elements if added alone.

And here is a good rule-of-thumb for any tool steel user to remember—

The more different alloys added—and the greater their quantity—the more difficult it becomes to keep the steel uniform and hold it under accurate control. Other things being equal, the steel having the simplest analysis is the one to be preferred.

CHAPTER 4

THE CHARACTER OF TOOL STEEL

The next step in getting acquainted with tool steel is to know something about its character, which we have already defined briefly as consisting of two factors, namely its **hardenability** and its **timbre,** or **personality.**

Much has been written in the past few years on the subject of the hardenability of steel. The term "hardenability" has now been universally adopted as describing the *tendency* of steel to harden, and not necessarily the *degree* to which it is capable of hardening. Under any one set of treating conditions, "hardenability" and "hardness penetration" or "hardening penetration" can be considered to be one and the same. The terms "hardness penetration" or "hardening penetration" are more commonly applied to the shallower-hardening steels, where a distinct depth of penetration can be seen such as shown in Fig. 51. In the "deeper hardening," slower-quenched

Fig. 51.—Hardened fracture of 1.05% carbon tool steel.

steels, where this line is not distinct, the term "hardenability" is often a more apt term. The reason for this will be more obvious after reading this chapter.

The word "timbre" was adopted by the Research Laboratory at The Carpenter Steel Company as a convenient name for that property of tool steel which controls grain-size, tendency toward grain coarsening at elevated temperatures, and toughness resulting from heat-treating operations. Timbre is a reflection of manufacturing history, rather than of bare chemical composition of the steel. In Chapter 2 we drew the analogy between personality in John Doe, and personality in a tool steel. Timbre in a steel, or personality in a man, are the result of many influences possibly not so apparent, but of extreme importance nevertheless. In a steel these influences go back to its birth as an ingot, and it is a fact that timbre is largely governed by the melting method itself. The effects of timbre are most apparent in the plain carbon tool steels.

What we have said thus far may be summed up in the following brief statements:

Hardenability is the tendency of steel to harden upon heat treatment, while hardness is the degree to which the steel actually hardens. Both are governed primarily by analysis.

Timbre is that property of tool steel which determines its grain size and toughness after a given heat treatment, and is governed primarily by its manufacturing history.

Hardenability and timbre taken together largely determine the character of a tool steel.

We shall now discuss these two properties in some detail.

HARDENABILITY (HARDENING PENETRATION)

It is a familiar fact to every hardener of tool steel that a piece of plain carbon steel with sufficient carbon—say .70% or above—and in a section about $\frac{3}{16}''$ round, will harden entirely through if heated to 1450°F. and quenched in water or brine. However if this section is 1″ round, under the same conditions it will harden on the surface only to a depth of about $\frac{1}{8}''$, the core remaining relatively soft. If, instead of being quenched in water, both pieces were quenched in oil (from about 1550°F.), the $\frac{3}{16}''$ section would harden through while the 1″ round section would not become fully hard, not even on the surface. It is obvious of course that the thing which changes the behavior is mass—the section of the piece—and upon thinking this through another step, it is apparent that it is the rate of cooling which determines whether or not the steel hardens. In the case of the 1″ round bar quenched in water, the core does not harden because the center portion of the bar cools too slowly, only the surface layer cooling rapidly enough to harden. In the case of the 1″ round bar quenched in oil, no part of the section, not even the surface, cools rapidly enough, and consequently no part of it becomes fully hard. The $\frac{3}{16}''$ section quenched in either oil or water cools rapidly enough to harden throughout. Thus mass is seen to affect the hardening behavior of tool steel (1) because various depths in the section cool at various rates during the quench, and (2) because the section size governs the over-all rate of cooling in any one medium.

These relations between the steel, the quenching medium and the section size can be better understood through a simple analogy. Let us imagine a cinder path such as illustrated in Fig. 52, and suppose a sprinter to be at the point T. The cinder path has a

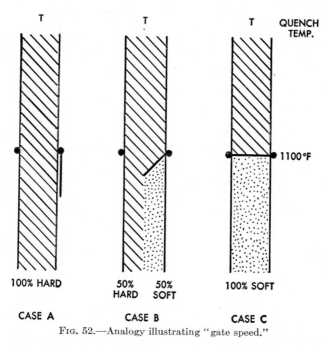

FIG. 52.—Analogy illustrating "gate speed."

gate at some point on its length, and this gate is equipped with a spring connected with a trigger at T so that the instant the runner starts down the path from the point T, a latch on the gate is tripped and the spring tends to close it. The trick is for the runner to get down the path fast enough to pass through the gate before it closes. If he gets through the gate while it is still wide open as in Case "A," he is considered entirely successful and has a score of 100%. If he gets through when the gate is partly closed, as in Case "B," he is only partly successful, or we might assume that only part of the runner got through. In any event let us say his score is 50%. If the gate is entirely closed before he arrives as in Case "C," of course he is entirely unsuccessful and does not get through the gate at all.

A piece of steel during quenching behaves in almost an exactly parallel manner. Let us think of our pathway as a range of temperature from T down to room temperature, and assume that our gate is placed at 1100°F. Suppose we heat a piece of carbon tool steel above the critical to temperature T, and imagine now that the steel is our runner and that the speed of cooling corresponds to the speed of our runner. The imaginary gate at 1100°F. acts exactly like our gate with the spring. If we are able to cool the steel rapidly enough from temperature T to get through 1100°F. before the gate starts to close, we have been 100% successful in hardening the steel. If we are too slow in getting from T to 1100°F. and the gate is half closed before the steel arrives, it will become only partially hard. If the gate at 1100°F., however, closes entirely before the steel arrives, it will not harden at all. The speed of cooling from T down to the gate is of course governed by the so-called quenching medium, the three most common being **water or brine** for extremely fast speed of quench, **oil** for intermediate speed of quench, and **air** for a relatively slow speed of quench.

But what about the gate speed itself? Is this the same for all steels? The answer to this question gives us the nub of the entire hardenability problem. The fact is that we regulate the gate speed, or the "critical quenching speed" as it is technically known, by adding alloys to the steel. Some alloy additions will slow the gate speed sufficiently so that an oil quench is fast enough to catch it open, while others slow it still further so that air-cooling is fast enough to harden the steel. Plain carbon steels have a very high gate speed, and therefore must usually be quenched in water. It should now be obvious why tool steels fall under three general classes—water-hardening, oil-hardening and air-hardening.

So far we have shown that the speed of quench and the critical quenching speed of the steel are the two factors which control the properties resulting from heat treatment. To simplify the discussion, we have assumed that the speed of cooling is uniform throughout the section being considered. This is true only of small sections. In large sections such as those commonly encountered in tools, it is not true, and another factor, that of "mass," must now be considered.

Mass is important in the quenching of tool steel only on account of the fact that tool steel, like all other materials, has a definite property of heat conductivity which limits the speed at which heat can be transferred. Since this is a constant property, the only other thing which determines the rate of flow from one point to another is the difference in temperature between these two points; and the greater the difference, the faster will the heat travel from the hot toward the cold part. Consequently the way to cool a body of steel fast is to maintain a big difference between the surface and the inside. This is accomplished by cooling in water, which carries heat away from the surface rapidly. If it is desired to cool more slowly, a medium like oil can be used, which will not take heat away so fast, or air which will take it away even more slowly. The rate at which steel will cool in any one quenching medium can be determined, and within practical limits will be the same for all types of tool steel.

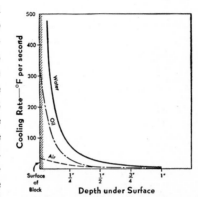

FIG. 53.—Cooling rates of steel block at various depths under a surface cooled in water, oil and air. (Cooled from a temperature of about 1500°F. Rates measured when cooling through 1100°F.)

If large blocks of tool steel are heated to the hardening temperature, and then quenched in three different media—water, oil and air—the rates of cooling in degrees per second from one surface inward can be represented by the curves in Fig. 53. Here the curve marked "water" indicates the rate of cooling at different depths under the surface when that surface is water-cooled. Likewise the curve marked "oil" indicates the cooling rate at various depths when the surface is cooled in oil; and the curve marked "air," the cooling rate when the surface is air-cooled. There are two things to note particularly in these curves, first, that they are "fixed" or constant for any one quenching medium and any one quenching temperature; and second, that the slopes of the three curves differ, the steeper curves indicating greater temperature difference between the surface and inside.

Let us now look at Fig. 54 which shows the same curve as that in Fig. 53 marked "water." The rate of cooling at the surface is something above 500°F. per second. Remembering now our gate speed discussion, it will be obvious that any steel having a critical quenching speed slower than 500°F. per second will harden to *some* depth. Suppose a certain steel which we shall call "A" had a critical quenching speed of 470°F. per second. It would follow that this steel, if quenched in water or brine in a

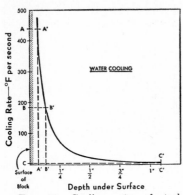

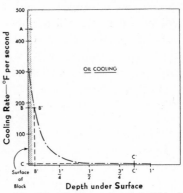

FIG. 54.—Cooling rates of steel block at various depths when water cooled, and resulting behavior of 3 steels of different gate speeds.

FIG. 55.—Cooling rates of steel block at various depths when oil cooled, and resulting behavior of 3 steels of different gate speeds.

large section, would fully harden to depth A since the entire layer from A to A' will be cooled faster than its gate speed. The hardness penetration, as indicated by A, will be about $\frac{3}{32}''$. If we now take a steel "B" having a much slower gate speed, and go through the same procedure, we shall find this to harden to a considerably greater depth as indicated by B'; and a steel "C," having a still lower speed, will harden to C'. What we are really doing is to pick the depth at which the rate of cooling of the steel coincides with the critical quenching speed, and this is our depth of hardening.

Suppose we consider the same three steels when cooled in oil, as illustrated in Fig. 55. It is obvious that steel "A" will not harden at all, while steel "B" will harden satisfactorily to a depth of B', and "C" will harden very deeply to a depth of C'. Carrying the comparison still farther and considering the air-cooling conductivity curve shown in Fig. 56, neither steel "B" nor "A" will harden, while steel "C" will harden satisfactorily to C'.

While our discussion up to the present point has assumed that the depth to which these various steels will harden can be represented by a definite point, as a matter of fact the dividing line between the hard surface and the softer interior is not sharply defined, but is actually a zone or range through which the hardness drops from one level to the other. This is because there is a time interval involved in "closing the gate," during which a corresponding range of mixed structure occurs. This is illustrated in Fig. 57, which shows a water-cooling curve as applied

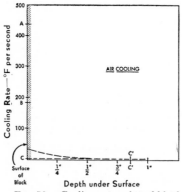

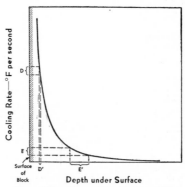

FIG. 56.—Cooling rates of steel block at various depths when air cooled, and resulting behavior of 3 steels of different gate speeds.

FIG. 57.—Curve illustrating difference in gradation zone in shallow and deep hardening steels.

to two steels "D" and "E." It is apparent, on account of the shape of this curve, that the shallow-hardening steels will have a sharper gradation zone as indicated by D', than the deep-hardening steels as indicated by E'. It is common experience that the water-hardening steels grade off sharply, the oil-hardening steels less sharply and the air-hardening steels very gradually.

To summarize what we have said, gate speed or critical quenching speed of any steel is governed primarily by alloy additions. Plain carbon steels have a high critical quenching speed, while the addition of certain alloys slows this speed down. The critical quenching speed of any steel determines the depth to which it will harden in any given cooling medium—in other words, it determines its hardenability. The hardenability of a tool steel may thus be expressed (1) as the depth to which a certain standard size will harden in a certain medium; (2), as the largest sized section which will just harden through; (3), as the depth to which a standard round specimen will harden in from the end when quenched only on that end; (4) and finally, as its critical quenching rate in degrees per second, from which any of the other values can be estimated.

A further word concerning plain carbon steels will be in order. While carbon tool steels are all much shallower hardening than the oil and air-hardening types, it has become customary to refer to deep-hardening, medium-hardening and shallow-hardening carbon steels to describe variations within this one family of steels. These terms refer only to comparison of one carbon tool steel with another, and should not be confused with any terms used to describe the much greater hardenability or hardness penetration effects obtained by alloy additions. The deepest hardening carbon steel will still be shallower hardening than the so-called oil-hardening types.

Before leaving the subject of critical quenching speed, it might occur to the reader to inquire how the steel behaves after it cools below the gate temperature of about 1100°F. We have stressed only the necessity of getting through this temperature before the gate closes, in order to produce hardening. What about speed of cooling after we are through the gate? The fact is that after the steel has successfully passed through the gate, the speed of cooling from there down is not so important. It is as though the steel, when it passes through the gate, makes a promise to harden, even though it will not do so actually until it reaches a considerably lower temperature. Between these two temperatures cooling can be delayed or even stopped without preventing ultimate hardening, the length of time which it is possible to hold at a constant temperature, or to delay cooling, depending upon the analysis of the steel. Manipulations in this range of temperature have given rise to several new and valuable methods of heat treatment which will be dealt with in Chapter 20.

TIMBRE

Earlier in this chapter it was said that the word "timbre" has been adopted as a name for a certain property of tool steel that controls the grain size and toughness resulting from heat treatment. It had been known for many years that there was a "something" in tool steel that affected its behavior—independent of its nominal analysis. This mysterious property had been variously referred to as "body," "nature," "quality," etc. Since the significance of these older terms was not very clear, it became desirable to pick out a new word to describe this property which was now being tested, measured and controlled. The word "timbre" was borrowed from music where it is used to distinguish between the character of tone produced by various different musical instruments or voices. It has been in use in connection with tool steel since about 1930, and is pronounced as though it were spelled *timber* (tĭm-bẽr). The manner in which it affects the behavior of tool steel readily suggests the analogy between "timbre" and "personality."

In the case of John Doe (applicant), his employer would want to know whether he was honest, industrious, careful and dependable. Especially would he be interested in his aptitude—that is, does he have the *kind* of mind and skill that will fit into the job in question? It is perfectly obvious that the man might present satisfactory specifications as to age, nationality, education, etc.; and he might be perfectly sound of body and yet his services would not be wanted because of some trait of character or personality.

It is just so with tool steel. Two steels can be made to the same analysis specification—both can be sound enough to pass the hot acid etch test with flying colors—and yet they might behave quite differently when hardened, because their timbre is different. Timbre is most easily studied in a plain carbon, water-hardening tool steel and it is in this type of steel that the greatest amount of timbre research has been conducted. Also, this is the steel—above all others—that a tool maker should know most about. This interesting property of tool steel will therefore be studied through its behavior in plain carbon tool steels containing about .90% to 1.15% carbon.

What causes timbre? Fundamentally, timbre is probably associated with the detailed chemical analysis of the steel, or with the arrangement or combination of elements not ordinarily determined in the usual routine of chemical investigation. For this reason the timbre will be uniform throughout an entire melt of steel, but can vary widely from one melt to another. In addition to the elements mentioned in Chapter 3, there are present in steel minute amounts of oxygen, nitrogen, hydrogen, aluminum, calcium, magnesium and other elements which cannot be determined by the usual chemical procedure. Much research is at present under way to evaluate these elements and particularly the manner in which they are combined among themselves and with iron or the other common elements. The microscope, the spectrograph, vacuum fusion and other methods are being employed in this work.

Until chemistry advances to a point where it can tell more about these minute quantities and their arrangement in the steel, they can be studied best by their effects upon the metal itself. This may seem like an unusual procedure—but it is not. For example, what chemistry in John Doe's brain would make him a thief—or a musical genius—or a lunatic? No one knows, and yet they do not hesitate to judge a man's character by the way he behaves. Or again, what is electricity? We generate it, measure it, control it and use it—without even knowing what it is. Many things must be studied by their effects—and timbre is one of them.

Is timbre something put into the steel? No. All steels have timbre just as all people have personalities. Timbre is simply one of the properties of a tool steel. Timbre should not be spoken of as though it were a *quantity*—for example, it is incorrect to say "How *much* timbre is there in this steel?"—or "Does this steel have *more* timbre than that one?" On the other hand, it would be correct to say "What is the timbre of that steel?"— in exactly the same manner as "What is the analysis of that steel?"

How is timbre determined? Timbre is evaluated by means of a *timbre test* which is described in its most comprehensive form in Chapter 16. A simplified procedure for timbre testing will be given here.

The timbre test specimen commonly used for plain carbon, water-hardening tool steel is a machined cylinder $\frac{3}{4}''$ round by about $3''$ long. A quick and easy test that will answer all ordinary purposes consists in heating this specimen to 1550°F., quenching in 5% to 10% salt brine,[1] and then breaking in half to expose the fracture.

Since carbon tool steel is naturally shallow hardening, the

---

[1] Brine is recommended because it is a more positive quenching medium than fresh water (see page 247). Fresh water *could* be used for a timbre test and might give reasonably satisfactory results—but brine is better.

fracture will appear somewhat as illustrated in Fig. 58. There will be a hard shell of varying depth and below this there will usually be a tough unhardened core. The timbre of the steel is determined by observing the **grain size** of the hardened case or shell. Sometimes this grain will be very fine and silky, while at other times it may be extremely coarse—or anything in between.

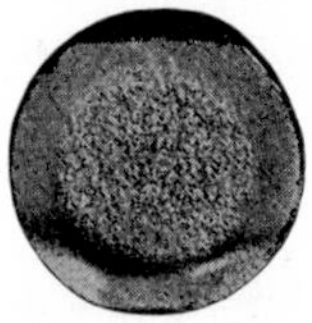

Fig. 58.—Typical hardened fracture of plain carbon tool steel.

What names are given to these different timbres? An excellent system for designating timbre by means of numerals is described in Chapter 16 of this book. For present purposes, however, timbre is divided into two groups as illustrated in Fig. 59,

Shallow hardening
tough timbre.

Shallow hardening
brittle timbre.

Medium hardening
tough timbre.

Medium hardening
brittle timbre.

Deep hardening
tough timbre.

Deep hardening
brittle timbre.

Fig. 59.—Carbon tool steel—varieties of timbre—broadly classified.

in which each group is illustrated for steels of three different hardenabilities. If the grain size of the case is very *fine*, it is called **tough timbre;** and if the grain size of the case is *coarse,* **brittle timbre.** The hardenability or hardness penetration is referred to as "shallow," "medium" or "deep." "Tough timbre" and "brittle timbre" are, of course, not very exact terms—but like the words "intelligent," "dishonest," "capable," etc., they do convey a definite meaning and serve to subdivide the different types of timbre as closely as is needed for most tool making purposes.

Can the timbre of a steel be changed? No, not after the steel has solidified in the ingot mold; from this time on, the timbre is as rigidly fixed as the chemical analysis. If timbre is fundamentally an "inherent" property, it is easy to understand why this property would not be influenced by hot forging, rolling, cold drawing or methods of heat treatment.

It is well to observe, however, that the *appearance* of a timbre test fracture can be affected by the history of the steel after the ingot stage. After all, the timbre test is nothing but a hardened fracture; and forging temperatures, annealing procedures, etc., are known to influence the appearance of a hardened fracture. In order to compare the timbre characteristics of two pieces of steel, they should be normalized or otherwise brought into the same structural conditions before testing. Such normalizing treatment should, however, not be applied to new steel purchased for tools (unless the user is going to forge the steel) because if the new material *as received* does not have the right grain size, tools made from it will reflect this discrepancy. In the last analysis, the tool maker wants steel that will respond uniformly to heat treatment and behave uniformly in service. When the timbre test warns him that a new piece of steel is abnormal, he should reject it and let the steel maker worry about what is wrong with it.

Why is the timbre test quenched from 1550°F.? This temperature is at least 100° above the normal hardening temperature of the steel; however, the purpose is not to harden the steel—but to *test* it. The timbre testing temperature was worked out by cut-and-try methods as the most effective for revealing the timbre of the steel. This can best be illustrated by looking at an example.

Suppose it was desired to compare the timbre of two bars of steel of the same analysis. Test pieces ¾″ round could be machined and given a *normal* hardening temperature of 1450°F. and quenched in brine. Upon breaking, the fractures would appear as in Fig. 60. Both samples show a fine grained case and both of them show about the same depth of case. At this hardening temperature, one might jump to the conclusion that they had the same timbre.

Fig. 60.—Two bars of carbon tool steel—brine quenched from 1450°F.   Fig. 61.—Same two bars as Fig. 60— brine quenched from 1550°F.

Now suppose two more test specimens are machined from the same bars and this time they are heated to 1550°F. and quenched in brine. The fractures will now appear as in Fig. 61. This is an altogether different story. One fracture still shows a fine grained case with a slightly deeper hardness penetration—because of the higher hardening heat. The other sample shows a very coarse overheated structure. Note that this section has hardened practically clear through. This is because of the extremely coarse grain, which has the effect of increasing the penetration just as a more elevated temperature would. It is now easy to see that the first sample is "tough timbre" and the second sample is "brittle timbre." This adequately answers the question as to why a temperature of 1550°F. is used for the test. When setting out to get certain

Tough timbre.   Brittle timbre.
Fig. 62.—Timbre test made on ¼″ thick discs cut from bars.

information it is necessary to use a procedure that will give the information desired.

Is it necessary to use a ¾″ round specimen? If the inspector is merely interested in determining whether the steel is "brittle" or "tough," it does not matter what size or shape test piece is used. A disc ¼″ thick sawed from the end of a bar will do nicely.

A disc timbre test on the two steels shown in Fig. 61 would appear as in Fig. 62. However, if he is also interested in seeing how much the coarsening effect increases the penetration, then a standard sized specimen must be used because the hardness does not penetrate as deeply on large sizes as on small sizes due to their slower quenching. Since a $3/4''$ round piece is inexpensive to machine, and provides the necessary information for the test, it is recommended for use on plain carbon tool steels.

Timbre in Alloy Steels.—The evidence of timbre is not nearly as clear cut or well defined in alloy tool steels as it is in plain carbon tool steel. This can readily be accounted for by the fact that alloy additions not only increase penetration (hardenability) as we have already seen, but also definitely tend to smooth out differences in grain size. While variations in the hardening behavior of alloy steels are frequently less conspicuous than they are in plain carbon steel, nevertheless alloy tool steels can, and do, vary in their hardening behavior. Much work has been done to control these variables, and a degree of uniformity has been achieved that was unknown only a few years ago.

Since timbre and small variations in hardenability are so vital to the user of carbon tool steel, the remainder of this chapter will be devoted entirely to a discussion of their effects on that type of steel.

THE EFFECTS OF TIMBRE AND HARDENABILITY IN CARBON TOOL STEEL

Having learned that the timbre in carbon tool steel can vary considerably—and having discovered a method for evaluating the timbre—the next question is—"What difference does it make?" Timbre affects in many ways the behavior of tool steel and these effects will now be considered.

Effect of Timbre on Toughness.—The use of the words "tough timbre" and "brittle timbre" is not without significance. Until about 1933 there was no satisfactory method available for measuring the toughness of hardened tool steel. At that time, the Carpenter Torsion Impact Testing Machine was invented and this has made available a tremendous amount of new information regarding the toughness of hardened tool steel. The torsion impact test is fully described in Chapter 11, but reference will be made here to some of the figures obtained in comparing tough timbre and brittle timbre steel.

Returning to the two bars whose timbre test was described on page 71, it will be remembered that when these two bars were quenched at 1450°F., both of them showed a fine grained case with no evidence of brittleness. Does this necessarily mean that they have the same toughness? If samples from both of these bars are hardened at 1450°F. and their toughness is measured on the torsion impact machine, the results will appear as follows:

	Rockwell hardness	Toughness, foot pounds
Brittle timbre steel.............	C-67	13[1]
Tough timbre steel.............	C-67	29[1]

[1] This figure indicates the energy needed to break the test specimen. 13 ft. lbs. is the equivalent of a 13 lb. weight falling one foot; 29 ft. lbs. is equivalent to a 29 lb. weight falling one foot.

Thus, while both steels become equally hard, one of them is more than twice as tough as the other. The above test was made in the "as hardened" condition when the steel is naturally in its most brittle form. Suppose both steels are now drawn (or tempered) at 350°F. This will greatly improve the toughness and a torsion impact will now show the following comparison:

	Rockwell hardness	Toughness, foot pounds
Brittle timbre steel.............	C-64	74
Tough timbre steel.............	C-64	116

Thus, while the fractures may *look* alike after a 1450°F. quench, the steels are *not* alike.

Since the brittle timbre steel becomes so coarse grained when it is overheated in hardening (as in the timbre test) and since the tough timbre steel does not show this evidence of overheat, an even greater difference in their toughness would be expected at higher hardening temperatures. The facts show that this is true. If the hardening furnace should accidentally get out of control and overheat the steel to 1500°F., the toughness figures would look like these:

	Drawing temperature	Rockwell hardness	Toughness, foot pounds
Brittle timbre steel...........	Not drawn	C-67	7
Tough timbre steel...........	Not drawn	C-67	21
Brittle timbre steel...........	350°F.	C-64	38
Tough timbre steel...........	350°F.	C-64	120

Effect of Timbre on Cracking in Hardening.—If a piece of tool steel is going to crack in hardening, it usually does so in the quenching bath after the steel has become practically cold. In the above paragraph a comparison was given between the toughness of tough timbre and brittle timbre tool steel in the hardened and undrawn condition. This is the amount of toughness that is available to resist cracking in the quenching bath. Since tough timbre steel shows from two to three times the toughness of brittle timbre steel in this condition, it is not surprising to learn that it is less subject to hardening cracks.

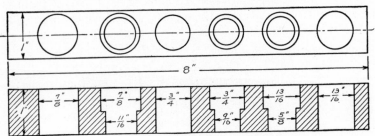

Fig. 63.—Design of specimen for cracking test.

Some interesting experiments can be made on the same two bars of tough timbre and brittle timbre steel that have been used in the above experiments to test their susceptibility to hardening cracks. To do this, a shape must be designed that will be quite dangerous to quench in water. Such a shape is sketched in Fig. 63.

A specimen like this is machined from each bar. They are placed in the hardening furnace together, heated to 1450°F. and quenched. When cold, they are removed from the quenching bath and appear as in Fig. 64. For purposes of photographing, the pieces have been etched in acid to emphasize the cracks.

It must not be assumed that it is impossible to crack a piece of tough timbre tool steel—because this is not true. The facts simply point out that, all other things being equal, tough timbre steel is *less likely* to crack in hardening than brittle timbre steel. An interesting problem illustrating this fact will be found in the story of the cutters shown on page 537.

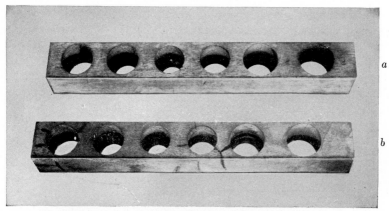

Fig. 64.—Cracking test specimens after hardening and etching. a. Tough timbre steel, Rockwell hardness C-65/68. b. Brittle timbre steel, Rockwell hardness C-66/68.

Effect of Timbre on Grinding Checks.—A grinding wheel produces intense local heat. This is obvious from the manner in which the tiny particles removed become white hot and burn up (grinding sparks). If the little chips that are removed get this hot, the spot from which they were torn must also attain a considerable temperature. These spots are, of course, instantly cooled by the surrounding metal and the coolant. If the action is very fast, and the temperature not too high, the ground surface will show no color. Under severe conditions, however, a bronze or blue temper color may be produced. When steel is heated, it expands—and when cooled it contracts. Thus, a surface that is being ground is continually expanding and contracting which causes rather heavy strains to be developed momentarily in the surface of the metal. If the strains are not too great and if the steel is tough enough, no permanent injury is done. Sometimes, however, tiny cracks will form in the surface of the steel and these are known as grinding checks. It is not necessary to actually "blue" the surface in order for these checks to occur.

Grinding checks are usually so fine that they cannot be seen by the naked eye—but, since they are sharp cracks in the surface of the steel, they greatly weaken the tool and make it much easier to break or chip in service. In order to reveal grinding checks for visual examination or for taking a photograph, the piece is etched in acid and this enlarges the checks until they are readily visible. (See Fig. 353, page 542.)

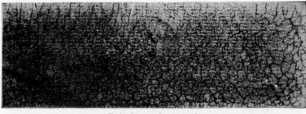
Brittle timbre steel.

Tough timbre steel.

FIG. 65.—Effect of timbre on grinding checks.

To investigate the effect of timbre on susceptibility to grinding checks, rectangular blocks about $1\frac{1}{2}'' \times 1'' \times 4''$ are machined from bars of tough timbre and brittle timbre steel. These are hardened just alike, but are not drawn (so that they will be particularly subject to grinding checks). The blocks are then put on a surface grinder and ground at the same time and in exactly the same manner. Upon etching the surface of the blocks, the brittle timbre sample is found covered with a number of fine grinding checks while the tough timbre steel is not (see Fig. 65). Obviously, if a dull loaded wheel is used and very heavy cuts (or very light ones either for that matter) are taken, sufficient strains might be set up to check *both* samples. However, the purpose of this paragraph is to show that, all things being equal, brittle timbre steel is *more likely* to check in grinding than tough timbre steel. Further reference to grinding checks will be found on page 542.

How does hardness penetration in a carbon tool steel affect size change in hardening? No one expects a plain carbon, water-hardening tool steel to hold its exact size when it is quenched. As will be seen in Chapter 20, this type of steel usually expands somewhat when hardened in small sections, and shrinks when hardened in large sections. It will also be pointed out that the amount of shrinkage or expansion depends upon the relative percentage of hardened case and tough core in the cross section of the piece. The deeper a piece of steel hardens, the more it tends to expand. Since deep hardening penetration would naturally cause a greater percentage of the cross section to become hard, such a steel would be expected to have a greater tendency to expand (or less tendency to shrink) than a shallow hardening steel. This is in accordance with the facts.

Although a tool maker does not expect his carbon tool steel to hold size accurately, he does not want to be badly fooled in its hardening behavior. For example, suppose he were making a draw ring to finish 2″ I.D. From past experience, he expects this ring to shrink about .010″ in hardening. He, therefore, machines it to exact size and figures he will have .010″ to grind out when it comes back from the hardening room. He happens to get hold of a deep hardening steel and, instead of shrinking .010″, it might shrink much less than this—or even open up a little. If it also goes out of round slightly—or has a slight soft skin of decarburization from the hardening, the chances are it will find its way into the scrap box. Unless he has a uniform hardenability to work with, the tool maker's only defense against this is to always allow an excessive amount for grinding. This costs money, it may cause other types of trouble to develop, and not infrequently serves to drive the tool maker into the use of an oil-hardening tool steel—when, from a service standpoint, he would prefer to use a water-hardening steel.

In making taps from water-hardening tool steel, it is quite customary to machine them with the lead slightly "fast" to allow for shrinkage in hardening. If the steel expands instead of shrinking, the lead is likely to be outside of the allowable tolerance. On the other hand, when a tool maker has a stock of tool steel that he knows will always be the same timbre, it is surprising

what he can do with it.   He gradually becomes so well acquainted
with the movement in hardening that he can make appropriate
allowances in machining and can finish up with results that are
much more accurate than would normally be expected of a water-
hardening tool steel.

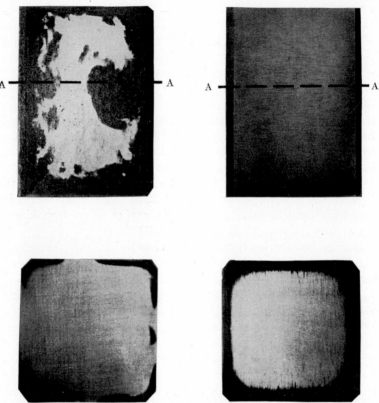

Fig. 66.—(Upper) Illustrating soft spots from quenching in fresh water.   (Lower)
Sections through A-A, after etching.

Effect of Hardenability on Soft Spots.—Soft spots are places on
the surface of a tool which fail to become hard.   They might well
be thought of as spots where the soft core projects through to the
surface.   These soft spots are not *caused* by variations in hardenability.   They are caused by something interfering with the
action of the quenching bath.   Sometimes gas pockets or steam
pockets will form on the surface and retard the action of the
quench just long enough to prevent the spot from hardening.

The only reason the matter is mentioned here is because quenching conditions that will produce a soft spot on a steel having shallow hardening characteristics may not produce any spots at all on a steel having deep hardening characteristics.

Fig. 66 shows at the top two blocks of carbon tool steel approximately 1½″ square × 2″ long. They have been heated together to a temperature of 1430°F. and then quenched in fresh water (which always contains considerable gas in solution). In order to bring out the soft spots so that they will be visible for photographing, both blocks were etched in acid. The large white area on the left hand piece is a soft spot; the other block contains no soft spots.

In order to explore these two pieces further, they are cut in half on the dotted line with a thin, flexible grinding wheel. Etching the cross section clearly reveals the hardness penetration. It will be seen from the lower pair of photographs that the left hand block hardens only about half as deep as the right hand block and that there are many places where there is no

Fig. 67.—Etched cross section of timbre test on the two steels used in Fig. 66.

hardened case at all. These are the soft spots. A round bar hardenability test made on these two bars of steel (etched, instead of fractured) turns out just as would be expected; Fig. 67 shows the left hand piece to be a shallow hardening steel and the right hand piece a deep hardening steel.

No tool maker should deliberately adopt a deep hardening steel—just to get rid of soft spots in hardening. If a 10% salt brine solution is used for quenching, soft spots are unlikely to appear on *any* carbon tool steel. The only reason for discussing soft spots in this chapter at all is because it is one of the ways in which variation in hardness penetration can make itself evident.

WHAT TO DO ABOUT HARDENABILITY AND TIMBRE IN A PLAIN CARBON STEEL

Having considered hardenability and timbre, and their effects on carbon tool steel, the next question is, "What can the tool maker do about it?" Obviously he should not ignore it. On the other hand, he might not feel justified in making a timbre test on every bar of carbon tool steel before he used it.   No hard and fast recommendations can be made because conditions and opportunity vary so much in different tool rooms.   Here are some of the ways this question is being handled in commercial tool rooms.

1. In many places the subject is completely ignored because it is not understood.   Tools that crack or misbehave are charged up to the "mysteries of tool steel."   If they have too much trouble with their water-hardening steel, they switch to an oil-hardening tool steel.   This adds to the expense of the steel and frequently adds to the cost of tool making and quite often the oil hardened tool will not give quite as good production as the water hardened tool would have given.   However, it is an easy way out of the trouble, and is a procedure that has been widely adopted.

2. The other extreme is found in a few shops where they carry an inventory of tool steel bars and make it a point to conduct a timbre and hardenability test on every bar received before placing it in the racks. In such shops, they usually make a hot acid etch test also.   The advantages of this are so obvious in shops where hundreds of dollars may be spent in making a single tool that the practice is likely to be adopted by many more shops.   This method has some minor disadvantages as follows:

(a) Tool steel that is badly needed for production might have to be rejected and a new shipment awaited.   Obviously, even this delay is better than spoiling the tool.

(b) There is some slight cost involved in making the inspection, but this is likely to be small compared to the value of the tools which are to be made.

(c) Many shops do not have the facilities—or the permission from the management—to make such tests but this is usually not insurmountable.

3. A practice intermediate between the first two mentioned is the one most commonly used.   Some tool steel manufacturers make timbre tests regularly on their carbon tool steel and are willing to guarantee the timbre of their product.   This is suggestive of the "doctor's certificate" referred to in Chapter 5 under the Soundness of Tool Steel.   It is not uncommon for tool supervisors, or those responsible for the purchase of tool steel to visit various steel mills and see with their own eyes just what timbre and hardenability tests the mill makes.

It might be supposed from this chapter that a tool maker is expected to analyze the requirements of his various tools and then specify some particular character of carbon tool steel to meet his needs. Actually, such procedure is very seldom recommended. Experience in hundreds of tool rooms has shown that **medium hardening tough timbre** steel is the best choice for the vast majority of tools. The thing that has played so much havoc with the use of water-hardening tool steel is not the inability to

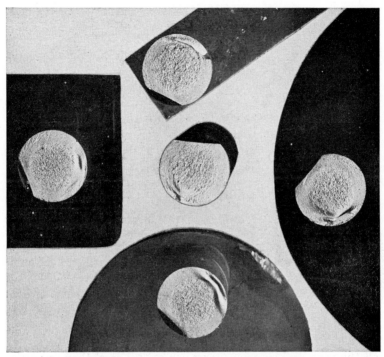

Fig. 68.—Illustrating effectiveness of timbre control. Five bars taken at random from a "certified" stock—pieces about $3\frac{1}{2}''$ long are cut from the bars, and a $\frac{3}{4}''$ round timbre test is machined and left attached to original bar section. The pieces are brine quenched from 1550°F. and fractured. Note uniformity of timbre and hardenability, regardless of size or shape of original bar.

secure the character needed—but rather the inability to get the *same* character twice in succession. All of this work on timbre and hardenability has been done within the past fifteen years. Prior to that time there were no tests, there was no recognized control in the steel mills, and if something went wrong in the tool room no one knew what was the matter. Now that these things are known, a tool maker has a right to expect steel of uniform character time after time.

CHAPTER 5

THE SOUNDNESS OF TOOL STEEL

The third and last step in getting acquainted with tool steel is to learn something about its internal soundness. When John Doe applies for a job, it is necessary to know something about his physical condition before putting him on the payroll. This does not necessarily mean that every employer must be an experienced doctor; he needs only to appreciate that different degrees of health and physical soundness exist in different individuals, and that certain types of ailment or weakness are harmful to a man's ability to work. Knowing this, he does not neglect to investigate the applicant's health before hiring him; but he does not make the examination himself, he depends upon the certificate of a reputable physician.

Just so, a purchaser of tool steel should realize that different degrees of soundness exist in different pieces of tool steel, and that certain types of ailment are detrimental to tools made from the steel. The least he can do is to make some inquiry as to what steps have been taken to make sure that the particular piece of steel he is buying is internally sound. Some buyers go all the way, and examine every bar of tool steel they purchase. Others depend on a "certificate of examination" which may be supplied by the steel maker. Still others make it their business to visit the plant of the steel manufacturer and see with their own eyes what type of inspection he is using for the protection of his customers. In any event, it is a subject that every tool steel user should know something about, and not completely ignore.

How is tool steel examined for internal soundness? For many years it has been the practice in tool steel mills to nick and break a small piece from each end of every bar as a part of the final inspection. It is surprising how much an experienced inspector can see on the fracture of these broken ends. Any gross defect such as pipe or bad surface seams can readily be detected and the bar is scrapped. The very cost of the pile of bar ends accumulated in this inspection testifies to the sincerity of the manufacturer's desire to protect his customers from getting steel containing internal defects. The difficulty lies, not in the intent or the amount of money spent in this crop-end inspection, but in what the unaided human eye can see.

Occasionally, tools would fail in hardening or in service and would be returned to the steel mill to determine the cause of failure. The first step in the investigation was always to determine the internal soundness of the steel. In the Metallurgical Laboratory, there developed the practice of boiling these specimens in hot acid in order to make the inspection more certain. The hot acid eats into any internal defects and so enlarges them that they are easily visible. Obviously, defects were found in this way that had escaped the unaided eye of the mill inspector.

Then the question arose—"If the hot acid etch test can be used to find trouble *after* it has happened, why not use it to find trouble *before* it happens?" To do this would involve cutting a disc from each end of a bar of steel, boiling it in acid and then inspecting the disc for defects. Contrary to general opinion, the expense of this inspection is not limited to making the test itself, but includes the large tonnage of steel that must be thrown away because it will not pass the test. The steel manufacturer who tackles this ambitious program must make up his mind to devote years of hard work to his melting and manufacturing processes in order that he may consistently make steel so perfect that it will pass the hot acid etch test without being scrapped. The routine use of this test in any steel mill bespeaks an extraordinary degree of soundness in that manufacturer's product—otherwise, the test would soon put him out of business.

It is interesting to compare the fracture test with the hot acid etch test in the following photographs. Fig. 69 shows two bars of tool steel which have been nicked and fractured for visual examination by the older method. Which would you choose?

From these same two bars are cut discs about ¼″ thick and boiled in hot acid. Now, referring to Fig. 70, which would you choose?

The disc at the left would be rejected according to almost any standards while the disc at the right represents practically perfect steel.

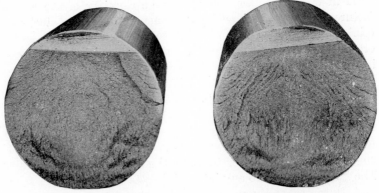

Fig. 69.—Crop test on two tool steel bars.

Fig. 70.—Hot acid disc inspection of same two bars.

Fig. 71 illustrates another fracture of a tool steel bar and beside it is shown the etched disc cut from the same bar. The fracture at the left contains no clue to the horrible condition of the steel as revealed by the hot acid.

After a mill has decided to make a 100% acid inspection of a certain grade of tool steel, the question arises "When should this inspection be made?" If the inspection is made on the finished bars—just before shipping—it will be necessary to scrap a certain amount of material and remake it. This usually involves expensive and annoying delays to the customer and it is obviously an expensive procedure for the tool steel manufacturer, because he has put all of his manufacturing cost into the bar.

There are many practical reasons for acid inspecting tool steel while it is still in the form of billets. In addition to the reasons already mentioned, the steel manufacturer must know what *kind* of defects the acid is revealing and what causes them—otherwise,

FIG. 71.—Another bar showing fracture and acid disc inspection.

he cannot hope to correct his practice to get rid of the defects in future bars. A defect is much larger and easier to study in a 4″ square billet than it would be in a 1″ round bar rolled from that billet. Since practically all of the internal defects originate in the ingot, it is perfectly safe to inspect the billet and it can readily be proved that sound billets will make sound bars. This is done by acid inspecting *both* billets and bars for a sufficient time to establish the facts.

In the routine acid disc inspection of tool steel at the mill, thin discs are sawed from the ends of the billets. Both the disc and billet are stamped with corresponding numbers for identification. The discs are then deep etched in hot acid, washed, dried and examined. Frequently they are then hardened and broken into little pieces for confirming observations. If, for example, the disc from one end of a billet shows a trace of a pipe, and the opposite end of the same billet is clean, a chunk perhaps 6″ long would be sawed from the piped end and scrapped; then a new disc would be sawed off and etched. If this second disc is clean, the billet would be passed for further manufacture. If the defect continued after reasonable discards, the entire billet would be scrapped. Fig. 72 illustrates examining of discs at the Carpenter plant, and Fig. 73 shows the label or "certificate of examination" that is pasted at the time of shipment on each bar made from acid disc inspected billets.

Recently there has come into use a non-destructive type of test for searching out internal defects. In this type of test high frequency vibrations are induced in a bar by means of a special crystal, usually quartz, and the reflection or echo caused by any internal defects is picked up and indicated on an oscillograph

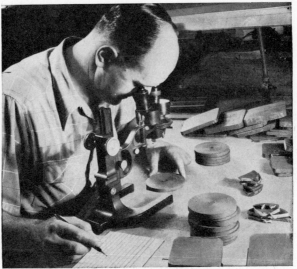

Fig. 72.—Inspecting deep etched discs.
(*The Carpenter Steel Company.*)

Fig. 73.—A label used to certify acid disc inspection.

screen. One such instrument is referred to as an ultrasonic reflectoscope, shown in Fig. 74.

This method has the advantage of making it possible to scan the *entire length* of the billet or bar. The indications obtained, however, must be interpreted carefully since the steel maker needs to know more about a defect than simply the fact that it is present. It is important, as we have stated earlier, that he know also its character and origin, and these are revealed with most certainty by disc inspection.

Thus while the ultrasonic test has proven a very valuable addition to our inspection procedure, its maximum value has been realized by properly incorporating it in the disc inspection

Fig. 74.—Ultrasonic testing machine. (*The Carpenter Steel Company.*)

procedure just described. Here it has provided an important additional safeguard to quality.

Emphasis has been placed on billet inspection because some steel buyers will specify that their tool steel must be acid inspected, and when they receive it they will look at the ends of the bar for evidence of freshly sawed discs. Lacking this evidence, they might assume that no acid inspection had been made. Obviously, in steel mills that employ only billet inspection, the ends of the finished bars will not show evidence of the inspection having been made.

Another point that will be discussed at some length in Chapter 15 must be emphasized here. There are many different kinds of tools and their steel requirements vary tremendously. Obviously, tiny internal defects that might precipitate the ruin of an expensive high speed steel hob, would pass unnoticed in a sledge hammer or even in a cold chisel. Furthermore, even if a rather gross defect did cause failure in a chisel, this loss would not be great, and certainly would not warrant increasing the cost of all chisels produced by specifying acid inspected steel. On the other hand, an intricate blanking die may involve only $5.00 worth of steel and $200 worth of labor, and any reasonable increase in

Fig. 75.—Acid disc inspection on bars taken at random from "certified" stock.

steel cost would be cheap insurance if it helped to assure the success of the tool. These rather extreme examples simply lead up to the statement that acid disc inspected steel is not required for all purposes; and even when it is advisable, rejection limits in the test may be loosened or tightened in accordance with the purpose for which the steel is used.

Because tool steel requirements do vary within such wide limits, even those tool steel mills that use the acid disc inspection do not apply it to *all* their grades. The reader can appreciate that it is an expensive and time consuming test and it is, therefore, reserved for the higher priced brands of tool steel; in fact, it is a very considerable element in the cost of these more expensive brands.   However, when a tool steel manufacturer advertises or guarantees that a certain brand of steel has been acid tested, it should be possible to pick bars at random from his warehouse stock, subject these bars to an acid disc inspection and find them all sound.   Such a group of discs cut at random from an acid inspected stock of tool steel is shown in Fig. 75.

This chapter has dealt with the hot acid etch test in a general way to enable the reader to become acquainted with methods used for insuring sound tool steel.   Those who are interested in actually making the acid disc inspection for themselves will find complete instruction in Chapter 15.

In concluding this section on "getting acquainted with tool steel," it will be profitable to skip swiftly over the history of the past and at least note the approximate dates when certain doors of acquaintanceship were opened.

From at least 3000 B.C. to the sixteenth century A.D., steel making and steel using were "arts" in the strictest sense of the word.   Scientifically, no one knew what tool steel was or why it hardened.   As late as 1540 A.D. metallurgical literature described steel like this:

"Steel is nothing else but iron worked up with much art and much soaking in the fire until it is brought to a perfect mixture and given properties that it did not before possess.   Likewise, it may have taken up suitable material of a dry or fatty tendency, also a certain moisture and thereby become white and denser. The long firing also opens up and softens its pores, which are drawn together again tightly by the power of the cold of quenching water.   The iron is thus given hardness and the hardness makes it brittle.   As iron can be made from any iron ore, likewise steel can be made from any pure iron."

About the time of the American Revolutionary War it was discovered that steel contained carbon and that this element enabled it to harden.   The first chemical laboratory in an American steel mill was installed about 1860 but chemical analysis remained largely a mill secret until the turn of the present century.   By this time the first door of acquaintanceship might be said to have opened.

The second door of "internal soundness" has been ajar for countless years.   No one knows when first a steel worker broke the end of a bar to inspect it for internal defects. Neither is it known when the more modern method of hot acid etching first came into use. Certainly, very little was heard of acid inspecting in this country prior to the First World War, and it was not until 1929 that the first complete stock of acid tested tool steel was advertised to the trade.

The story of timbre, as such, dates from 1930[1]—but this door opened rapidly. By the close of the same year stocks of tool steel made under timbre control methods and having a definite and uniform timbre were available to industry. A full understanding of hardenability of both carbon and alloy tool steels, springing from this earlier work, did not come until later, when in 1940 adequate tests were devised to determine critical quenching rate as a part of routine control in manufacture.

Thus it will be seen that the reader of this book is not gathering the moss of centuries, but is sharing in an acquaintanceship with tool steel that the steel maker himself has enjoyed for only a very few years. It makes it easier to understand why the simplified methods to be described in the next two sections have so recently come into existence. The Matched Tool Steel Method of selecting tool steel as well as the simplified procedures for heat treatment are both the outgrowth of developments that are less than twenty years old.

[1] G. V. Luerssen (The Carpenter Steel Co.). *Some notes on the Behavior of Carbon Tool Steel on Quenching.* Transactions of the American Society for Steel Treating, Vol. 17, 1930, page 161.

PART II

SELECTING THE RIGHT TOOL STEEL FOR EACH KIND OF TOOL

CHAPTER 6

THE MATCHED SET METHOD[1]

On page 3 were listed four things that are essential to the making of a really good tool:

1. Proper design.
2. Accurate tool making.
3. The right tool steel.
4. Correct heat treatment.

It was further said that item #3 gave the tool maker the most difficulty, and was the one standing in greatest need of simplification. This Part II is devoted to a simplified and workable method of tool steel selection. It is known as the Matched Set Method. It is simple because it deals entirely with tools and tool requirements—things with which the tool maker is already familiar, and requires practically no knowledge of the tool steels themselves. It is workable because it works. At this writing, the Matched Set Method has been in commercial use for about ten years and it has been definitely proved that when a tool maker is confronted by a tooling problem, he can select a tool steel that he may never have used before, and he will get the results that he set out to obtain. Chapter 8 contains many reports from tool rooms on the workings of the Matched Set Method. The present chapter will be devoted to the method itself.

There is one thing about tool steel that a tool maker must know in order to use the Matched Set Method; he must understand the modern tough timbre carbon tool steel and have a pretty good idea of what can be expected of it. It is for this reason that plain carbon tool steel has been dealt with so fully in the earlier chapters. The reader now knows that the term "plain carbon tool steel" is not very definite, but embraces a broad class of steels that may vary widely in carbon precentage, physical soundness,

[1] This method of selecting Tool Steel was originated by one of the authors in conjunction with the Research Department of The Carpenter Steel Company.

and timbre.   A much more exact term than merely "carbon tool steel" must be used in a chapter that undertakes to recommend specific steels for specific uses.   As a matter of convenience, the name "WATER-HARD" will be used to apply to one very definite kind of plain carbon tool steel, the characteristics of which are as follows:

CHARACTERISTICS OF WATER-HARD

Average analysis

Carbon...................................... 1.05%
Manganese................................... .20
Silicon..................................... .20
Alloys...................................... None

Soundness—O.K. on acid disc inspection.
Timbre—Tough timbre, medium hardness penetration.

The Matched Set Method of selecting tool steel can best be introduced by quoting a passage from Chapter 3:

If plain carbon tool steel had been perfectly satisfactory for all tooling problems, there would have been no need for alloy steels.   Alloys are put into steel to enable it to do things that a plain carbon steel cannot do.   Strangely enough, these *extra* requirements can all be assembled under four heads.

1. To secure greater wear resistance for cutting or abrasion.

2. To secure greater toughness or strength.

3. To secure hardening accuracy and safety—and increased hardenability.

4. To give the steel "red-hardness," or the ability to do its work when the tool is heated so hot that a plain carbon steel would soften.

If exactly the same thing is said in different words, it plunges us directly into the Matched Set Method—

There are four reasons why a tool maker might want to switch from plain carbon tool steel (WATER-HARD)—

1. To get more wear resistance.

2. To get more toughness.

3. To get greater hardening accuracy and safety.

4. To get red-hardness.

Conversely, if a tool is *not* lacking in any of these four things, it should be made of WATER-HARD.   This immediately suggests the answer to the question—"What kind of tools should be made from WATER-HARD?"   The answer is the first rule of the Matched Set:

Rule 1.—All tools should be made from WATER-HARD *unless there is some good reason for making them from something else.*

A tool maker should not think of WATER-HARD as "just another tool steel." He should think of it as "home." Home is the place where a person stays all the time unless he has a good reason for going somewhere else. It is just so with WATER-HARD. A tool maker should ask himself this question "Is there any good reason

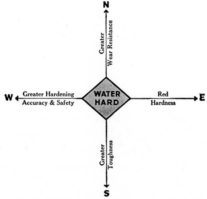

Fig. 76.—Four reasons for switching from carbon tool steel.

why the tool should *not* be made of WATER-HARD?" If no good and sufficient reason presents itself, then this is the steel to use.

But suppose the tool maker decides (or discovers by trial) that the tool in question should *not* be made from WATER-HARD. Then he asks himself the second question—"Why not?" There can only be four answers to this question as has already been seen. This makes it possible to draw a map and to assign to each answer one of the four directions of the compass. The diamond in the center of the map (Fig. 76) represents the field of WATER-HARD. If, for any reason, this steel fails to handle the job satisfactorily, there are four directions available for the tool maker to go to secure the extra property he desires. These constitute the next four rules of the Matched Set Method—

Rule 2.—To secure greater wear resistance, travel north.

Rule 3.—To secure greater toughness, travel south.

Rule 4.—To secure greater hardening accuracy or safety, travel west.

Rule 5.—To secure red-hardness, travel east.

It cannot be emphasized too strongly that if the tool maker does not want extra values in any of these directions, he *stays at home*.   There are more different kinds of tools that can, and should, be made from WATER-HARD than from any other tool steel in existence.

The reader is now asked to use his imagination a little.   Suppose the tool maker is thoroughly acquainted with WATER-HARD—but knows nothing whatever about any other kind of tool steel. Let us imagine that he keeps in his tool box a pepper shaker containing a magic powder labeled "Wear Resistance."   When

Fig. 77.—To add wear resistance.

he comes to a tool requiring greater wear resistance than can be secured with WATER-HARD, he simply cuts off a piece of WATER-HARD steel and sprinkles the magic powder over it.   This adds the extra property that he wants but changes nothing else.   He now has a piece of steel that will behave in every respect like the familiar WATER-HARD steel—excepting that it will wear in service many times longer.

Suppose again that he had another pepper shaker labeled "Toughness."   Confronted by a tool that would break in service when made from WATER-HARD, he would simply sprinkle his steel with this magic powder—nothing else would change—and he would be able to make a tool many times tougher than he had before.   It is perfectly obvious that the tool maker would not need to know the formula for his magic powders—just so they worked.

The above story is not as fantastic as it seems.   In real life, there are no magic powders but there are **alloys** which can be put into steels when they are melted and thus add the extra properties that were conferred by the magic powders. Practical experience shows that in adding the kind of alloys that will produce great wear resistance, a certain percentage of toughness is lost. Also, in adding those alloys which make the steel very much tougher, a certain percentage of wear resistance is lost. This is exactly

Fig. 78.—To add toughness.

what would be expected from looking at the map on page 95— when the tool maker is travelling north toward wear resistance he is moving away from toughness which is south. Likewise, when he is moving toward greater toughness, he is getting away from wear resistance. The tool maker with his magic powders—or the steel maker with his alloys—has now made a group of three steels which will hereafter be referred to as a "Matched Set." They are all water-hardening, and they are as nearly alike as possible in every respect excepting in their relative wear resistance and toughness. Each steel is supposed to pick up its work where the other leaves off so that the tool maker can travel from one to another and know in advance just what to expect.

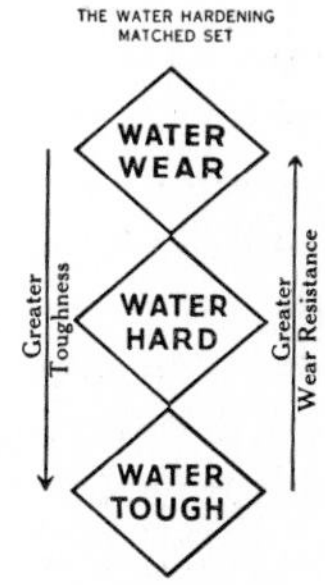

Fig. 79.—The Water-Hardening Matched Set.

The Water-Hardening Matched Set is illustrated in Fig. 79. For convenience the super wear resisting steel will be called WATER-WEAR, and the super tough steel WATER-TOUGH. The arrows are used to show which way to travel to gain the extra properties desired. All of this seems so simple and understandable that the reader will wonder why Matched Tool Steels have come into existence so recently. The answer will become evident when he stops to realize the territory that each of these three steels is asked to cover. Among the three of them, they are expected to make every tool of every description that can be made from a water-hardening tool steel. In earlier years there have been dozens of water-hardening steels used to cover all this territory—and only three steels are now expected to take the place of all of them. This is an extraordinary demand and tool steels of this capacity were not available until recently. This situation can be better understood after taking a look at the tool steel picture as it existed only a few years ago.

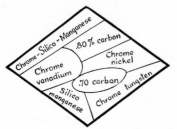
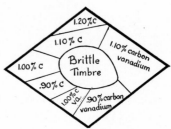

Fig. 80.—Tool steels formerly used to fill the bottom diamond.

Fig. 81.—How the middle diamond would look without timbre control.

For example, Fig. 80 represents the bottom diamond—which is the field of WATER-TOUGH—filled with some of the tough tool steels previously used. It will be seen that some of the space is occupied by plain carbon tool steels containing .70% or .80% carbon. These steels are tougher and less wear resistant than a 1.05% carbon tool steel, and they therefore belong in the bottom diamond. However, such lower carbon steels did not begin to have the capacity to take care of all the tough tools that industry wanted to make. As a result, other tough alloy steels were developed to fill up the space. None of these steels had the capacity to do the job alone; together they were able to cover the territory, but each of them had different properties and therefore presented to the tool maker just the kind of problem in selection that the Matched Set Method seeks to avoid.

Now look at the middle diamond (Fig. 81). Up until quite recently, "plain carbon tool steel" was not a "thing"—it was an extremely variable product. These were the days before timbre was controlled and the tool maker was asked to continually change the carbon content of his steel in order to solve his water-hardening tool steel problems.

Tool makers need not be very old to remember situations where a certain type of carbon steel tool would be going along fine for a while—then suddenly tools would begin to crack in hardening or break in service. Investigation of the trouble, in the light of knowledge then available, showed that the analysis of the steel was the same as had always been used and cause for the sudden appearance of trouble would remain a mystery. The solution recommended might be to switch to a lower carbon steel. If this did not work, a new source of tool steel would be tried—or some alloy tool steel would be substituted. Carbon-vanadium tool steel was a development of this period aimed at this particular type of trouble. The real trouble was **timbre,** and with this factor "running wild," the correctives were somewhat akin to operating for appendicitis when the patient was really suffering from gall stones.

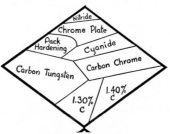

Fig. 82.—The top diamond without matched tool steel.

Constant recurrence of this sort of thing gradually drove many tool rooms into alloy tool steels or heat treating practices that sacrificed much of the efficiency of their carbon tool steels. It is of more than passing interest in this connection that when controlled timbre steels were finally offered to industry, many tool makers said with some surprise "Why we are not having any trouble with our carbon tool steel." And this was true—over a period of years, they had weeded out all the troublesome applications and retained carbon tool steels for only the most unimportant tasks. Since about 1930, this "flight from carbon tool steel" has been reversed, and today the trend is definitely back toward this easy machining, glass hard, keen cutting product—without which the Water-Hardening Matched Set would be impossible. If a single, timbre controlled carbon tool steel will completely cover the area of that middle diamond, the advantages to the tool maker are obvious.

A study of the top diamond in Fig. 82, shows a curious assortment of steels and processes that the tool maker resorted to in order to increase the wear resistance of his tools. It is not necessary that the new WATER-WEAR steel should exceed the capacity of all of these various processes and analyses put together. If a steel can be found that will adequately cover the territory assigned to this top diamond, it will do away with the errors that would result from improper selection among the older alternatives—will eliminate the uncertainties which attend many of these special heat treating processes—and will average to greatly increase the production secured from wear resisting tools.

Tool steels are available today that will *satisfactorily* fill these three diamonds of the Water-Hardening Matched Set. It must

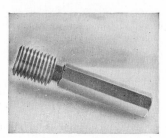

Fig. 83.—Master thread gauge.

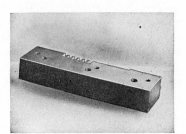

Fig. 84.—Jack die.

not be assumed that they represent ultimate perfection. The tool steel industry will always learn how to make better and better steels. The three diamonds, with their respective needs, can remain there for many years to come, and as better tool steels are developed to fill the requirements of these diamonds, the older ones will become obsolete and the newer ones will take their places. The reader can easily see that such changes can be made with practically no confusion to the tool maker. It will be much as though he had simply discovered a better "magic powder" in the Land of Make-Believe.

It is now time to return to the map. The tool maker's needs for greater wear resistance and greater toughness have been discussed, and solved by the use of two alloy steels called WATER-WEAR and WATER-TOUGH.

Sometimes the tool maker's problem does not involve either wear resistance or toughness. Suppose he were making a master thread gauge like the one illustrated in Fig. 83. If this were made from WATER-HARD it might readily have all of the wear resistance and toughness that he wanted. However, he finds that when he hardens his gauge, it shrinks so much that it is no longer accurate enough to be used as a master. What he now wants is a steel that is as nearly like WATER-HARD as possible—but which will *hold size* accurately when quenched. Or, suppose he were called upon to make a tool of hazardous shape like the piece illustrated in Fig. 84 where those little square cornered teeth would almost surely crack if quenched in water. He knows that if the tool could be brought out of the hardening operation in one piece, it would give perfectly satisfactory performance. He does not want greater toughness or greater wear resistance—he wants greater *safety in hardening*. **Hardening accuracy** and **hardening safety** go hand in hand, and he finds them both on the map (Fig. 85) by traveling west.

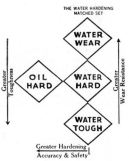

FIG. 85.—To secure hardening accuracy and safety, and deeper hardening.

Without again discussing "magic powders," it is sufficient to say that the steel maker can add to the steel other alloys which will have very little effect on the wear resistance or the toughness but which will make the steel oil-hardening and will give it the added properties of accuracy and safety. This steel will be called OIL-HARD.

It will be appreciated that there are hundreds of different kinds of tools which require either hardening accuracy or hardening safety, or both. After all, neither of these requirements directly affects the *serviceability* of the tool after it goes to work. The tools themselves will be subject to all of the requirements which were found in the Water-Hardening Matched Set. That is, a tool maker might make a certain tool out of OIL-HARD and when he placed it in service he would find that it was not *tough* enough and breakage would follow. On the other hand, the tool might be a blanking die that must produce millions of pieces and his OIL-HARD steel might lack the *wear resistance* desired so that he would want to add this extra property. Thus it is necessary to place to the north of OIL-HARD a steel which will retain all of the hardening accuracy and safety—but which will have super wear resist-

ance.   This steel is called OIL-WEAR.   Likewise, there must be
placed south of OIL-HARD a safe and accurate steel having super
toughness and this would be called OIL-TOUGH.

As illustrated in Fig. 86, these three oil-hardening steels form
a Matched Set of their own known as the Oil-Hardening Matched
Set.   They bear exactly the same relationship to each other as
did the three water-hardening steels,
and they are used in exactly the same
way.

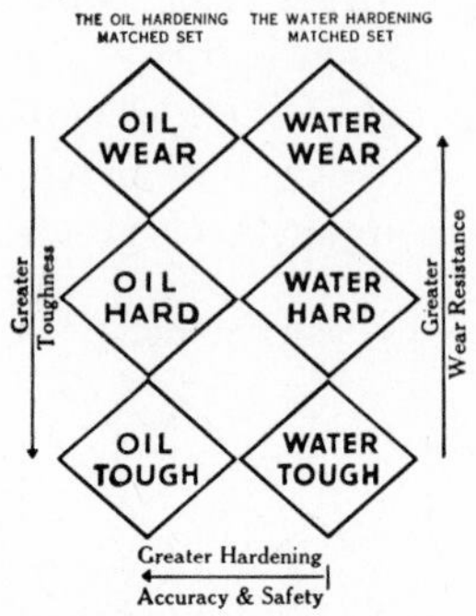

In   discussing   the   Oil-Hardening
Matched Set, hardening accuracy and
hardening safety have been given as
the   primary   reasons   for   travelling
west from the water-hardening steels.
No   mention   has   been   made   of   the
possible advantage of the deeper hardness penetration which goes hand in
hand   with   these   properties   in   the   oil-
hardening steels.   Deeper penetration
in itself is desirable and helpful in
certain types of tools, such as some types of blanking dies,
where it makes possible a greater number of regrindings than
would   be   allowable   were   the   tool   made   from   a   shallower
hardening steel.

Sometimes the tool maker is confronted by a problem involving
either an extremely intricate or a very large sized tool in which
even an oil-hardening steel will not answer.   As the science of tool
engineering progresses, more and more of the "impossible"
things are being done with tools.   The natural result is that tool
designers need more latitude, both in design and in the size of
sections.   There is consequently a trend toward more intricate
tools with the emphasis on extreme accuracy in hardening and a
very minimum of finish grinding, lapping and fitting.   Under
such circumstances cases could arise in which it might be hazardous to use an oil-hardening steel.   There is also the trend toward
considerably larger sections, and there might be cases in which on
account of the size of the tool, an oil-hardening steel would not
become sufficiently hard.   Such a case is illustrated in Fig. 105
(page 124).

FIG. 86.—The Oil-Hard-
ening and Water-Harden-
ing Matched Sets.

Confronted by problems such as these it is apparent that in some instances the tool maker needs even greater hardening accuracy and safety than are obtainable in an oil-hardening steel, and greater hardness penetration. He finds these by continuing to travel west on the map. (Fig. 87.) The steel maker has now added sufficient of the proper alloy to make possible full hardening by air cooling, thus gaining both the advantage of hardening in very large sections as discussed in Chapter 4, and the ultimate in freedom from size change in hardening. This steel will be termed "AIR-HARD."

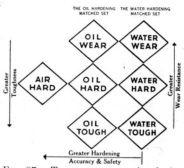

FIG. 87.—To secure extreme hardening accuracy and penetration.

As in the case of the Water and Oil-Hardening Matched Sets, tools made from air-hardening steels will be subject to requirements other than that the tools retain accurate size or harden in large sections. As in the previous cases, they must be adapted to the particular service intended for them, so that again it is necessary to provide to the north of AIR-HARD a steel with all the qualities of AIR-HARD relating to size change and penetration, but with the added quality of extreme wear resistance. This steel is called AIR-WEAR. Similarly it is necessary to provide to the south an air-hardening steel having extreme toughness, and this will be called AIR-TOUGH (Fig. 88).

FIG. 88.—The Air-Hardening, Oil Hardening and Water-Hardening Matched Sets.

It is interesting to examine this group of nine steels from another direction. At the top there are three super wear-resisting steels—AIR-WEAR, OIL-WEAR and WATER-WEAR. These three steels are "running mates" and, theoretically, the only difference between them is the fact that OIL-WEAR and AIR-WEAR possess the extra properties of hardening accuracy and safety, and progressively deeper hardening penetration. Thus all three would be used for making the same tools, and their production ability would be expected to be substantially the same, (except in the case of those tools in which deeper penetration of the oil and air-hardening steels increases production by virtue of a greater number of possible regrindings in service). The tool maker is likely to choose between them, not so much for production reasons, but rather for *tool making* reasons. Likewise, AIR-HARD, OIL-HARD and WATER-HARD are running mates. They are used for the same tools and give very much the same production, with the same reservation concerning the possible advantage of added hardness penetration as you proceed toward the west. WATER-HARD is the one selected unless the extra properties of hardening accuracy and safety are desired in which case OIL-HARD is used, or if super accuracy and deeper hardness penetration are wanted, then AIR-HARD is used. AIR-TOUGH, OIL-TOUGH and WATER-TOUGH are also running mates used for the same purpose. The tool maker chooses OIL-TOUGH whenever the design or requirements of the tool necessitate holding accurate size during hardening, or whenever the shape of the tool would make it unsafe to quench in water. Or he chooses AIR-TOUGH when the tool is required to hold extremely accurate size during hardening, or when the tool is of such large size that an air-hardening steel is necessary in order to obtain the required over-all hardness. In all other cases he chooses WATER-TOUGH.

Based on the actual steels that are currently assigned to these nine diamonds, the tool maker should be prejudiced in favor of the Water-Hardening Matched Set. In only a few cases will there be a difference in production in favor of the oil or air-hardening steels. As a general rule, the water-hardening steels are either less expensive to purchase, or less expensive to machine, or both. Of course, an oil-hardening or air-hardening steel which comes from the hardening room in one piece is much more to be desired than a water-hardening tool that comes from the hardening room broken or cracked. Therefore, in case of doubtful hardening, it is the part of wisdom and safety to choose the oil or air-hardening steel—otherwise, both economy and production point to the water-hardening steel.

There remains one more point of the compass to consider—east. The fourth reason why WATER-HARD might not be satisfactory for a tool lies in the fact that some tools get hot in service. A lathe tool, for example, is heated by the friction of cutting so that the edge may become blue or even a dull red. Under these circumstances, WATER-HARD would lose its temper and become quite soft and useless. Many hot forging tools

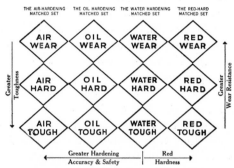

FIG. 89.—The complete Matched Set Diagram.

have the same requirement. This extra property is called **red-hardness.** Alloys like tungsten, molybdenum, chromium and vanadium have the ability, when properly combined, to make a steel red-hard. That is, the tool can become heated in service—sometimes even as high as 1000°F.—and when it cools off it will be just as hard as it was when it started. Furthermore, such steels will be reasonably hard while they are still at the high temperature. For example, a high tungsten steel will remain hard enough to cut metals continuously while the cutting edge is up to a dull red temperature—or about 1000°F.

When red-hardness is the extra property desired, the tool maker proceeds east, as indicated in Fig. 89, and there he finds a steel called RED-HARD. North of RED-HARD there is a red-hard steel having super wear resistance called RED-WEAR and in the south there is another having super toughness called RED-TOUGH. These three steels comprise the fourth and last of the Matched Sets. They are known as the Red-Hard Matched Set.

One could scarcely call these three steels running mates of their corresponding three steels in the Water-Hardening Set, because in each instance they are used for entirely different purposes. So we must recognize a rather basic difference between the Red-Hard Set, and the set of nine steels first described. The latter are used for tools which never get hot in service, while the Red-Hard steels have been specifically designed to operate at elevated temperatures, and in this respect fall into a specialized field of applications. It would be well to keep an imaginary line between the two groups, thinking of the set of nine steels at the left of this line as *cold work die and tool steels*, and the set of three steels to the right of this line as *hot work die and tool steels*. It is interesting to anticipate a little and note that the steel which occupies the RED-WEAR diamond is *high speed tool steel*.

The alloys used in the formula for making red-hard steels are expensive and must be used in quite large quantities. Therefore these red-hard steels will average to cost more than the corresponding members of the Water-Hardening Matched Set. Also, due to their high alloy content, they will usually cost more to machine—and even more to heat treat. There is, therefore, never any excuse for calling upon these red-hard steels except-ing in cases where the tools get so hot in service that it is simply impossible to use the steels from the other three Matched Sets.

The reader should note and remember one point in which the direction arrows of the Diagram cannot be taken too literally. It was pointed out that in travelling north for greater wear resistance, the toughness decreased; and when travelling south for toughness, the wear resistance decreased. This is indicated by the direction arrows on the Diagram and it is also true in practice. Therefore, it would be entirely logical to suppose that in traveling west for hardening accuracy and safety, the steels would lose red-hardness; and that in travelling east for red-hard-ness, they would lose accuracy and safety. This is **not** true. The east-and-west arrows are "one-way" arrows, and the reader must simply tax his memory with this fact.

The twelve steels described comprise the complete Matched Set Diagram. With these twelve steels a tool maker can solve almost any tooling problem that may present itself. The interesting thing is that, thus far, not a word has been said about analysis. So far as using the Matched Diagram is concerned a tool maker could use it just as accurately if he had never heard of analysis. He could even think in terms of "magic powders" and get along just as well.

Obviously, the success of this method depends upon the availability of twelve tool steels that are truly matched with each other —and each steel must have sufficient capacity to completely fill

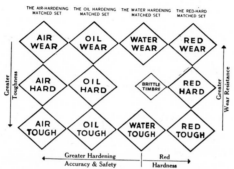

Fig. 90.—Matched Diagram using brittle timbre carbon steel.

the diamond to which it is assigned. This becomes clear upon consideration of what might happen if there were no tough timbre tool steel to fill the WATER-HARD diamond. Brittle timbre steel is so much more limited in its application that, if this kind of steel were used, the diagram might look like the illustration in Fig. 90. Brittle timbre steel is so brittle in service that it is limited on the south and does not extend far enough to connect with WATER-TOUGH. Its very brittleness compels the use of heat treatments that limit its wear resistance, and for many purposes it will not reach up north far enough to contact WATER-WEAR. Its susceptibility to cracking in hardening keeps it quite some distance removed from the hardening safety of OIL-HARD. The "red-hardness" is not affected so it would still touch RED-HARD on the east. In other words, it is not matched with the steels that surround it.

Here is what might happen. The brittleness of the brittle timbre steel might drive a tool maker south toward WATER-TOUGH. After the tool was made of WATER-TOUGH, it might lack sufficient wear resistance for its purpose. What would he do then? It is evident that this particular tool falls in the open space between the brittle timbre steel and WATER-TOUGH. His only recourse would be to hunt *outside* the Matched Diagram for some other steels to fill the gap. This defeats the very purpose of the diagram, which is to use the smallest possible number of steels and have them so closely matched that the tool maker can go from one to the other without embarrassing gaps.

It will be appreciated that this diagram throws a tremendous responsibility on the shoulders of the tool steel manufacturer. He must find for each of the twelve steels a chemical formula that has sufficient capacity to fill the diamond. He must then so control his method of manufacture that the properties of his steel are *uniform* from one shipment to another—so that the tool maker can depend upon the results he will get.

It is not claimed that perfection has been arrived at in these particulars, and there is ample room in the future for the steel manufacturer to develop more perfect steels to put into these diamonds. In truth some of the steels filling the various diamonds have already been modified since the Matched Set idea was first published, and an additional set, the air-hardening steels, has been added. These changes have been made as better steels have been found to fill present spaces, and as new steels have proved their worth to justify new spaces. This is all testimony to the fact that instead of interfering with improvements, the Matched Set Method actually suggests them. The basic idea is one which lends itself to considerable flexibility; and even further improvements, and possibly additions, may be expected in the future.

In spite of minor imperfections, therefore, the advantage of the Matched Set Method greatly outweighs its disadvantages. This was the first definite method of tool steel selection ever presented to the tool maker, and its results continually speak for themselves in tool rooms all over the world. Take two tool makers of equal ability and ask them each to make exactly the same tool or die. Give one of them a number of the old-fashioned tool steel catalogs to read and give the other a Matched Set Diagram. The matched set man will have his answer in a few minutes and the chances are ten to one that his finished tool will give less trouble and more production than the other fellow's. Somewhere in all of those tool steel catalogs it is entirely likely that there is *one* steel that might exceed the performance of the Matched Tool Steel picked from the Diagram—but the chances of finding this one steel among so many (on the first trial) is so remote that the odds are long in favor of the Matched Set Method. Multiply this by hundreds of tools and dies of every conceivable variety, such as might be made in the tool room of an average metal working plant, and it will be seen why the Matched Set Method works so well—in spite of its minor deficiencies.

The Matched Set Method sounds so easy that the reader is likely to expect that he will never make a mistake. This is not the case. Errors *will* be made—and wrong steels will be selected from the Diagram. But—each error points the tool maker more accurately to the proper diamond on the Diagram and it is seldom necessary to make more than two trials. The examples given in Chapter 8 show cases where the right steel was found on the *first* trial, the *second* trial—and in one instance—on the *third* trial.

Furthermore, errors will be made in heat treatment that will start the tool maker off in the wrong direction. For example, suppose a tool is made of WATER-TOUGH, and through careless heat treatment, it is badly decarburized on the surface. If this is not noticed (and corrected) the tool goes into service and appears very soft and lacking in wear resistance. The tool maker might jump to the conclusion that he should travel *north* for greater wear resistance and make the tool of WATER-HARD. If the tool is up against very severe service, WATER-HARD might break or chip—and the tool maker might then erroneously assume that *neither* steel would do the job. As a matter of fact WATER-TOUGH was the right choice in the first place, but the heat treatment had everyone fooled. As long as we are human, we will make errors in practice, and errors in judgment. No method of tool steel selection can be made proof against such errors, and Part IV of this book has been written just so these mistakes can be kept at a minimum.

Prima Donnas.—It is not the intention to leave the reader with the impressions that some day there will only be twelve tool steels left in the world. Even today in tool rooms where the Matched Set Method has been completely adopted, other tool steels find occasional use.   If the authors may be pardoned for naming things to suit themselves, we will call all tool steels that do not appear on the Matched Diagram "prima donnas."   This is more than a name because it really describes the situation quite accurately.   On the stage, a prima donna is an *artist* with a *temperament*.   She can do *one* thing almost perfectly—maybe she is a ballet dancer or an opera singer—but whatever that one thing is, she does it mighty well.   But she can't (or won't) darn socks, fry eggs, play tennis or redecorate the living room.   She is a little hard to understand—they call it "temperamental." There are tool steel "prima donnas"—and we shall use this term to apply to all special analysis tool steels that can do a few things very well but can't do enough jobs to entitle them to a place on the Matched Diagram.

The Matched Set Method is not going to retire all of these prima donnas.   If the Matched Set will take care of 90% of the tools that come up in the tool room, it will have done a wonderful job.   There will always be exceptional tools that will require exceptional consideration.   Such exceptional consideration is seldom justified in a tool that must be renewed only perhaps once or twice a year.   Finding the right prima donna to use for a tool might easily require cutting-and-trying eight or ten different tool steels—with quite a variety of heat treatments being applied to each one.   Not only is this expensive, but if the tool is made only occasionally, it would take years to work the problem out— and by that time, either the prima donna or the tool itself might be obsolete.   On the other hand, consider a bolt and nut plant. In the tool room, they might make thousands of cold header dies every year.   They can well afford to spend considerable time and money hunting for a prima donna that will give them better results than they could get from WATER-HARD or any of the other members of the Matched Set.   Or consider the the tool manufac- turer who makes tools for resale.   For example, a tap manufac- turer might make hundreds of thousands of taps per year and he is in competition with others who are doing the same thing.   No trouble or expense is too great for these manufacturers to perfect their product.   Incidentally, they buy tool steel in such large quantities that the tool steel manufacturer is generally willing to make up a special "custom made" analysis to suit their particular needs. A further discussion of these special steels is beyond the scope of this book but it is important for all tool makers to know that such steels are available—because they never know when they may be called upon to use them. Prima donnas are best worked out in direct personal contact with the tool steel manufacturer.

CHAPTER 7

THE TWELVE MATCHED TOOL STEELS

The theory of Matched Tool Steels presented in the last chapter enables a tool maker to put his finger on a certain diamond and say, "That is the steel I want to try first." If for any reason the first tool is lacking in some particular, he can simply follow the proper arrow and correct the difficulty. The tool designer might even put on his blueprint "To be made of OIL-TOUGH Tool Steel." But this is as far as any theory can go. The tool maker cannot tear a page out of a textbook and make the tool of it. He must have a real piece of tool steel.

This chapter will name, and give the analysis of the twelve Matched Tool Steels that The Carpenter Steel Company has fitted into the Matched Diagram. Not only does this give reality to the chapters that have preceded, but makes possible the chapters that follow. Part III is devoted to describing the properties, heat treatment, and testing of Matched Tool Steels, and it is necessary to have something more definite to talk about than the twelve idealized diamonds of the Matched Diagram. For example, the Matched Diagram says that OIL-WEAR will hold size accurately in hardening. The tool maker wants to know *how* accurately. Exact figures can be given only when talking about one definite steel. Heat treating instructions must also be specific—otherwise we are compelled to fall back upon the general *theory* of heat treatment as it is dealt with in textbooks on metallurgy. Just as far as possible the names OIL-WEAR, OIL-HARD, etc. will be adhered to, because these names are fundamental to the Matched Set Method and will stay in existence—even while the steels themselves may be continually improved.[1] **Brand names** are necessary to the identification of a tool steel— because they describe not only the analysis, but the "soundness"

[1] Examples of this will be found in the RED-HARD and RED-TOUGH diamonds —to which two improved hot work tool steels have been assigned in the revised diagram.

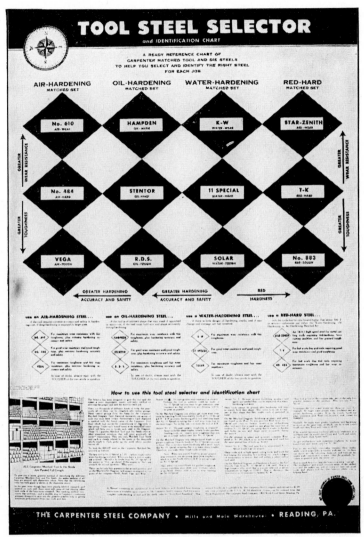

FIG. 91.—Wall chart using the Matched Diagram as a tool steel selector. (*Copyright 1948, The Carpenter Steel Co.*)

and the "personality" of the steel as well.   For example, The Carpenter Steel Company makes no less than four brands of tool steel having the same type *analysis* as WATER-HARD, but only one of them has been definitely matched into the Diagram.   An analysis specification could mean *any* of them—but the brand name picks out the right *one*.

THE TWELVE MATCHED TOOL STEELS

WATER-HARD

Carpenter Brand Name—"*No. 11 Special*"

Type Analysis

Carbon	1.05%
Manganese	.20
Silicon	.20
Alloys	None

WATER-TOUGH

Carpenter Brand Name—"*Solar*"

Type Analysis

Carbon	.50%
Manganese	.40
Silicon	1.00
Molybdenum	.50

WATER-WEAR

Carpenter Brand Name—"*K-W*"

Type Analysis

Carbon	1.30%
Manganese	.30
Silicon	.30
Tungsten	3.50

OIL-HARD

Carpenter Brand Name—"*Stentor*"

Type Analysis

Carbon	.90%
Manganese	1.60
Silicon	.25

OIL-TOUGH

Carpenter Brand Name—"*R. D. S.*"

Type Analysis

Carbon	.75%
Manganese	.35
Silicon	.25
Chromium	1.00
Nickel	1.75

OIL-WEAR
Carpenter Brand Name—*"Hampden"*
Type Analysis

Carbon	2.10%
Manganese	.25
Silicon	.25
Chromium	12.50
Nickel	.50

AIR-HARD
Carpenter Brand Name—*"No. 484"*
Type Analysis

Carbon	1.00%
Manganese	.70
Silicon	.20
Chromium	5.00
Molybdenum	1.00
Vanadium	.20

AIR-TOUGH
Carpenter Brand Name—*"Vega"*
Type Analysis

Carbon	.70%
Manganese	2.00
Silicon	.30
Chromium	1.00
Molybdenum	1.35

AIR-WEAR
Carpenter Brand Name—*"No. 610"*
Type Analysis

Carbon	1.50%
Manganese	.30
Silicon	.30
Chromium	12.00
Molybdenum	.80
Vanadium	.90

RED-WEAR
Carpenter Brand Name—*"Star-Zenith"*
Type Analysis

Carbon	.72%
Manganese	.25
Silicon	.20
Chromium	4.00
Tungsten	18.25
Vanadium	1.15

Carpenter Brand Name—"*Speed Star*"
Type Analysis

Carbon	.82%
Manganese	.25
Silicon	.25
Chromium	4.25
Tungsten	6.25
Vanadium	1.90
Molybdenum	5.00

RED-HARD
Carpenter Brand Name—"*T-K*"
Type Analysis

Carbon	.35%
Manganese	.30
Silicon	.30
Chromium	3.50
Tungsten	9.00
Vanadium	.40

RED-TOUGH
Carpenter Brand Name—"*No. 883*"
Type Analysis

Carbon	.40%
Manganese	.35
Silicon	1.10
Chromium	5.00
Vanadium	.90
Molybdenum	1.35

For actual use in the tool room, the above trade names are incorporated in the Matched Diagram shown in Fig. 91, page 113.

CHAPTER 8

THE MATCHED SET METHOD IN USE

It is the purpose of this chapter to give examples of how the Matched Set Method is applied. First will be illustrated a number of real tools that will be discussed from the theoretical

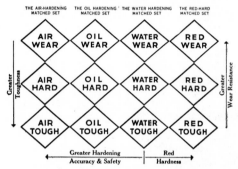

FIG. 92.—The Matched Set Diagram.

angle. We will put ourselves in the place of a tool maker who might be required to make these tools and then we will "think out loud" about the selection of the proper Matched Tool Steel. The Matched Diagram (Fig. 92) is reproduced here for convenience.

Note that in each case we first ask the key question "Why not use WATER-HARD?" This question is asked—even when it may seem foolish—because in answering the questions as to *why* WATER-HARD will not work, we point ourselves in the direction of the steel that *will* work.

FIG. 93.—Draw die and steel cup.

Fig. 93. Draw ring for drawing a 23 gauge steel cup. Why not use WATER-HARD? This tool presents no cracking hazards— it is easy to grind after hardening, so size change is not vital—

117

yes, WATER-HARD is O.K.   If production were very large, and
WATER-HARD did not wear long enough, travel north and use
WATER-WEAR.

Fig. 94.   Compound blanking and perforating die and punch.
Blanking 26 gauge steel.   For the die: Why not use WATER-

FIG. 94.—Blanking and perforating tools.

HARD?   Because it can't be ground to exact size after hardening.
What is the tolerance on this stamping?   If the contour and
holes must be held within a thousandth or two—an oil-hardening,

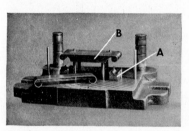

FIG. 95.—Tools for curling brass strip.

non-deforming tool steel must
be used.

OIL-HARD is the oil-hardening running mate of WATER-
HARD.   Why not use OIL-
HARD?   Great toughness is not
involved—OIL-TOUGH is not
needed.   The choice lies between OIL-HARD and OIL-WEAR
depending on the production
required per dressing.   OIL-WEAR dies will cost considerably
more than OIL-HARD—will the production pay for the extra cost?

The punch: To get accurately fitted tools—accurate holes and
freedom from stoning or lapping—OIL-HARD or OIL-WEAR must be
used—just as in the dies.

The small punches: Why not use WATER-HARD bar stock or
Drill Rod?   No question of grinding or size change is involved.
Either one can be used—and drill rod is the easiest to get.

Fig. 95.   Bending die (*A*)—and mandrel (*B*).   The punch is
not shown.   Used for curling .020″ brass.   This type of tooling
is useful only for soft materials.   The flat strip is laid on the top
of the mandrel, the punch bends the ends straight down then
forces the mandrel down until the edges of the brass catch the

lugs on the side of the dies which start the material curling under. The wear is all on the dies.

The dies: Why not use WATER-HARD? It would be O.K. For long production use WATER-WEAR. There is no size change and little cracking hazard involved.

The mandrel: Why not use WATER-HARD? It is a mean unbalanced shape to harden in water—also the mandrel needs strength and toughness more than it needs wear resistance. Hence we want both more toughness and more hardening safety than would be expected from WATER-HARD. Travel west for safety and south for toughness and we come to OIL-TOUGH—the tough member of the oil hardening family. That is the steel to use for the mandrel.

FIG. 96.—Marking die.

What about the guide pins on which the mandrel slides? Use WATER-HARD Drill Rod. In sizes $\frac{3}{16}''$ round and smaller, WATER-HARD Drill Rod will harden file hard in oil and this makes it definitely tougher for small pins, punches, etc.

NOTE: Do not confuse WATER-HARD Drill Rod with ordinary "commercial drill rod." WATER-HARD Drill Rod is made from high quality timbre-controlled tool steel. Therefore, it will do a lot of things that commercial drill rod will not do.

Fig. 96. Interchangeable stamping die for marking brass and steel strip.

For the die: This is a perfectly flat plate involving no requirement but hardness. Use WATER-HARD.

For the punch: This graduated punch is also the holder for the replaceable stamps. Why not use WATER-HARD? Because it would crack in hardening—note those sharp slots on either side. To get hardening safety, go west and use OIL-HARD.

For the individual stamps: Use WATER-HARD. If the screw

holes in the stamps constitute a hardening hazard, quench only the face and let the balance of the stamp remain unhardened.

Fig. 97. Square punches for punching switch slide plates. The plates (shown much reduced in size) are .45% carbon steel $1\frac{1}{4}''$ thick, partly machined down to $1\frac{3}{16}''$ thick. The holes are $\frac{3}{4}''$ square and while three sides of the punch are cutting through $1\frac{1}{4}''$ metal, the fourth side is cutting $1\frac{3}{16}''$ metal.

FIG. 97.—Switch slide plate and punch (enlarged).

FIG. 98.—Progressive marking and stamping die.

Why not use WATER-HARD? Because it would break in service —the side thrust is tremendous. Since greater toughness is needed, use WATER-TOUGH. No oil-hardening requirements are involved.

Fig. 98. Progressive blanking and stamping die. (Note the lettered stamp in the punch holder indicated by the arrow.) The first stage perforates the curved slots and stamps the letters —the second stage blanks. The material is galvanized iron.

Why not use WATER-HARD? A water-hardening steel would be hopeless for the punch or die—cracking hazard, warpage and accuracy are all involved.

The lettered stamp can and should be made of WATER-HARD. OIL-HARD could be used but it would not last as long as WATER-HARD and an oil-hardening steel is not needed here.

The die must be made from an oil-hardening or air-hardening

steel and either OIL-HARD or OIL-WEAR would be the first selection, depending on production required per dressing, since no superior toughness is required on this light gauge material.

The thin curved punches are an interesting problem. On very light material OIL-HARD or OIL-WEAR would be O.K.— if any breaking or chipping were encountered in service, go south for greater toughness and use OIL-TOUGH.

The large rectangular punch would be the same steel as used in the die.

Fig. 99. Thread rolling die. The job is cold rolling threads

FIG. 99.—Thread rolling die.

on soft and mild steel bolts or studs under flat dies. The requirements are, first, extreme accuracy in hardening, since no finish grinding is permissible on the teeth; and second, good wear-resistance to provide long production runs.

Why not use WATER-HARD? In this case great hardening accuracy is necessary, and furthermore water quenching would be hazardous on account of the sharp corners at the base of the teeth. We therefore travel west. OIL-HARD could be used but would not meet the wear requirement. We now have two directions we might travel, northward to gain wear-resistance, or westward to gain greater safety and accuracy along with greater wear-resistance. In this case it is wise to go both westward and northward, and use AIR-WEAR.

Fig. 100. A slitting cutter. There is little about the shape of the tool to prevent using any steel we care to. However, people who make these shears get tired of having them warp or dish in hardening—so they go to an oil-hardening steel to keep them flat and straight.

FIG. 100.—Rotary metal slitting cutter.

Slitting cutters are usually made from either OIL-WEAR or OIL-TOUGH depending on service. For slitting thin gauge metal, or such other materials as paper or fibre where abrasion is high and stresses are low, OIL-WEAR is preferred. For the big majority of miscellaneous work, OIL-TOUGH is the best. Chipping on the edge is a common fault in slitting shears and the toughness of OIL-TOUGH is the answer to that.

Fig. 101.   Cold heading gripper dies.

Why not use WATER-HARD? No good answer presents itself so we make them of WATER-HARD. As a matter of practical experience, we know that WATER-HARD would do a reasonably good job in these dies —and try as we might there would be no other steel in the

FIG. 101.—A pair of cold heading gripper dies.

entire Matched Set that would do better.   However, in bolt shops they make thousands of these dies and they have worked with the tool steel manufacturers to develop custom-made "prima donnas" that are specially suited for header dies.   Such steels will outperform WATER-HARD by a considerable margin.

This example is included to show that—even with the Matched Set and all the jobs the Matched Set can do—there will still be a few jobs that can be done better with special "custom-made" tool steels.

Fig. 102.   Dies for coining automobile brake drum.   In making a brake drum, after the rim is formed it is placed in a press for a coining operation to give the drum exact shape and size.   On this operation very heavy pressure is applied and the metal is reduced .002″ to .003″ in thickness.

FIG. 102.—Dies for coining brake drum.

Tendency for wear on the die is very severe.

Why not use WATER-HARD?   In this case the tools are quite heavy in section and the operating pressures high.   Deep penetration and resistance to wear are necessary.   Neither a water nor an oil-hardening steel are advisable under these conditions, and it is necessary therefore to travel west for greater hardening penetration.   AIR-HARD, however, would not give the desired wear-resistance, and the logical direction to travel from there would be northward to AIR-WEAR.

The illustration in Fig. 102 shows the brake drum to the left of the male part of the die.   All parts are AIR-WEAR except the flat machine steel pieces attached to the right and bottom of the male parts of the die.

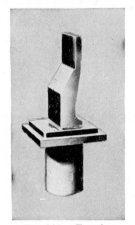

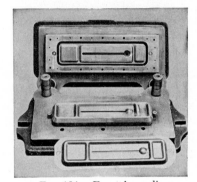

FIG. 103.—Forming punch.

FIG. 104.—Escutcheon die.

Fig. 103.   Forming punch.

Why not use WATER-HARD?   There is nothing in the design of this tool to prevent WATER-HARD from being used.   The choice of steel will depend entirely on the type of service.   If WATER-HARD breaks due to heavy strains in service—switch to WATER-TOUGH.   If WATER-HARD is plenty tough—but wears out or galls—use WATER-WEAR.

Fig. 104.   Escutcheon die for forming the steel stamping illustrated.   This stamping is about 18″ long.

Why not use WATER-HARD?   The die is made up in three sections and the punch in two sections.   This is a good job for WATER-HARD providing the hardener is familiar with the heat treatment of these large chunks in water.   Most escutcheon dies are made of water-hardening steel.

If an inexperienced man were to harden these tools, he would be better off with an oil-hardening steel (OIL-HARD) so they would not warp.

Fig. 105.   Large rolls for the roll forming of .150″ thick pickled and annealed SAE 1010.

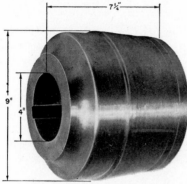

FIG. 105.—Large forming rolls.

It is obvious from the illustration that there is nothing in the design of this tool which would prevent using any steel we choose. However, this roll is subjected to very high compression, and consequently a high degree of hardness, and a great depth of hardness, are both necessary. These requirements would rule out both water-hardening and oil-hardening steels.

If we were to make these rolls for the first time, the logical starting point would be AIR-HARD. Experience would indicate whether it would be desirable to go either northward for more wear resistance, or southward for greater toughness. Actual experience on this particular case indicated that it was preferable to go southward, and best results were obtained on AIR-TOUGH.

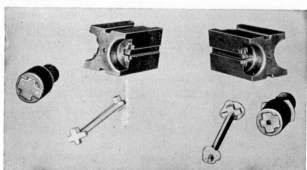

FIG. 106.—Tools for hot upsetting special forgings.

Fig. 106.   Gripper dies and punches for hot upsetting a special steel wrench.

Why not use WATER-HARD? These tools will become *hot* in service and the temper would quickly be lost in WATER-HARD. What we need here is *red-hardness*. The first red-hard steel encountered going east on the Diagram is RED-HARD. Why not use this? No satisfactory objection can be found and hence this steel is the one to use.

NOTE: On further acquaintance with the Red-Hard Matched Set, it will be found that RED-WEAR is not tough enough to be even considered for making dies of this sort (although possibly it might make the punches). Therefore, at all times, in selecting a steel for hot *forging* tools, the choice lies between RED-HARD and RED-TOUGH.

Fig. 107. Hot extrusion mandrel.

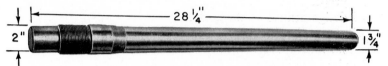

FIG. 107.—Hot extrusion mandrel.

The job is that of extruding aluminum tubing. The requirements are red-hardness to withstand high operating temperatures, good toughness, and the ability to withstand water cooling when necessary.

Why not use WATER-HARD? These tools will become hot in service, and as a result a plain carbon steel would quickly soften. Moving eastward on the diagram from WATER-HARD the first diamond encountered is RED-HARD. Why not use this? RED-

FIG. 108.—An assortment of metal cutting tools.

HARD has sufficient strength and hardness at elevated temperatures, but does not have the desired toughness. Neither will it stand water cooling in service, and is very likely to develop surface checks under those conditions. The logical direction to move therefore is southward to RED-TOUGH.

Fig. 108. Here is a whole group of metal cutting tools.

Why not use WATER-HARD? There is not a tool in this assortment that cannot be made of WATER-HARD. In fact, tools like hand taps which operate at very slow speeds *are* made of WATER-

HARD. However, machine tools today operate so rapidly that the cutting tools become very hot and WATER-HARD would soften.

Here we need red-hardness and maximum wear resistance, so we go east for red-hardness and north for wear resistance and come to RED-WEAR. This is a high speed tool steel and is the obvious answer to most machine driven metal cutting tools.

It will be noticed in the above examples that there are many "ifs."

IF production is to be large . . .

IF proper heat treating facilities are available . . .

IF design cannot be changed . . . etc. . . . and etc. . . .

These are the "ifs" the steel manufacturer never knows—but the tool maker does. The purpose of the Matched Diagram is to place the most up-to-date knowledge of the steel maker in the hands of the tool maker. When he adds this to what he already knows about his own tooling problems, the solution is not difficult to see.

REAL PROBLEMS THAT HAVE BEEN SOLVED

At this writing, the Matched Tool Steel Method has been in commercial use for about ten years. During this time it passed through a period of trial, and emerged as a widely recognized and established method for the selection of tool steels. When the first edition of this book was written in 1937, the author in commenting on the practicability of the Matched Set Method, said: "Sometimes the most attractive theories do not work out in practice, but in this case, this book might have been written two years ago—because it has not been found necessary to change the Diagram, remove a single steel or even alter the instructions." The ensuing eight years of experience with the Matched Set have fully confirmed this observation. Time and again during those eight years the soundness of the Matched Set principle has been demonstrated. It has been proven such a valuable implement that the only modification has been in the form of an addition— that of a fourth set of steels, the Air-Hardening Set.

During the period through which the Matched Set Method has been in use, many interesting stories have been received from commercial tool makers who have solved their problems by means of the Matched Set Method. In many cases, they adopted steels which they had never before used—they heat treated the tools by the simplified methods described in PART III—and they achieved results that heretofore might have been expected only with the assistance of a tool steel expert. Several of these stories are reproduced below with photographs taken of the actual tools which were made. The wording is the authors'—each story being presented in the most instructive form possible—without changing any of the original facts.

THE STORY OF A PUNCH

The first story concerns one of the simplest of all tools—a plain, round punch.

The Job (Fig. 109).—To punch two holes $\frac{7}{32}''$ round through a section $\frac{7}{32}''$ thick, of cold drawn carbon steel showing about 187 Brinell hardness. It was a big production job. The punches were being made of a good grade of plain carbon, water-hardening tool steel (not WATER-HARD). The results were not very uniform because most of the punches failed by breaking. The average was about 4,000 holes per

FIG. 109.—A difficult cold punching job.

punch. It was one of those annoying little jobs that are a headache both to the tool room and the production department.

The tool maker decided it was a good place to try out the Matched Diagram. He said to himself, "I'm using a plain carbon, water-hardening tool steel. Of course, it is not WATER-HARD but it is the same *analysis*, so I should be in the Water-Hardening Matched Set."

Next he argues—"This punch doesn't get hot, so I can forget the red-hard steels. It is an easy shape to harden in water and I grind it all over anyway, so I don't need an oil-hardening steel. The answer must be somewhere in the Water-Hardening Matched Set. Since the punches are breaking, I want more toughness, so I go south and here is WATER-TOUGH. I'll try that." And he did.

Sure enough, the breakage stopped entirely and the production went up to an average of 6,000 holes per punch. But—now the WATER-TOUGH punches finally failed by galling. If he could get rid of that, he could get more production.

It took a lot of nerve to travel north for greater wear resistance —because it seemed as though that was where he had just come from. But he argued that he had never used tough timbre WATER-HARD steel and he was going to find out whether the Diagram knew what it was talking about. Strange as it may seem, the WATER-HARD punches did not break—and they did wear longer. The production was now up to an average of 8,000 holes per punch.

This looked like a good place to stop—but said he, "Let's just take a chance and see what is up north in that top diamond. They can't do any more than break." So he made a few punches from WATER-WEAR. Believe it or not, they didn't break either and production increased to 14,000 pieces per punch.

WATER-WEAR was adopted for the job and everything was going fine—then something else happened. The engineering department decided that that particular piece ought to be a little heavier so they added to its thickness. This caused punch breakage to develop again—so what? The tool maker simply "backed up" to WATER-HARD and again the job was licked.

There are two interesting things to note in this experience. The first thing to observe is the fact that, while the tool steel originally used was probably a good steel, it wasn't on the Matched Diagram—it wasn't matched with WATER-TOUGH and WATER-WEAR. For this reason it was necessary to make *three* trials to arrive at the best steel. The Matched Diagram has this in common with all "maps"—you must get *on* the map first, before you can use the direction signs.

The second thing to notice is how easily the tool maker found his way around, once he got firmly settled on the Diagram. When they thickened up the section and WATER-WEAR punches started breaking, he did not need to do a lot of experimenting—he *knew* what to do and he did it. The best tool steel expert from the steel mill could have done no better. In fact, with this Diagram, the tool maker has some advantages over the expert—because he knows both the *job* and the tool steel, while the steel man usually knows only the steel.

THE STORY OF A PERFORATING DIE

The Job (Fig. 110).—To punch at one stroke 1,600 holes $\frac{9}{64}''$ diameter in $\frac{1}{8}''$ thick cardboard to form a punchboard. On account of limitations of press equipment the user of the die insisted on a one-piece job, so the tool designer had no choice but to build it that way, although ordinarily he would have designed

an indexing die. This is one of the cases previously mentioned in which the designer is allowed no latitude, and consequently an added burden must be thrown on the steel and the heat treatment. The die as de-
signed measured 10″ × 8″ × 2″. It was originally made from OIL-HARD, but cracked in hardening between the light and heavy sections along the junction of the drilled out center and the edge. In order to get greater safety in harden-ing the tool maker decided to move west to an air-hardening steel.

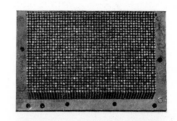

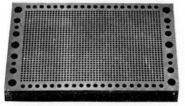

Fig. 110.—Perforating die.

The die was made from AIR-HARD, which solved the prob-lem completely. The die hardened free from cracks and without noticeable size change. Production was satisfactory. Since the punches presented no hardening problem, they were made from WATER-HARD.

THE STORY OF A PLUG GAUGE

The Job (Fig. 111).—A small round plug for gauging the hole in steel pump gears. The gauges are hardened, ground and

Fig. 111.—Plug gauge for pump gears.

lapped and their dimensions checked on a P. & W. Electro-limit Comparator. The allow-able wear is .0003″ (three tenths) after which the gauge is discarded.

Originally these gauges were made of OIL-HARD, hardened and drawn to C-62 Rockwell hardness. The average production was 965 holes before they wore undersize.

Somebody suggested chromium plating the OIL-HARD tools. They were sent out and plated and this increased their life to 1,280 holes.

Then they turned to the Matched Diagram for greater wear resistance and the arrow pointed north to OIL-WEAR. The OIL-WEAR gauges showed C-62/63 Rockwell hardness after hardening and drawing—not much harder than OIL-HARD—but the production jumped to an average of 2,390 holes per gauge.

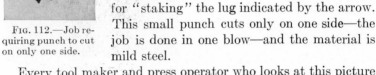

FIG. 112.—Job requiring punch to cut on only one side.

In this case, the tool maker was on the Diagram when he started and it was only one step to the right steel.

A DIFFERENT KIND OF PUNCH

This is the story of an unusual kind of punch.

The Job (Fig. 112).—A "shaving" punch for "staking" the lug indicated by the arrow. This small punch cuts only on one side—the job is done in one blow—and the material is mild steel.

Every tool maker and press operator who looks at this picture will know what the trouble was—punch breakage. A *good* punch lasted a few hours and the rest didn't pay for setting them up. They had tried "everything."

This problem was handed to a tool maker and he was told "to lick that job." As luck would have it, just about that time he received some literature on Matched Tool Steels. He wasn't going to "fool" with this one—he picked the *toughest* steel in the lot—WATER-TOUGH. To the amazement of everybody, the first WATER-TOUGH punch put in the press ran for a week. The job was licked—and stayed licked.

THE STORY OF A MANDREL

The Job (Fig. 113).—This job is to punch holes in the wall of a brass tube. The operation consists in slipping the tube on the mandrel, punching 11 holes through both sides of the tube on one stroke, then giving the tube a quarter turn and punching a second set of holes, thus completing each tube in two strokes. The operation was done on an ordinary punch press, the normal production being 1,000 per hour.

Requirements on the mandrel in this case were particularly severe. It must be kept perfectly straight in hardening, and it must have considerable strength and toughness, since it could be supported only on one end. OIL-TOUGH was first used, but the tools wore rapidly, and production was not satisfactory. The tool maker therefore decided to move northward to greater wear-resistance. OIL-WEAR was considered, but having in mind the ultimate in accuracy obtainable in Air-Hardening Steels,

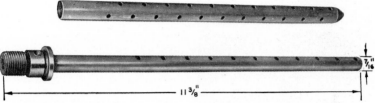

FIG. 113.—Mandrel for punching holes in the wall of a brass tube.

and the possibility of greater toughness, it was decided to move westward to AIR-WEAR.

The punches were originally made of WATER-HARD, but in search of greater accuracy and toughness, had later been changed to OIL-TOUGH. When the mandrel was changed to AIR-WEAR, the punches also were made of AIR-WEAR.

The production on the tools when made of OIL-TOUGH was 80,000 pieces for the life of the tool. After changing to AIR-WEAR, the production stepped up to 240,000 pieces.

It is interesting in connection with this case that, in order to obtain greater toughness in the shank of this mandrel, the shank was redrawn at a higher temperature than the remainder of the tool, demonstrating how modifications in heat treatment sometimes can be used to good advantage.

FIG. 114.—Combination punch and draw die.

FOLLOWING THE ARROWS TO GREATER PRODUCTION

The Job (Fig. 114).—Here is shown a combination punch and draw die that works on cold rolled strip steel.

This tool had been made of high carbon tool steel—and also carbon-vanadium tool steel; but it seemed impossible to get away from galling and scratching the work. Efforts to make the die "glass hard" only served to make the tool so brittle that the thin wall would break. The best production had been 600 pieces.

The tool maker turned to his Matched Diagram; he put his finger on the WATER-HARD diamond and said, "Here is about where I am—and I want greater wear resistance."

The arrow pointed north to WATER-WEAR and the next tool was made from that steel. He didn't hear from the production

department for a long time— but when he did—the figure was 12,000 pieces. This was not a "freak" because later dies made in several different sizes have shown the same improvement.

NO TRAVELING NECESSARY

The Job (Fig. 115).—Note the two round prongs at the crank shaft end of this connecting-rod. The trimming die was designed to cold trim the flash between these prongs.

Fig. 115.—Drop forged connecting rod and trimmer die.

The Matched Diagram found them working with air-hardening high carbon, high chrome tool steel for this die. It chipped in service. They tried other high alloy tool steels and the same thing happened.

Then they looked at the Diagram and asked the Number One question: "Why not make this of WATER-HARD?" There didn't seem to be any good reason not to— so they did.

The WATER-HARD dies not only cost much less, but they out-performed the high carbon, high chrome tools because they did not chip or spall. The user also reports that after the dies have been ground down about $\frac{1}{4}''$, they rework them and get just as good production as before.

It is surprising how often a tool maker finds that he does not *need* to travel to any

Fig. 116.—Metal forming rolls.

alloy tool steel after he has standardized on a tough timbre water-hardening steel.

TWO JUMPS TO FIND THE ANSWER

The Job (Fig. 116).—These 3″ diameter rolls are used for rolling a bead on stainless strip .008″ thick. Note the thin edge on the bead.

When made of carbon tool steel, the thin bead cracked in hardening, so they followed the arrow to OIL-HARD for "greater hardening safety." When made of OIL-HARD, the bead stayed on in hardening safe enough, but when placed in service the strain was too much for the thin sections in this hard steel, and the edges chipped.

So the tool maker said, "Now what I want is greater toughness"—and he followed the south-bound arrow to OIL-TOUGH. Made of OIL-TOUGH, they had made "miles" of molding when this picture was taken and the bead is still there.

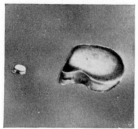

A—Take a punched slug of tool steel so big.

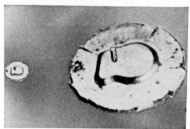

B—Cold coin it and extrude the pin like this.

C—Trim and prick punch to make a finished part like this.

D—The coining die, actual size.

FIG. 117.—Cold coining a tiny watch part. In each case, the photo at the left is actual size, the other is highly magnified.

SEEN THROUGH A WATCH-MAKER'S GLASS

The Job (Fig. 117).—Here is a coining die required to cold coin the shape illustrated in photograph C. Since the material being coined is high carbon tool steel and the tiny shaft (only .010″ in diameter) must be extruded into a hole in the die, it makes a nice tooling problem.

Extreme hardness is needed so that the edges of the extruding cavity will not wash away.　Good compression strength is needed to prevent the entire impression from sinking under the heavy pressure needed to coin this high carbon steel.　And above all, the steel must be tough to avoid chipping.

The tool maker started with WATER-HARD—and he never had occasion to go further.　He reports that he is getting 5,000 pieces per die, which is entirely satisfactory.

A SMALL PUNCHING JOB

The Job (Fig. 118).—Here is a tiny punching job—not as small as the watch part—but very small, and plenty tough nevertheless.

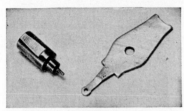

FIG. 118.—A small but difficult punching job.

The stock is .050″ cold rolled strip.　The small end is cold swaged down to .038″ thick and then punched.　This cold swaging naturally hardens the material and adds to the difficulty of punching.　The hole is only .040″ in diameter.

This is another of those jobs where "everything" had been tried—including many special alloy punch steels.　The best production had been 300 holes per punch.

When the tool maker got his Matched Diagram, he followed the arrow "for greater toughness" and picked WATER-TOUGH. The first WATER-TOUGH punch did 3,500 holes and since then he has improved the performance until now he *averages* 4,600 holes per punch.

Some of these stories read like magic—but they aren't.　The tool maker lives with his job every day, he understands his tool problems better than any outsider can, and he usually knows what he *wants*.　Until the Matched Diagram was available, the average tool maker was confronted with hundreds and hundreds of different tool steels, and about all he knew about them was their brand names; how could he choose among so many?　In solving the problems described in these pages these tool makers are confronted with only twelve steels—and each steel is matched to its neighbor so that it picks up its work where the other leaves off. It is the first time that the tool maker has had a chance to show what he could do when possessed of a really workable method of tool steel selection.

WHICH STEEL ON THE DIAGRAM WILL GIVE GREATEST PRODUCTION?

Every tool maker wants greater production, but sometimes *greater production* is confused with *greater wear resistance*. The two are not necessarily the same. If they were, greater production would always be secured from the steels at the top of the Matched Diagram, and less production from the steels at the bottom.

Actually, big production exists in every diamond—and in every Matched Tool Steel. It's there waiting like a reward for the tool maker who selects it at the right time, and gives it the right heat treatment.

Sometimes maximum production will be found in the north— but just as often it is in the south, east, or west. The requirements of the job will determine in which diamond greatest production will be found—as the following example will illustrate.

WANTED: BIG PRODUCTION

The Job (Fig. 119).—Here is a case where maximum production was found at the bottom of the Diagram. The work

FIG. 119.—Circular thread roller dies.

consisted in rolling a 14-pitch thread on .020″ unannealed brass. This is a drawn shell 3.205″ diameter and the threads must be held to a tolerance of plus or minus .0035″. The shell and a pair of circular thread rolling dies are shown in the photograph.

An oil-hardening, non-deforming tool steel is indicated for these dies. While there would be no danger of this shape cracking in water, the tools must stay round—flat and accurate in pitch.

They chose OIL-HARD as an oil-hardening steel having a good

combination of wear resistance and toughness. It developed, however, that if OIL-HARD was left hard enough for good wear resistance, there was a tendency after long service, for the thread to chip. If the tools were drawn back far enough to resist chipping, the threads flattened and production suffered. Everyone who uses thread roller dies is familiar with this situation. The production with OIL-HARD ran between 50,000 and 75,000 shells.

One of the rules that will be learned in Part III is—*Never buy a hard steel and then draw it down soft in an effort to make it tough. In so doing, the hardness and wear resistance that cost good money to buy, is thrown away—and the result is a tool that is **neither** hard nor tough. If more toughness is needed, start out with a tough steel in the first place.* Accordingly, this tool maker travelled south on the Matched Diagram and came to OIL-TOUGH.

OIL-TOUGH will show a Rockwell hardness of C-59/60 when properly heat treated—and is much tougher than OIL-HARD would be if drawn back to this same hardness. As a result, OIL-TOUGH dies are producing 800,000 shells without any repair work on the tools at all. The tools shown in the illustration had actually made this production when they were photographed.

Although in the above case greater production was found at the *bottom* of the Diagram, this same shop uses WATER-WEAR for the draw rings and mandrels for drawing these brass shells. Where they used to get 50,000 shells from a plain carbon water-hardening tool steel, they now get 300,000 from WATER-WEAR. In that case big production was found up north—but then the carbon steel dies didn't chip—they "picked up" or wore out and the thing that was needed in that case was greater wear resistance. Tool makers who know their tools, and know what they want, are doing some fancy sharpshooting with the Matched Diagram.

FIG. 120.—Punch and die for punching heavy sheet.

PRODUCTION INCREASED
100%

This story is an example of how one manufacturer, faced with the problem of getting more production out of existing equipment, did just that by applying the Matched Set Method.

The Job (Fig. 120).—This manufacturer was punching 3/16″

thick open hearth steel sheet, 19 punches and dies to the set-up. As the job was considered a difficult one, and thought to require a very tough steel, OIL-TOUGH was first used. This gave about 190,000 holes between grinds, which was rated good.

At this point, the problem was put to the tool maker to step up production per grind so as to reduce shut-down time required for regrinding. Reference to the Matched Set Diagram indicated that greater wearing qualities could be obtained by going northward to OIL-HARD. When the punches and dies were made from OIL-HARD, production stepped up to about 387,000 holes per grind—an increase of over 100%; and here is an important point—while OIL-HARD was chosen on account of its greater *hardness*, it proved to have sufficient *toughness* to handle the job.

A MILLION AND A HALF PIECES

Here is a story which illustrates how important it is to think clearly on the subject of tool steel.

The Job (Fig. 121).—This manufacturer is making the formed stamping illustrated at the right from .033″ cold rolled strip steel. The operation in question is the forming of the "hook" around a tool steel closing die which is also shown in the picture—and it must be hammered down *tight*.

When the Matched Tool Steels first came upon the scene, this die was being made of high carbon, high chrome tool steel and production was running around 70,000 to 80,000 pieces per tool, after

FIG. 121.—Closing die and stamping.

which the die broke. When a tool breaks without an "accident" after this much work, the cause is *not* brittleness—it is *fatigue*.

When the tool maker applied his Matched Diagram to this problem, his first question was "Why not make this of WATER-HARD?" Well, really it was difficult to answer that question. It seemed that the best way would be to start at scratch—with WATER-HARD—and then work in the direction indicated by the first tests.

The tool maker, however, decided to start with WATER-TOUGH and work "north" for greater wear resistance if necessary. After all, he didn't want his first Matched Tool Steel to *break* if he

could help it.   The first WATER-TOUGH die did 1,500,000 pieces—
so he cancelled his reservations and did no more travelling.

Now, here's the deceptive part about a story like this.   One
is liable to forget the details and circumstances and just remember that WATER-TOUGH did 1,500,000 pieces compared to 80,000
for high carbon, high chrome tool steel (which belongs up in the
OIL-WEAR diamond).   First thing the reader knows he gets the
idea that WATER-TOUGH will *outwear* high carbon, high chrome tool
steel nearly 20 to 1—and the minute he does, he will start
misapplying WATER-TOUGH.   WATER-TOUGH solved this problem
because it has a measured strength of 323,000 pounds per square
inch with 4.5% elongation in a tensile test.   That's why it did
the job.

THE STORY OF THREE TOOLS

This story tells how one parts manufacturer discovered that
production efficiency depends to a
large extent upon the selection of the
right tool steel for the specific job—
and he discovered it through the
Matched Set Method.

It started with an effort to break a
production bottleneck where the tools

FIG. 122.—Shaving die.

wore too rapidly, causing frequent and costly shutdowns and tool
replacement.

Job No. 1 (Fig. 122).—This shaving die used in a punch-press
operation represented a sore spot on account of rapid wear
resulting in frequent regrinds.   The die
was being made of OIL-HARD.   Reference to the Matched Set Diagram
prompted the tool maker to go north for
greater wear-resistance.   When OIL-
WEAR was selected, production was
stepped up 400%.

Success with the first selection problem
induced the tool maker to return to the

FIG. 123.—Staking punch.

Matched Set Diagram to correct a condition involving tool breakage—a source of constant irritation and high production cost.

Job No. 2 (Fig. 123).—This staking punch, used to stake nuts
on a spindle, was being made from a water-hardening steel not
guaranteed for timbre.   It broke when treated for maximum

hardness, and battered out of shape when drawn soft to secure greater toughness. Reference to the Matched Set indicated not a change to another diamond, but rather a change to a water-hardening steel that would *fill* the WATER-HARD diamond— timbre-tested carbon tool steel. When tough-timbre WATER-HARD was applied, it could be treated for maximum hardness without fear of breakage, with the result that service life of the tool was increased from 40 hours to over 6 months.

With such good results in the solution of tool problems, the tool maker gained confidence in the method, and proceeded to review other tools to see if their performance could not be improved by proper selection of steels.

Job No. 3 (Fig. 124).—A burnishing punch, made of high speed steel, failed to impart the desired finish or to hold up as expected in service. RED-HARD properties were not necessary. The Matched Set indicated

FIG. 124.—Burnishing punch.

therefore that a misapplication had probably been made. Arguing that a water-hardening steel would do this job, the tool maker traveled north from WATER-HARD to get additional wear-resistance. When WATER-WEAR was selected, a smoother, cleaner finish was obtained, and the pieces produced during the life of the tool increased from 384,000 to 576,000.

IN CONCLUSION

It must be evident to the reader by this time that, while the tool maker need not know a lot about tool steel (aside from WATER-HARD) he *must know his tools*. Being itself in a sense a tool, the Matched Set must be used with the same intelligence and good judgment exercised in the use of any of the actual tools in the shop.

And finally, it must be understood that "changing steels" is the *last* thing the tool maker does. Tools may fail because of faulty design, improper heat treatment, or accidents in service. "Buck-passing" is still a popular pastime—the designer hates to admit that the design is wrong—the hardener hesitates to acknowledge that the heat treatment on a certain tool got away from him—or the press operator tries to cover up the fact that he got two pieces in the die at one time and broke it. If the blame can be passed along to the tool steel, it seems like such an *easy* solution to the problem. However, to change tool steel under such circumstances is obviously futile, and even the "buck-passer" will find himself in trouble when the new tool comes through made of the wrong steel.

"Trouble-shooters" from the tool steel mill are frequently criticized when they come on a job because they "try to find trouble with everything excepting the steel." If such critics would only stop to realize that the expense of sending a service man is frequently much greater than the cost of the piece of steel involved, they could readily see how much *easier* it would be for the steel mill to issue credit for the piece of steel, and have done with it. However, the steel maker knows that he would not be "done" with it. If the trouble is not with the steel, he would be in exactly the same position as the dentist who pulled the wrong tooth.

Chapter 9 which follows, presents a simple and practical tool steel selector which has been included here at the suggestion of many tool makers as a means of arriving at the right steel for the job. Part III then describes a simplified method of arriving at the proper heat treatment for tools; a simplification that has done much to eliminate errors and costly experiments in this department.

CHAPTER 9

THE TOOL STEEL SELECTOR

In Chapter 8 a number of examples were given to show how the Matched Set Method is applied in actual practice. In all cases the question was asked, "Why not use WATER-HARD?," and with that question as a starting point, the proper direction on the Matched Set Diagram was found which would lead us to the right steel. Practical tool makers have told us that once they are on the Matched Diagram this method works successfully. They can move with assurance from one steel to another and know in advance just what results they will secure.

However, the tool maker is not always "on the diagram," and in some cases wants a good safe guide to the best steel for a *first choice*. The Tool Steel Selector was designed as a convenient means for making that choice. It puts into direct practical use the Matched Set idea. We feel that it is particularly valuable on account of the fact that practical tool room men helped materially in determining upon the form and contents of the charts—and we gratefully acknowledge their assistance.

How to Use the Selector.—
1. Locate the name of the tool you wish to make.
2. Check the purpose and requirements of the tool.
3. Locate the right tool steel to start with.

Precaution in Using the Selector.—A case might arise in which you are making a certain tool from one of the Matched Set tool steels with entirely successful results. If you look up the name of that tool in this chapter, and find that the Selector Chart recommends some other steel as a starting place, do not abandon your present position, but continue using the steel which is working successfully. You arrived at this by actual experience. If you had originally started with the steel recommended on the chart, the chances are you would have later moved to your present steel as better suited to your particular shop conditions.

When you have a *new* type of tool to make, then use the chart as a guide. It represents the aggregate best judgment of a great many competent tool engineers, and as such will afford a very reliable compass to steer you on the right course.

ARBORS

(with Shoulders and Threads)

Require toughness plus a good combination of strength and wear-resistance—preferably minimum warpage in hardening.

—then use OIL-TOUGH

(If the part is tapered for holding work—see MANDRELS)

AUTOMATIC
SCREW MACHINE TOOLS

—Box Mill Tools
—Form Tools
—Parting Tools
—Shaving Tools

Must have high-speed cutting qualities plus a keen, non-chipping edge to give smooth finish.

—then use RED-WEAR

142

BATTERING TOOLS

See PNEUMATIC TOOLS—Chisels, Rivet Sets, etc.

BEADING TOOLS
—Bootleg, Pneumatic

Must have high fatigue-resistance, great toughness, and wear-resistance—simple to heat treat.

—then use
WATER-TOUGH

BENDING DIES

See DIES, Forming

BITS   ROUTER

Must have ability to hold a keen, tough edge at high speeds.

For cutting metals and wood.

—then use
RED-WEAR

BITS TOOL HOLDER

For average machine shop use on miscellaneous work—roughing and finishing.

—*then use*
RED-WEAR

BLACKSMITHS' TOOLS

Maximum combination of hardness and toughness—easy to heat treat.

—*then use*
WATER-TOUGH

BLADES SHEAR

See *SHEAR BLADES*

BLANKING DIES

See *DIES, Blanking*

BOLT CUTTERS

See CUTTERS

BOLT DIES

See DIES, Header; also HAMMERS, Header

BORING TOOLS

Require high-speed cutting properties; resistance to abrasion and chipping—certain types must be forgeable.

—then use
RED-WEAR

BOX MILL TOOLS

See AUTOMATIC Screw Machine Tools

BRASS FINISHING TOOLS

See FINISHING TOOLS (For Finishing Brass)

BRASS FORGING DIES

See DIES, Brass Forging

BROACHES

Require keenest possible cutting edge; maximum wear-resistance—must stay straight in hardening.

- For high-speed steel broaches. → **—then use RED-WEAR**
- For extremely long and slender broaches. → **—then use AIR-WEAR**
- For short-run "specials" (and when high-speed hardening facilities are not available). → **—then use OIL-HARD**

BULL RIVETERS

Require maximum toughness and strength to resist upsetting; good surface hardness to resist wear. → **—then use RED-TOUGH**

BUNTERS

For Cold Heading

Need high compression strength; a hard surface backed by a tough core; good resistance to side thrust.

—*then use*
WATER-HARD

BURNISHING TOOLS

Also Burnishing Rolls

Require slick, glass-hard surface that will not pick up or gall.

—*then use*
WATER-WEAR

BURRS

Require file-hard, non-chipping cutting edge—must harden free from decarburization—smaller sizes can't be ground.

For metal cutting.

For wood cutting.

—*then use*
RED-WEAR

—*then use*
WATER-HARD

BUSHINGS

—Collet
—Pusher
—Plain
—Screw
—Shoulder
—Slip

Require a hard wearing surface.

Simple sections to be sized by grinding.

—then use
WATER-HARD

Irregular sections and thin walled sections—ground or unground.

—then use
OIL-HARD

BUTTON DIES

See DIES, Threading

BUTTON SETS

Need fatigue-resistance to resist breaking in shank; wear-resistance plus strength to resist upsetting.

—then use
WATER-TOUGH

BUTTONS LOCATING

Require maximum surface hardness with tough core, if possible.

—then use
WATER-HARD
or 1.20% Carbon Tool Steel Drill Rod

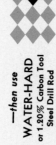

CAULKING TOOLS

Must resist shock and fatigue—must be tough on striking end to resist spalling.

—*then use*
WATER-TOUGH

CAMS

Should hold exact size and shape in hardening to avoid cam-grinding operation—no decarburization (soft skin) in hardening.

—*then use*
OIL-HARD

CENTERS LATHE

Dead centers require maximum life, greater wear-resistance, freedom from galling, resistance to frictional heat.

—*then use*
RED-WEAR

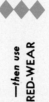

Live centers or ball-bearing centers require hardness plus toughness and strength.

—*then use*
WATER-HARD

—*Dead*
—*Live*

149

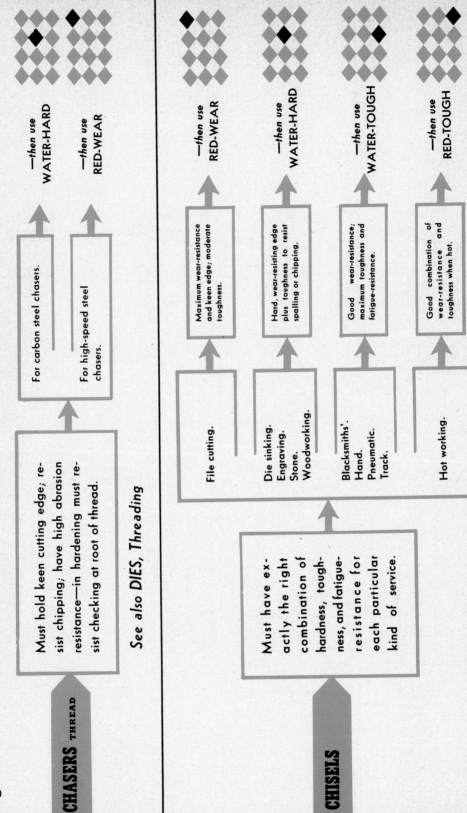

CHASERS THREAD

Must hold keen cutting edge; resist chipping; have high abrasion resistance—in hardening must resist checking at root of thread.

For carbon steel chasers.

—then use WATER-HARD

For high-speed steel chasers.

—then use RED-WEAR

See also DIES, Threading

CHISELS

Must have exactly the right combination of hardness, toughness, and fatigue-resistance for each particular kind of service.

File cutting.

Maximum wear-resistance and keen edge; moderate toughness.

—then use RED-WEAR

Die sinking. Engraving. Stone. Woodworking.

Hard, wear-resisting edge plus toughness to resist spalling or chipping.

—then use WATER-HARD

Blacksmiths'. Hand. Pneumatic. Track.

Good wear-resistance; maximum toughness and fatigue-resistance.

—then use WATER-TOUGH

Hot working.

Good combination of wear-resistance and toughness when hot.

—then use RED-TOUGH

CHUCK JAWS

Each type must have the proper combination of hardness and toughness.

For simple shapes requiring high hardness (and which can be ground after hardening if necessary) such as drill chucks, detachable jaws, jaw inserts, wrenchless chucks, etc.

—then use
WATER-HARD

For box chucks, step jaws and other irregular shapes —or shapes which cannot be ground after hardening.

—then use
OIL-TOUGH

CLUTCH PINS

or Dogs
—Pin
—Roller
—Shuttle
—Wedge

Require maximum resistance to shock and fatigue and ample hardness to resist peening.

For shapes that are simple enough for water-hardening.

—then use
WATER-TOUGH

For badly unbalanced sections which are likely to crack in water.

—then use
OIL-TOUGH

COLLETS

—Screw Machine
—Lathe

For maximum wear resistance—plus toughness.

—then use
WATER-HARD

For wear resistance and toughness—with added safety in hardening.

—then use
OIL-HARD

For maximum toughness, with some sacrifice of hardness.

—then use
OIL-TOUGH

CONCRETE BREAKERS

Moil Points

If longer than about 15 inches, or if equipped with collar, steel must have a tough core to resist fatigue.

—then use
WATER-HARD

Short, stubbly points, which transmit most of the blow to the job, are not so subject to fatigue.

—then use
WATER-TOUGH

152

COUNTER-BORE PILOTS

Inserted

Require extremely high resistance to abrasion and galling.

For maximum resistance to galling.

—*then use*
WATER-WEAR

For good resistance to galling.

—*then use*
WATER-HARD
or 1.20% Carbon Tool Steel Drill Rod

COUNTERBORES
AND COUNTERSINKS

Require ability to hold keen cutting edge under all conditions; fair toughness—easy to heat treat.

—*then use*
RED-WEAR

CROWNERS

Should be hard enough to resist sinking; tough enough to withstand chipping on steep crowning effects.

If the work is done cold.

—*then use*
WATER-HARD

If the work is done hot.

—*then use*
RED-HARD

153

CUT-OFF TOOLS

See PARTING TOOLS

CUTTERS

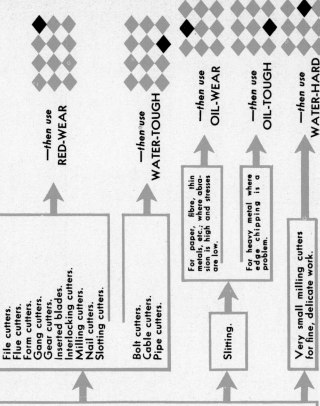

There are all kinds of "cutters" to meet all kinds of service . . .

1. First of all, a steel must be selected from which the tool *can be made;* i.e., if a tool cracks or deforms excessively in hardening, it is worthless—no matter what its theoretical cutting efficiency may be.

2. Next in importance, the tool must be tough enough so it will not break outright in service.

3. Next, the cutting edge must have enough "red-hardness," so it will not soften at the highest temperature attained in service.

4. Next in importance, the cutting edge must stay keen enough to produce an acceptable finish.

5. After *all* the above requirements are satisfied, you can then pick the steel that will wear the longest and give the greatest production.

File cutters.
Flue cutters.
Form cutters.
Gang cutters.
Gear cutters.
Inserted blades.
Interlocking cutters.
Milling cutters.
Nail cutters.
Slotting cutters.

—then use
RED-WEAR

Bolt cutters.
Cable cutters.
Pipe cutters.

—then use
WATER-TOUGH

Slitting.

For paper, fibre, thin metals, etc.; where abrasion is high and stresses are low.

—then use
OIL-WEAR

For heavy metal where edge chipping is a problem.

—then use
OIL-TOUGH

Very small milling cutters for fine, delicate work.

—then use
WATER-HARD

DIES BENDING

See DIES, Forming

DIES BOLT HEADER

See DIES, Header

DIES BOLT THREADING

See CHASERS

DIES BRASS FORGING

Must have red-hardness with good toughness to resist sinking and breaking—also resistance to heat checking.

—then use
RED-HARD

DIES BLANKING —HOT

—Hot Nut
—Hot Punching

Require good red-hardness, with toughness to resist chipping.

→ For long runs on well-heated stock.

—then use
RED-HARD

→ For short runs on well-heated stock—for any length runs where tool breakage is likely.

—then use
RED-TOUGH

DIES BLANKING —COLD

—Lamination
—Shaving
—Stamping

When die must hold size accurately in hardening; or is of non-uniform shape (likely to crack in hardening)—also shaving dies.

—then use
OIL-HARDENING
or
AIR-HARDENING
MATCHED SET

→ If it must give extremely long production; or if it works on fibre, asbestos, mica, silicon sheets, high phosphorus or other abrasive stock; AND the die sections are not subject to heavy breaking load or excessive shock.

—then use
OIL-WEAR
or
AIR-WEAR

→ For average production; intermediate toughness and wear-resistance; short runs on abrasive materials.

—then use
OIL-HARD
or
AIR-HARD

→ If it must handle very heavy stock; or has very fragile projections; or is exposed to heavy shock.

—then use
OIL-TOUGH
or
AIR-TOUGH

WATER-WEAR is seldom used for blanking dies excepting in very simple shapes. As a general rule, blanking dies for maximum wear-resistance should be made of OIL-WEAR.

—*then use* OIL-WEAR

For average production and average hardness and toughness.

—*then use* WATER-HARD

For handling very heavy stock; for tools having fragile projections; or for heavy shock.

—*then use* WATER-TOUGH

When die need not hold size accurately in hardening (can be ground all over) —when section is uniform enough to permit water-quenching—also sectional dies.

—*then use* WATER-HARDENING MATCHED SET

NOTE: In general, the same steel can be used for the blanking punch as for the die. For perforating punches, see PUNCHES.

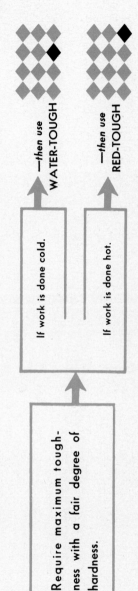

Require maximum toughness with a fair degree of hardness.

If work is done cold.

—*then use* WATER-TOUGH

If work is done hot.

—*then use* RED-TOUGH

DIES BULLDOZER
—*Bending*
—*Simple Upsetting*
—*Straightening*

157

DIES BURNISHING

If die is of irregular shape and cannot be ground—if it must hold size accurately in hardening.

—*then use*
OIL-WEAR

For the majority of burnishing dies, which can be ground and lapped to accurate size and can be safely water-quenched. These steels shrink in hardening and rehardening.

For maximum wear-resistance and non-galling.

—*then use*
WATER-WEAR

For good hardness and wear-resistance.

—*then use*
WATER-HARD

NOTE: Water-hardening steels are preferable—and the working surface should always be flush-quenched if possible.

DIES CARTRIDGE SHELL

See DIES, Drawing

158

DIES COINING

Requirements for coining dies—

1. They must not split.

2. They must not sink, which is usually followed by spalling.

3. They must not crumble or chip on sharp edges.

4. They must not gall or pick up (usually due to soft skin from hardening).

NOTE: All water-hardened coining dies should be quenched with a flush in the impression and given an extra long draw.

For maximum wear-resistance and longest possible life:

a. For flat-faced dies—for very shallow impressions made from solid tool steel.

b. For deeper impressions, subject to splitting stresses, when shrunk or pressed into a shoe.

—then use OIL-WEAR or AIR-WEAR

For average coining dies to be made from solid tool steels:

a. For shallow impressions with excessive sinking pressure (harden between 1525° and 1600° F.).

b. For deep impressions, subject to excessive splitting stresses (harden between 1450° and 1525° F.).

—then use WATER-HARD

For large coining dies requiring deep hardness penetration (such as dies used for cold coining drop forgings).

—then use WATER-TOUGH

DIES COINING —HOT

—Sizing

Requirements:

1. Red-hardness to resist washing and abrasion.

2. Resistance to heat checking.

3. Toughness to resist splitting.

For maximum red-hardness and resistance to washing and abrasion.

—then use RED-HARD

For maximum toughness and resistance to heat checking.

—then use RED-TOUGH

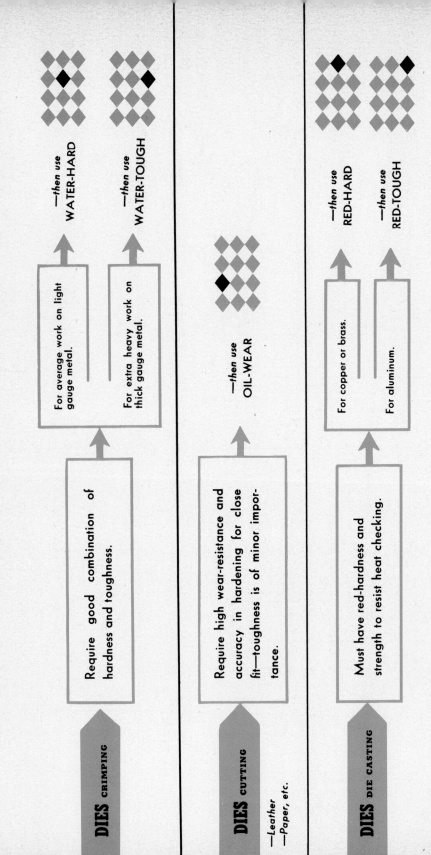

DIES CRIMPING

Require good combination of hardness and toughness.

For average work on light gauge metal.

—*then use* WATER-HARD

For extra heavy work on thick gauge metal.

—*then use* WATER-TOUGH

DIES CUTTING

—Leather
—Paper, etc.

Require high wear-resistance and accuracy in hardening for close fit—toughness is of minor importance.

—*then use* OIL-WEAR

DIES DIE CASTING

Must have red-hardness and strength to resist heat checking.

For copper or brass.

—*then use* RED-HARD

For aluminum.

—*then use* RED-TOUGH

DIES DRAWING

Dies to be used for *cold drawing* must have a hard, slick, non-galling wearing surface.

For irregular shaped dies that must hold accurate size in hardening and cannot be ground.

—*then use*
OIL-WEAR
or
AIR-WEAR

For round draw dies use a steel from the Water-Hardening Matched Set (these steels tend to shrink in hardening). For maximum safety and best results, draw dies should be spout quenched in the hole only. If suitable flushing equipment is not available, air or oil-hardening steels should be considered.

For maximum life—for eyelet dies—particularly good for brass, aluminum and other non-ferrous metals.

—*then use*
WATER-WEAR

For average draw dies, large or small—to give good all-around production.

—*then use*
WATER-HARD

Dies for *hot drawing* ferrous or non-ferrous metals.

—*then use*
RED-HARD

161

DIES EMBOSSING

Require a good, hard, wear-resisting surface with enough strength to resist sinking; toughness to resist chipping; freedom from soft skin.

→ Whenever size-change requirements permit, use preferably a water-hardening steel.

—then use
WATER-HARD

→ When accurate size must be held in hardening.

—then use
OIL-TOUGH

DIES EXTRUSION —COLD

Must have a hard wear-resisting surface to avoid galling and abrasion.

→ For irregular shaped dies that must hold accurate size in hardening.

—then use
OIL-WEAR
or
AIR-WEAR

→ For simple shapes, to get maximum wear-resistance and long runs—for bolt extruding inserts, collapsible tube dies, etc.

—then use
WATER-WEAR

→ For simple shapes, to get average wear-resistance—especially for highly stressed dies made of solid tool steel.

—then use
WATER-HARD

DIES EXTRUSION—HOT

—*Also Extrusion Die Holders*

Must have red-hardness and wear-resistance—strength to resist up-setting.

For extruding copper or brass.
—*then use* RED-HARD

For extruding aluminum.
—*then use* RED-TOUGH

DIES FORGING—HOT

Must have good red-hardness.

For maximum red-hardness and resistance to washing.
—*then use* RED-HARD

For maximum toughness, or if dies are water cooled.
—*then use* RED-TOUGH

163

DIES FORMING BENDING
—Sectional
—Unit

When dies must hold size accurately in hardening—or are of non-uniform section (likely to crack in hardening).

—then use
OIL-HARDENING
or
AIR-HARDENING
MATCHED SET

For maximum wear-resistance with fair toughness—wire forming—forming non-ferrous sheet, and light gauge steel—for inserts at wearing points in large cast forming dies.

—then use
OIL-WEAR
or
AIR-WEAR

For good average combination of wear-resistance and toughness in small or medium size dies—dies which must also "iron" the metal—for both steel and non-ferrous.

—then use
OIL-HARD
or
AIR-HARD

For maximum toughness with fair wear-resistance—especially heavy gauge material —extra large size dies.

—then use
OIL-TOUGH
or
AIR-TOUGH

When dies need not hold accurate size in hardening (can be ground all over) and the section is simple enough to permit water quenching.

—then use
WATER-HARDENING MATCHED SET

For maximum wear-resistance with fair toughness—wire forming—forming non-ferrous sheet, and light gauge steel—for inserts at wearing points in large cast forming dies.

—then use
WATER-WEAR

For good average combination of wear-resistance and toughness—dies which must also "iron" the metal—for both steel and non-ferrous.

—then use
WATER-HARD

For maximum toughness with fair wear-resistance — especially heavy gauge material—extra large size dies—bulldozer dies for bending and forming.

—then use
WATER-TOUGH

DIES HEADER —COLD

—Gripper
—Inserts
—Solid

Requirements:

1. They must not split.

2. They must not sink (sinking is usually followed by spalling).

3. They must not crumble or chip on sharp edges.

4. They must not gall or pick up.

*See Fig. 101.

NOTE: Flush quench all solid dies through the holes.

For solid die inserts, to secure maximum wear-resistance and longest possible runs.

—then use
RED-WEAR

For solid or open dies $1\frac{1}{2}$″ dia. or smaller—for bodies of insert dies.

—then use
WATER-HARD
or
WATER-WEAR

For solid or open dies larger than $1\frac{1}{2}$″ dia.

For this purpose a carbon tool steel containing approximately .90% Carbon is usually recommended.*

166

DIES **HEADER—HOT**

—Gripper
—Inserts
—Spike

Requirements:

1. Toughness to resist splitting.

2. Strength to resist sinking.

3. Red-hardness to resist washing away, and provide cutting ability.

4. Resistance to heat checking.

For maximum production on hand or automatic headers.

—*then use* RED-HARD

For short runs—for any length runs where die breakage is a serious problem.

—*then use* RED-TOUGH

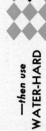

DIES **JEWELERS'**

Must have high surface hardness with best possible toughness to resist chipping—must take and retain good finish.

—*then use* WATER-HARD

DIES LAMINATION

See DIES, Blanking

DIES NAIL

Must hold keen edge with good toughness against shock—must hold size in hardening and not decarburize.

For hard wire and unusual jobs requiring extra wear-resistance.

—*then use*
RED-WEAR

For average work.

—*then use*
WATER-HARD

DIES NOTCHING

Must have good toughness to re-sist shock and be hard enough to retain good cutting edge.

—*then use*
AIR-TOUGH

DIES NUT

—Blanking Dies
—Piercing Dies
—Trimming Dies

Must be hard enough to hold size and a good cutting edge—tough enough to withstand some shock.

NOTE: For nut punches, see PUNCHES.

For cold work.

—then use
WATER-HARD

For hot work.

—then use
RED-WEAR

DIES NUT BURNISHING

Must have extremely hard wearing surface and ability to hold size without splitting or galling in service.

—then use
WATER-WEAR

DIES PIPE THREADING

See DIES, Threading

169

DIES POWDER METAL

Require exceptional wear resistance and high strength.

—then use
OIL-WEAR
or
AIR-WEAR

See also PUNCHES, Powder Metal

DIES RIVETING

Must have toughness to resist rapid blows and fatigue—hardness to hold shape.

—then use
WATER-TOUGH

DIES SHAVING

Must hold keen edge—resist abrasion—hold size in hardening.

—then use
OIL-WEAR

DIES STRIKING

Must have hard surface with good toughness to resist chipping—hardness must penetrate deep enough to avoid sinking—core must be tough to resist splitting.

—*then use*
WATER-HARD

NOTE: On larger dies, when sufficient penetration of hardness cannot be secured in WATER-HARD by raising the hardening temperature, a tool steel containing approximately .90% Carbon is usually recommended.

DIES SWAGING

Must have a good hard surface, supported by a tough core to resist splitting and provide fatigue-resistance.

For half-round, or shapes subject to splitting.

—*then use*
WATER-HARD

For flat-faced dies, particularly in large sizes.

—*then use*
WATER-TOUGH

DIES TACK

Require very good cutting ability and toughness to withstand repeated high-speed impacts—must be forgeable.

—*then use*
WATER-HARD

171

DIES THREAD ROLLER

Must hold lead and shape in hardening—must have an unusual combination of hardness and toughness.

When dies are severely stressed—working the most difficult type of material, particularly heat-treated bolts—all types of threads —roll pointing.
—*then use* RED-WEAR

For all-around performance.
—*then use* AIR-WEAR or AIR-HARD

For simple jobs— easy working stock.
—*then use* OIL-TOUGH or AIR-TOUGH

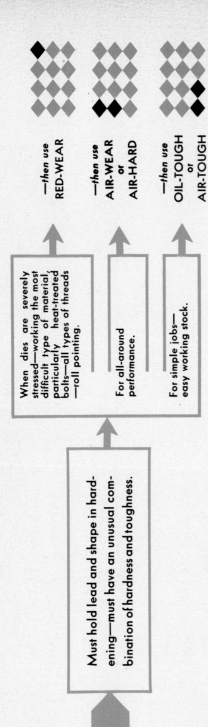

DIES THREADING

Must hold keen, tough cutting edge —must not crack at root of thread.

For carbon steel: Button dies. Screw plates. Spring dies.

For closest accuracy
—*then use* OIL-HARD

For average work.
—*then use* WATER-HARD

For high-speed steel: Chasers. Collapsible dies. Wood screw chasers.
—*then use* RED-WEAR

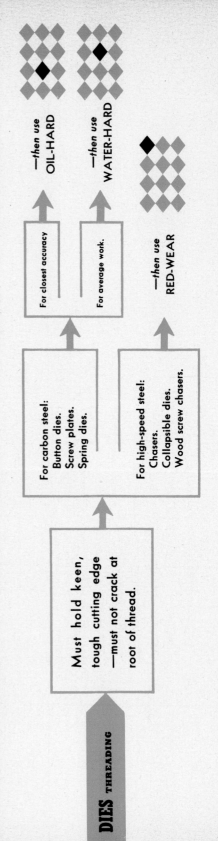

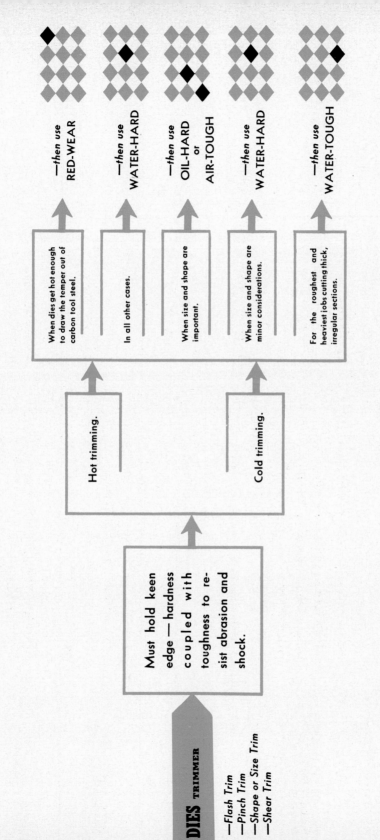

DIES TRIMMER

—Flash Trim
—Pinch Trim
—Shape or Size Trim
—Shear Trim

Must hold keen edge — hardness coupled with toughness to resist abrasion and shock.

Hot trimming.

Cold trimming.

When dies get hot enough to draw the temper out of carbon tool steel.

—then use
RED-WEAR

In all other cases.

—then use
WATER-HARD

When size and shape are important.

—then use
OIL-HARD
or
AIR-TOUGH

When size and shape are minor considerations.

—then use
WATER-HARD

For the roughest and heaviest jobs cutting thick, irregular sections.

—then use
WATER-TOUGH

DIES TUBE DRAWING

Must have a very hard, non-galling surface—should shrink on rehardening.

For maximum wear-resistance on both ferrous and non-ferrous metals—can be reshrunk. —*then use* WATER-WEAR

For good wear-resistance and the ability to stand maximum number of re-hardenings (shrinks). —*then use* WATER-HARD

For hot drawing non-ferrous tubing—does not shrink. —*then use* RED-HARD

NOTE: Flush-quench water-hardening dies only in the hole, leaving outside of die soft if possible.

DIES VANSTONING —COLD

Must have great toughness. —*then use* WATER-TOUGH

DIES VANSTONING —HOT

Must have red-hardness and resistance to shock. —*then use* RED-TOUGH

DIES WIRE DRAWING

Require extremely hard, slick surface to resist abrasion. —*then use* WATER-WEAR

NOTE: If possible, quench only the hole (leaving outside of die soft) by means of a water flush. Will shrink on each rehardening.

DOWELS

Very hard surface to avoid galling —enough toughness to resist chipping or splitting when driven or pressed.

—then use
WATER-HARD
or 1.20% Carbon Tool Steel Drill Rod

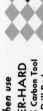

DRIFTS

Must have maximum strength and toughness to resist breaking from side thrust, upsetting, or spalling on striking end.

—then use
WATER-TOUGH

DRILL BUSHINGS

See BUSHINGS

DRILL PLATES

Require good hardness and accuracy in hardening.

—then use
OIL-HARD
or
AIR-TOUGH

DRILLS

—Center
—Flat
—Gun Barrel
—Twist

High-speed drills require red-hardness and wear-resistance with best possible toughness.

—then use RED-WEAR

For carbon steel drills.

—then use WATER-HARD

DRILLS STONE

Require hardness and fatigue-resistance, plus resistance to chipping.

—then use WATER-HARD

DUMMY BLOCKS

Require maximum strength to resist upsetting at a dull red heat.

—then use RED-HARD

END MILLS

—Ball End
—Double End
—Fishtail
—Shell End
—Single End
—Taper Shank

Require keen, tough cutting edges; resistance to chipping—must have tough body in long end mills.

—then use RED-WEAR

ENGRAVERS' TOOLS

Must have all the properties of a good chisel steel plus a harder, keener edge.

—*then use*
WATER-HARD

EXTRUSION DIES

See *DIES, Extrusion*

FILE CUTTERS

See *CUTTERS*

FINGERS

—*Chucking*
—*Clutch*
—*Cut-off*
—*Feed*
—*Spring*

Require "tough" hardness.

Chucking fingers.
Clutch fingers.
Feed fingers.

Cut-off fingers.
Spring fingers.

—*then use*
OIL-TOUGH

—*then use*
WATER-TOUGH

FINISHING TOOLS

Require keen, non-crumbling cutting edges—must resist chipping on intermittent cuts—easy to sharpen.

For finishing iron and steel, where speed can be sacrificed for best possible finish. —*then use* WATER-WEAR

For finishing brass at maximum speed. —*then use* RED-WEAR

For finishing brass at moderate speed for best possible finish. —*then use* WATER-WEAR

FIXTURES

—Gauging Fixtures
—Holding Devices
—Locating Studs and Wear Points

Require easy workability and good hardness.

For most applications, unless too difficult to harden in water. —*then use* WATER-HARD

Where size change or cracking hazards prevent use of water-hardening steel. —*then use* OIL-HARD

FLATTERS

See BLACKSMITHS' TOOLS

FLUE CUTTERS

See CUTTERS

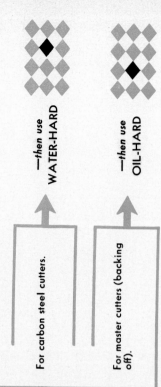

FLUE ROLLERS

See ROLLS, *Expander*

FORM CUTTERS

—Circular
—Flat
—Fly
—Master
—Milling

Require keen, accurate cutting edge—toughness to resist edge crumbling or chipping.

For high-speed cutters. —*then use* RED-WEAR

For carbon steel cutters. —*then use* WATER-HARD

For master cutters (backing off). —*then use* OIL-HARD

FORM TOOLS

See AUTOMATIC *Screw Machine Tools;* FORM CUTTERS; *also* CUTTERS

FORMING DIES

(Sheet Metal)

See DIES, *Forming*

179

FULLERS

See BLACKSMITHS' TOOLS

GAUGES

—Plug
—Ring
—Snap
—Thread Plug
—Thread Ring

All gauges require wear-resistance and must take a good finish—some gauges must hold size accurately in hardening.

Plug.
Ring.
Snap (wearing points).

—*then use*
WATER-HARD

Thread plug.
Thread ring.

Plugs over about 1½ inch diameter—rings with wall thickness over about 1 inch —for extra wear-resistance on all sizes.

—*then use*
OIL-WEAR

Plug and ring gauges smaller than above.

—*then use*
OIL-HARD

GEAR CUTTERS

See CUTTERS, Gear

GRADING ROLLS See ROLLS, Grading

GRIPPER DIES See DIES, Header

GUN BARREL DRILLS See DRILLS, Gun Barrel

HEADER DIES See DIES, Header

HEADER HAMMERS See HAMMERS, Header

HAMMERS

—Bush
—Header
—Machinists'
—Nail Machine
—Pulverizing
—Swaging Machine

Require the proper combination of hardness and toughness.

Bush.
—*then use* WATER-HARD

Machinists' (ball peen). Pulverizing. Swaging machine.
—*then use* WATER-TOUGH

Nail machine.
—*then use* RED-WEAR

Header.

For deep impressions subject to splitting.
—*then use* WATER-HARD

For flat or shallow-faced hammers subject to sinking.
—*then use* WATER-TOUGH

HEADER PUNCHES *See HAMMERS, Header*

HOBS

Require a keen, wear-resisting cutting edge, with the ability to hold an accurate form.

For high-speed hobs. —then use RED-WEAR

For carbon steel hobs. —then use OIL-HARD

HUBS

Must have high compression strength and the right amount of transverse strength to resist splitting—must hold accurate size in hardening.

For flat or convex-faced hubs; stresses almost entirely compressional. —then use OIL-WEAR or AIR-WEAR

For hubs having slight concave face; medium splitting stresses. —then use OIL-HARD or AIR-HARD

For hubs having deep notches or impressions on face; subject to maximum splitting stress. —then use OIL-TOUGH or AIR-TOUGH

HOLLOW MILLS

Must hold keen cutting edge and the corners must "stay put" to insure clearance—should hold size in hardening.

For high-speed mills or cutting heat-treated steel.

—then use RED-WEAR

For carbon steel mills used on brass, aluminum, etc.—short runs on steel.

—then use OIL-HARD

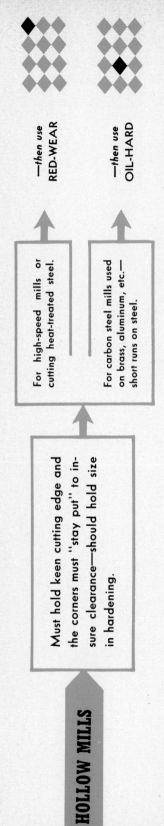

INSERTS

See DIES, Blanking; DIES, Forming; DIES, Drawing, etc., depending on what the insert does.

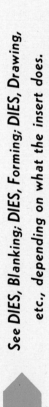

JAWS

—Chuck
—Fixture
—Jig Gripper
—Vise

Must have the proper combination of hardness and toughness for each type of service.

Chuck.

See CHUCK JAWS

Jig and fixture.

—then use WATER-HARD

Vise.

—then use WATER-TOUGH

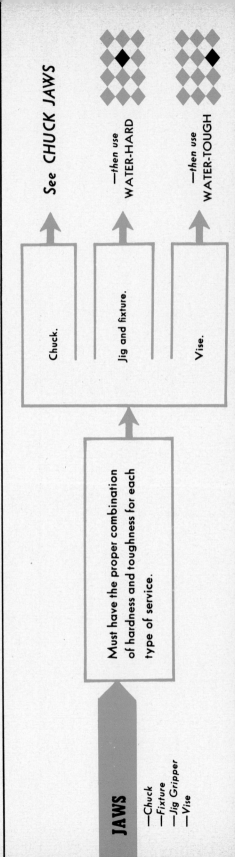

JIGS WEAR POINTS

See FIXTURES, Wear Points

KNIVES MACHINE

—Circular
—Composite
—Solid

Require hardness and wear-re-sistance with ample toughness to prevent edge chipping.

High-speed steel knives.

—then use
RED-WEAR

Carbon steel knives.

—then use
WATER-HARD

KNIVES SHEAR

See SHEAR BLADES

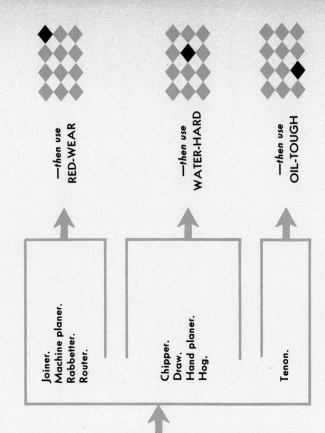

KNIVES WOODWORKING

—Chipper
—Draw
—Hand Planer
—Hog
—Joiner
—Machine Planer
—Rabbetter
—Router
—Tenon

Require a keen, tough edge, and some types also need resistance to heat.

Joiner.
Machine planer.
Rabbetter.
Router.

—then use RED-WEAR

Chipper.
Draw.
Hand planer.
Hog.

—then use WATER-HARD

Tenon.

—then use OIL-TOUGH

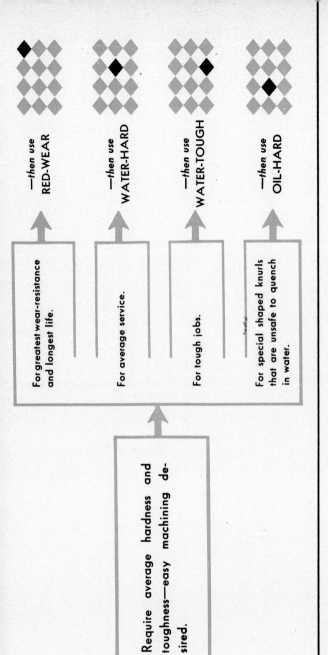

KNURLING TOOLS

Require average hardness and toughness—easy machining desired.

For greatest wear-resistance and longest life.
—then use RED-WEAR

For average service.
—then use WATER-HARD

For tough jobs.
—then use WATER-TOUGH

For special shaped knurls that are unsafe to quench in water.
—then use OIL-HARD

LAMINATION DIES

See DIES, Blanking

LATHE CENTERS

See CENTERS, Lathe

L

LATHE TOOLS

Require good cutting efficiency at the temperature attained by tool—tough for intermittent cuts—forgeable.

→ For high-speed roughing and finishing. *—then use* RED-WEAR

→ For special finishing of steel and non-ferrous metals (at reduced speed). *—then use* WATER-WEAR

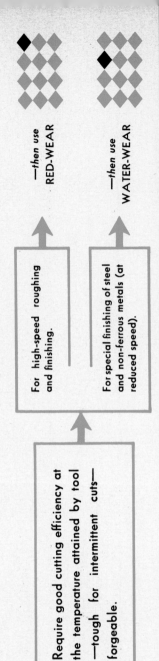

LEATHER KNIVES

See KNIVES, Machine

LINERS MOLD

—For Abrasive Materials

Require resistance to pure abrasion above all else.

→ Whenever design makes it possible to quench in water. *—then use* WATER-WEAR

→ When shape is such that oil-hardening is necessary. *—then use* OIL-WEAR

MANDRELS COLD
—Drawing
—Extrusion
—Work Holding

For good resistance to abrasion and minimum size change in heat treatment.
—*then use* AIR-WEAR

When design makes it possible to water quench.
—*then use* WATER-HARD

Where distortion is of primary importance.
—*then use* AIR-TOUGH

MANDRELS HOT
—Drawing
—Extrusion

For copper or brass.
—*then use* RED-HARD

For aluminum or if tools are water cooled.
—*then use* RED-TOUGH

MAULS

Require "tough hardness."
—*then use* WATER-TOUGH

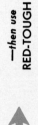

MILLING CUTTERS

See CUTTERS

MOIL POINTS

See CONCRETE BREAKERS

MOLDS FOR PLASTICS

Require very clean, sound steel—accuracy in hardening—must take good finish.

For "tool steel" molds.

For other types of mold steel.

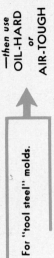

—then use
OIL-HARD
or
AIR-TOUGH

—ask for special leaflets

NAIL CUTTERS

See CUTTERS

NAIL SETS

Require hardness to resist upsetting; strength to resist bending; and toughness to resist spalling.

—then use
WATER-HARD

NUT PIERCERS
(Hot)

Must resist heat and abrasion.

—then use
RED-WEAR

PARTING TOOLS

Require maximum ability to hold keen edge, with sufficient strength to avoid breaking under severe strain—must not pick up or gall—frequently must be forgeable.

—then use
RED-WEAR

PAWLS

Require "tough hardness."

When shape permits hardening in water.

—then use
WATER-TOUGH

When shape is unbalanced, and must be quenched in oil.

—then use
OIL-TOUGH

N–P

PILOTS

—Dowel
—Drift
—Guide
—Knockout
—Locating
—Plastic Mold
—Relief

Stationary pilots require good hardness and fair toughness—rotating pilots need extra resistance to galling.

NOTE: When absolutely necessary because of design, use OIL-WEAR or OIL-HARD.

For maximum resistance to galling and wear.

—then use
WATER-WEAR

For good hardness and added toughness.

—then use
WATER-HARD
or 1.20% Carbon Tool Steel Drill Rod

PINS

Require hardness plus strength.

For practically all purposes except when maximum toughness is required.

—then use
WATER-HARD
or 1.20% Carbon Tool Steel Drill Rod

When extra toughness is needed in knockouts, drift or mold pins.

—then use
WATER-TOUGH

PIPE CUTTER WHEELS

See CUTTERS, Pipe

PLANER TOOLS   See LATHE TOOLS

PLUG GAUGES   See GAUGES, Plug

PLUNGERS

Degree of wear-resistance and toughness varies according to the service.

For highly abrasive conditions with relatively low breaking stress (compression stress may be high).

For resisting high transverse (breaking) stresses and shock.

Very long or irregular shapes that require oil-quenching. —then use OIL-WEAR

Simple sections that can be water-quenched and ground. —then use WATER-WEAR

Very long or irregular shapes that require oil-quenching. —then use OIL-TOUGH

Simple sections that can be water-quenched and ground. —then use WATER-TOUGH

PNEUMATIC TOOLS

—Backing Out
—Beading
—Button Sets
—Caulking
—Chisels
—Hammers
—Rivet Busters
—Rivet Sets
—Scarfing Tools

Require a tough, hard steel that can withstand shock and fatigue.

—then use
WATER-TOUGH

PUNCHES HOT

—Blanking
—Drawing
—Piercing

Require wear-resistance and strength when hot—resistance to heat checking.

For simple compression jobs—little side thrust—no water-cooling—long runs.

—then use
RED-WEAR

For moderate side thrust—long, deep punches—hot nut punches.

—then use
RED-HARD

For maximum toughness—hot piercing mandrels—piercing irregular sections—can be water-cooled.

—then use
RED-TOUGH

PUNCHES COLD

—Backing Out
—Blanking
—Center
—Drawing
—Forming
—Nut
—Perforating
—Pharmaceutical
—Piercing

Complicated shapes; unsafe to quench in water or which can't be sized by grinding.

—then use
OIL-HARDENING
or
AIR-HARDENING
MATCHED SET

For maximum hardness and wear-resistance or working very abrasive material; when breaking stresses are moderate.

—then use
OIL-WEAR
or
AIR-WEAR

For average combination of wear-resistance and toughness.

—then use
OIL-HARD
or
AIR-HARD

For maximum toughness, punching heavy materials and irregular sections—for punches that break in stripping — pharmaceutical punches.

—then use
OIL-TOUGH
or
AIR-TOUGH

Simple shapes; safe to quench in water, or easy to size by grinding.

—then use
WATER-HARDENING
MATCHED SET

For maximum hardness and wear-resistance, or working very abrasive material; when breaking stresses are moderate.

—then use
WATER-WEAR

For average combination of wear-resistance and toughness.

—then use
WATER-HARD

For maximum toughness, punching heavy materials and irregular sections—for punches that break in stripping—pharmaceutical punches.

—then use
WATER-TOUGH

195

PUNCHES POWDER METAL

Require good toughness to resist breaking, and high strength to resist upsetting.

—*then use*
OIL-TOUGH
or
AIR-TOUGH

See also *DIES, Powder Metal*

QUARRY TOOLS

See STONE TOOLS

QUILLS

—*Cut-Off*

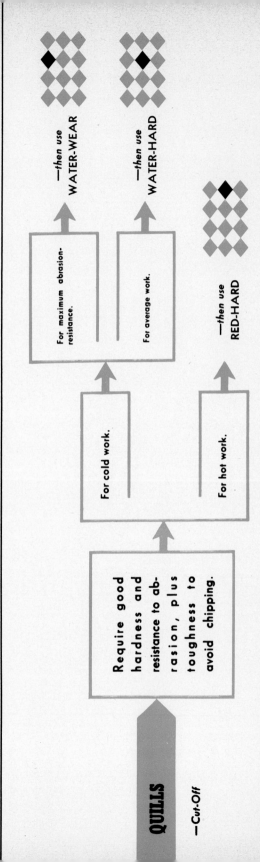

Require good hardness and resistance to abrasion, plus toughness to avoid chipping.

For cold work.

For maximum abrasion-resistance.

For average work.

For hot work.

—*then use*
WATER-WEAR

—*then use*
WATER-HARD

—*then use*
RED-HARD

REAMERS

—Adjustable
—Bridge
—Chucking
—Expansion
—Hand
—Inserted Blade
—Machine
—Rose

Must hold a hard, keen cutting edge, without chipping or galling.

Chucking. Inserted blade. Machine. Rose. → For high-speed steel reamers. → *—then use* **RED-WEAR**

Bridge. Hand. → For carbon steel reamers. → *—then use* **WATER-HARD or WATER-WEAR**

Expansion. → In addition to a good, keen cutting edge, must be tough to permit expanding. → *—then use* **OIL-HARD**

Blades for adjustable reamers. → Should stay straight in hardening and hold a keen edge. → *—then use* **OIL-HARD**

RIFLING TOOLS

Require extra keen cutting edge with freedom from chipping and galling. → *—then use* **RED-WEAR**

Q-R

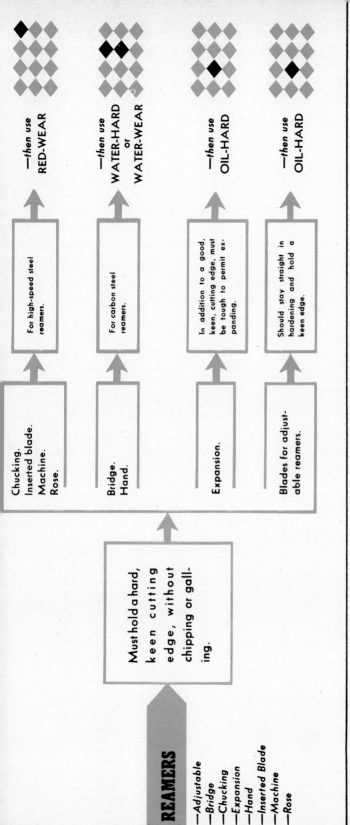

197

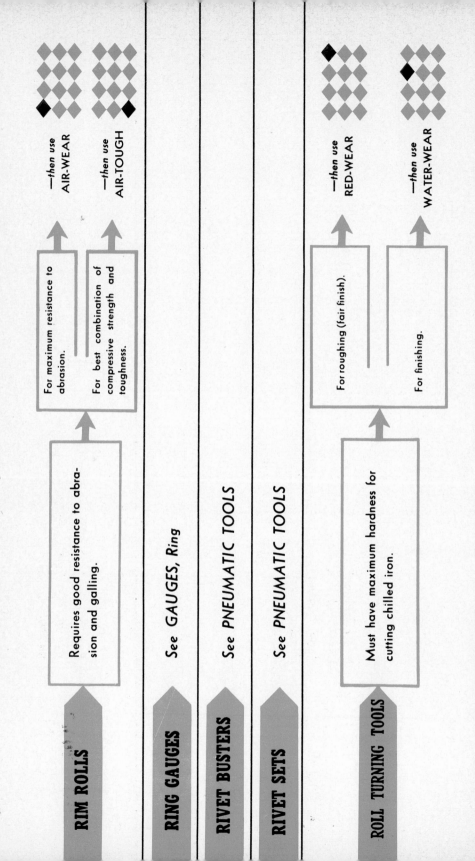

RIM ROLLS

Requires good resistance to abrasion and galling.

For maximum resistance to abrasion.

—*then use* AIR-WEAR

For best combination of compressive strength and toughness.

—*then use* AIR-TOUGH

RING GAUGES

See GAUGES, *Ring*

RIVET BUSTERS

See *PNEUMATIC TOOLS*

RIVET SETS

See *PNEUMATIC TOOLS*

ROLL TURNING TOOLS

Must have maximum hardness for cutting chilled iron.

For roughing (fair finish).

—*then use* RED-WEAR

For finishing.

—*then use* WATER-WEAR

ROLLS COLD WORK

—Beading
—Bending
—Burnishing
—Crimping
—Embossing
—Engravers'
—Expander
—Forming
—Grading
—Rim
—Seaming
—Swaging

For intricate or accurate shapes.

→ —then use OIL-HARDENING or AIR-HARDENING MATCHED SET

For maximum hardness and wear-resistance — burnishing rolls.
→ —then use OIL-WEAR or AIR-WEAR

For average hardness and toughness — bending; forming; embossing; crimping; seaming.
→ —then use OIL-HARD or AIR-HARD

For rolls with delicate beads subject to side thrust.
→ —then use OIL-TOUGH or AIR-TOUGH

For simple shapes safe to quench in water—or which can readily be ground.

→ —then use WATER-HARDENING MATCHED SET

For maximum hardness and wear-resistance—rim rolls.
→ —then use WATER-WEAR

For average hardness and toughness — bending; forming; embossing; crimping; seaming; engravers' rolls; expander.
→ —then use WATER-HARD

For rolls with delicate beads subject to side thrust—heavy duty forming rolls.
→ —then use WATER-TOUGH

ROLLS HOT WORK

—Bending
—Expander
—Forming
—Grading, Inserts

For maximum wear-resistance with minimum breaking stress—grading roll inserts.

—then use
RED-WEAR

For maximum toughness when rolls do not get excessively hot—flanging rolls, etc.

—then use
RED-TOUGH

ROUTER BITS

See *BITS, Router*

SAW TEETH

Require high-speed cutting efficiency with toughness to avoid corner chipping and prevent breaking from wedging action.

—then use
RED-WEAR

SCARFING TOOLS

See *LATHE TOOLS*

200

SCRAPERS

Must hold a super-hard, keen edge.

For maximum wear-resistance. → *—then use* WATER-WEAR

For general work. → *—then use* WATER-HARD

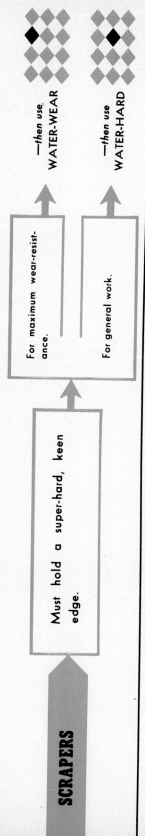

SCREW DRIVER BLADES

—Hand
—Power

Must have high torsional strength to resist shear, and hardness to resist rounding of edges. → *—then use* WATER-TOUGH

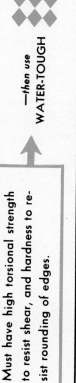

SCREW PLATES

See DIES, Threading

SHANKS

—Tipped Tools

Require maximum toughness and fatigue resistance.

For resistance to abrasion from chips. → *—then use* AIR-HARD

For maximum toughness. → *—then use* WATER-TOUGH

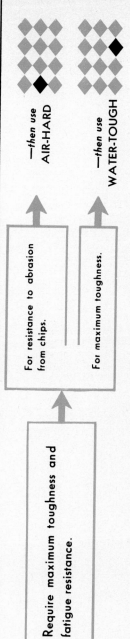

SHAPER TOOLS *See LATHE TOOLS*

SHAVING DIES *See DIES, Shaving; also DIES, Blanking*

SHAVING TOOLS *See AUTOMATIC Screw Machine Tools*

SHEAR BLADES

Should have all the hardness and wear-resistance possible, but they must not chip or break.

For cold shearing, smooth or notched.
—*then use* WATER-TOUGH

For cold shearing—where accuracy in heat treatment is important.
—*then use* AIR-TOUGH

For hot shearing, smooth or notched.
—*then use* RED-HARD

SIZING DIES *See DIES; Coining, Hot*

SLEDGES

Require "tough hardness" to resist upsetting and spalling. —then use WATER-TOUGH

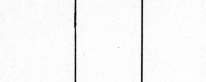

SLITTING CUTTERS

See CUTTERS

SLOTTING CUTTERS

See CUTTERS

SPIKE DIES

See DIES, Header—Hot

SPINDLES

Must have good wear-resistance and accuracy in hardening.

For average wear resistance. —then use OIL-HARD

For maximum wear resistance. —then use OIL-WEAR

SPINNING TOOLS

Require maximum resistance to abrasion and galling.

For all spinning tools except those which are impossible to harden in water.

—*then use* WATER-WEAR

For such tools as would crack if water-quenched.

—*then use* OIL-WEAR

SPOT FACERS

See COUNTERBORES

STAMPING DIES

See DIES, Blanking, Cold

STAMPS

(Stencils)

Must have adequate hardness with toughness to resist upsetting or chipping.

For intricate or very accurate roller stamps.

—*then use* OIL-HARD

For hand stamps and simple roller stamps.

—*then use* WATER-HARD

For good all around stamp steel—hot or cold—heavy duty.

—*then use* WATER-TOUGH

STAYBOLT TAPS

See TAPS

STONE TOOLS

Must have abrasion-resistance plus toughness to resist chipping and fatigue-resistance—should be easy to forge and heat treat.

Bush hammers.
—*then use* WATER-HARD

Chisels.
Four points.
Hand points.
—*then use* WATER-TOUGH

STRIKING DIES

See DIES, Striking

STRIPPER PLATES

—*Hardened*

Must hold size accurately in order to support punches.
—*then use* OIL-HARD or AIR-TOUGH

SWAGING TOOLS

See name of part, i.e., DIES, Swaging; ROLLS, Swaging; HAMMERS, Swaging

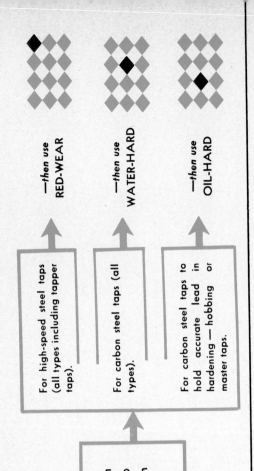

—then use
RED-WEAR

For high-speed steel taps (all types including tapper taps).

—then use
WATER-HARD

For carbon steel taps (all types).

—then use
OIL-HARD

For carbon steel taps to hold accurate lead in hardening — hobbing or master taps.

Must have keen cutting edge with various degrees of toughness to resist chipping or breaking—often require accuracy in hardening.

TAPS

—Collapsible
—Hand
—Hobbing (Master)
—Machine
—Pipe
—Staybolt
—Tapper Taps

THREAD CHASERS

See CHASERS

THREAD GAUGES

See GAUGES

THREAD ROLLER DIES

See DIES, Thread Roller

206

TIRE TURNING TOOLS

Must have good red-hardness to hold edge in spite of hard spots—toughness to resist chipping.

—then use **RED-WEAR**

TOOL BITS

See BITS, Tool Holder

TOOL SHANKS

See SHANKS

TRACK CHISELS

See CHISELS, Track

TRIMMER DIES

See DIES, Trimmer

VISE JAWS

See JAWS, Vise

T - W

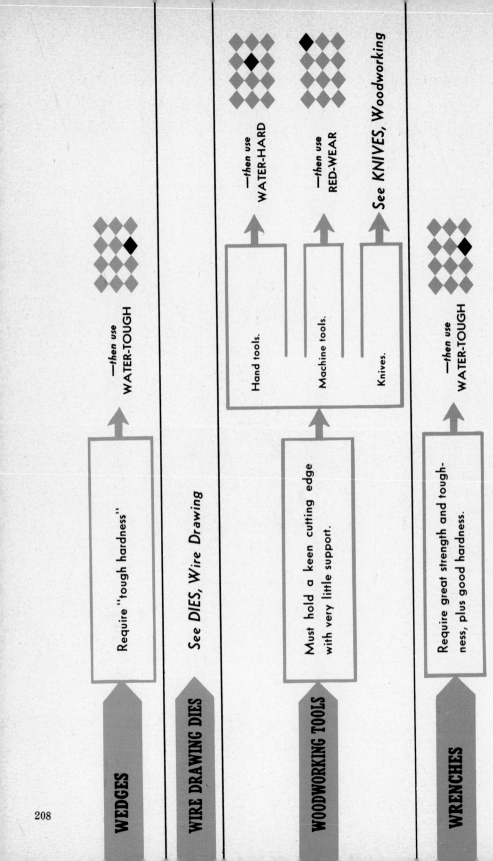

WEDGES

Require "tough hardness"

—*then use*
WATER-TOUGH

WIRE DRAWING DIES

See DIES, Wire Drawing

WOODWORKING TOOLS

Must hold a keen cutting edge with very little support.

Hand tools.

Machine tools.

Knives.

—*then use*
WATER-HARD

—*then use*
RED-WEAR

See KNIVES, Woodworking

WRENCHES

Require great strength and toughness, plus good hardness.

—*then use*
WATER-TOUGH

PART III

PROPERTIES, HEAT TREATMENT AND TESTING OF TOOL STEEL

In order to understand the properties of tool steel, it is necessary to know something about its heat treatment and testing. In order to understand the heat treatment, a knowledge of the properties and testing are necessary. Likewise, a study of testing involves knowledge of heat treatment and properties.

While every effort will be made to present these three subjects as clearly and as logically as possible, the reader will find it desirable to read straight through this entire Part III and then, having acquired the background, reread the entire part. Many things will be clear on the second reading that were not thoroughly understood on the first.

CHAPTER 10

HEAT TREATING METHODS AND EQUIPMENT

HEAT TREATING METHODS

Strictly speaking, all heating and cooling operations constitute heat treatment—whatever their purpose. Sometimes this expression is used in a more restricted sense to mean simply the hardening and tempering treatments.

Normalizing.—Normalizing, as used in these pages, consists in heating the steel in excess of the usual hardening temperature in order to clear up some undesirable condition in the structure. It is a sort of corrective treatment used after forging, or after an improper job of hardening in order to put the steel back into a more "normal" condition. In most cases, the steel is cooled in air from the normalizing temperature.

Annealing.—Annealing may be performed for several reasons, only two of which are of interest to the tool maker.

(a) **Annealing to Soften.**—A tool steel forging, as it comes from the hammer, is too hard to machine and must be annealed; or perhaps a tool that has already been hardened must be annealed for some additional machine work. For this type of anneal, it is customary to heat the steel slightly above its critical range and then cool very slowly. The steel maker always furnishes annealing temperatures as a part of the instructions for handling his steel. In connection with this subject, it will be interesting for the reader to review the comments on machinability, page 41.

(b) **Annealing for Strain Removal.**—No matter how carefully a piece of tool steel may have been annealed in the first place, considerable internal strain can be set up by certain tool making operations. It is frequently desirable to get rid of these strains before the tool is hardened. If a large amount of metal is removed by machining, the resulting strains are likely to cause the tool to go out of shape during hardening—even though an oil-hardening, non-deforming tool steel is used. Where extensive

211

machining is necessary on a tool requiring extreme accuracy, it is good practice to rough machine, give the piece a strain relieving anneal, and then finish machine with a light cut. Cold hobbing operations, bending, forming, coining (or even deep stamp marks) will cause internal strains in the metal which should likewise be removed by a strain relieving anneal. If not relieved, these may be so great that, when the additional strain of hardening is introduced, the tool will crack.

A strain relieving anneal is conducted by heating the steel to a temperature below the critical point and then cooling. Furnace cooling is best—cooling in lime or dry ashes is fairly good—and even air cooling is much better than no strain relieving anneal at all. If the steel manufacturer does not publish the temperature for this anneal, the range between 1275° and 1325°F. can be used for almost any tool steel—regardless of analysis.

Hardening.—Tools are hardened to develop their strength and wear resistance. The operation consists in heating the steel to some temperature above the critical and then cooling rapidly enough to cause the steel to harden.

The hardening temperature is supplied by the steel manufacturer and this temperature should be adhered to unless the user is willing to do the experimental work necessary to find a temperature that will suit his own particular requirements better.

The quenching medium is also prescribed by the steel maker. Some steels should be quenched in water (or brine), others should be quenched in oil, and still others are hardened by cooling in air. The reasons for the difference in behavior of water-hardening, oil-hardening and air-hardening steels during quenching were discussed in Chapter 4, and it was indicated that hardening actually takes place in two separate and distinct steps. The first step is that of cooling through a temperature of approximately 1100°F. faster than the gate speed (or critical quenching speed) of the steel, so as to insure hardening. The second is the actual hardening itself which in a plain carbon steel starts at about 500°F. and approaches completion as the steel cools below the boiling point of water, or about 200°F. It is therefore important in quenching to make sure that the entire section of the tool from center to surface be cooled to below 200°F. if it is to fully harden. It is not necessary, and in many cases not desirable, to quench a tool "stone cold," but it should become cold enough not to boil a drop of water before it is considered safe to go into the draw.

Since actual hardening takes place in the range of approximately 500°F. to room temperature, it follows that the so-called quenching stresses which sometimes result in cracking, must also develop in this range. Special methods of hardening have recently been devised which aim to minimize these stresses, and thus reduce the danger of cracking, by means of retarded cooling through this low temperature range. These methods are known by various names such as "time quenching," "martempering," "isothermal quenching," etc. They were developed primarily for the heat treatment of hardened parts rather than tools, and since accurate timing is quite essential, they lend themselves rather to production hardening than to the hardening of miscellaneous or occasional tools or parts. They have not been used much in the hardening of tools up to the present time, but will doubtless find wider application in the future.

The behavior of tool steel in the hardening process is covered more in detail in Chapter 20. Before leaving this subject, however, a word should be said about special hardening mechanisms. These consist of a furnace for heating the steel and some sort of an appliance for automatically telling the operator when the steel goes through its critical point. Some of these appliances show a "hump" on the pyrometer chart, others are actuated by the expansion and contraction of the steel and still others take advantage of the fact that steel loses its magnetism when heated above the critical point. It is sometimes recommended that the hardener needs only heat the steel "safely" above the critical point so indicated and then quench. There is nothing *safe* about this procedure. Many alloy steels must be heated 100°F. or more above the critical point in order to get best results. Some alloy steels require soaking at the hardening heat and others do not. These automatic appliances are excellent if the hardener will not attribute to them any more information than they actually give—namely, the location of the critical point. He should depend upon instructions from the steel manufacturer—or his own experimental work—to determine how *far* above the critical the steel should be heated, and how *long* it should be soaked.

Pack Hardening.—This is a modified hardening procedure frequently recommended for certain types of tool steel. It consists in packing the tools in a container with a suitable carbonaceous material, preferably clean cast iron borings, and then heating the entire pack to the hardening temperature. Obviously, heating progresses more slowly and the time necessary for soaking is increased. When the proper time comes, the tool is removed from the pack and quenched. Aside from the effects of slow heating and long soaking—which are sometimes desirable—this procedure keeps the surface of the tool free from scale and often helps to avoid surface decarburization. Charcoal should never be used for pack hardening below 1600°F. because it encourages decarburization. Cast iron borings are preferable at all times.

Tempering (or drawing).—This operation involves reheating a tool that has been hardened in order to relieve the hardening strain and increase the toughness. Incidentally, it usually causes the tool to lose some of its hardness—but this is not the *purpose* of tempering. The tool maker would rather leave his tools glass hard if he knew they would not break or go out of shape from strain. Drawing is usually conducted at a relatively low temperature—as compared to the hardening heat.

The length of **time** that the tool is soaked at the drawing heat is important. The desired results are really secured by a combination of *time* and *temperature*. No tool should be soaked at the drawing heat for less than one hour. Even in the few cases where the hardener could "get away with" a shorter time, he will do the tool more good than harm by allowing it to remain for the full hour at heat. Throughout this book "one hour draw" means one hour soak after the tool has come up uniformly to the drawing temperature. The time necessary to heat a tool up to the drawing temperature depends upon the section size of the tool, the drawing temperature and the heating medium. The larger the tool and the lower the drawing temperature, the longer will be the time required. Liquid baths and circulating air furnaces heat faster than ordinary oven drawing furnaces. Since hardened tools are drawn at low temperatures where the eye cannot tell when the tool is up to temperature, it is important to have some sort of guide in estimating the probable time necessary to reach temperature. Such a guide will be found on page 492.

The length of soak necessary after the tool has come up to

temperature depends upon the size and character of the tool. Large or intricate tools should be drawn longer than one hour. For example, the progressive blanking and stamping tools shown on page 120 (Fig. 98) might well be drawn for two hours if the die were about six inches square—and four or five hours if it were twice as large. The escutcheon tools shown on page 123 (Fig. 104) are about 15″ long. If made in one piece, four hours would not be too long to draw them—whereas, made in three sections, one hour would probably be sufficient. Generally speaking, the highly alloyed tool steels should be drawn longer than those containing little or no alloy.

Cold Treating (Deep Freezing).—Earlier in this chapter it was stated that the hardening of tool steel approaches completion "below the boiling point of water"—in other words, close to room temperature. For many years it has been known that while quenching or cooling down to room temperature would result in almost complete hardening, still there is often a small part of the structure of the steel which, even though it makes the "promise" to harden as it cools through the "gate," does not fulfill this promise at room temperature. It will fulfill its promise, however, if it is cooled below room temperature, and in recent years equipment and materials have been made available to remove these last traces of unhardened structure by cooling to low temperatures. These methods are referred to as "cold treating," "deep freezing," etc., and are carried out by cooling the tools in dry ice or in special refrigerating equipment. The cooling treatment is applied preferably after a preliminary draw to lessen the danger of cracking, and should be followed by a second draw.

Aging.—While the primary purpose of cold treating is to complete any hardening which has not taken place at the usual temperature of the quenching bath, it has another important result, that of stabilization of the hardened steel. Certain very accurate gauges or tools must be ground and lapped to exact size—and must then hold this size indefinitely. As ordinarily made, a hardened tool may change size or shape to the extent of a few ten thousandths over a period of years. This comes about through a natural aging process. Obviously, tool makers cannot wait for years for a tool to reach stability. Many years of aging can be crowded into a few hours of applying a modified cold treatment as follows:

After the tool has been properly hardened and thoroughly drawn, it is ground to the point of lapping. It is then heated for an hour or two to the temperature of boiling water and cooled back to room temperature. This is followed by cooling in "dry ice," or suitable refrigerating equipment for a similar time and allowing to warm up to room temperature. It is then put through the same cycle of heating and cooling four or five times more. This brings the steel to a stable condition after which the final lapping operation is completed.

HEAT TREATING EQUIPMENT

In a discussion of heat treating equipment it is important to remember that all heat treating operations are a question of temperature, time and atmosphere. If the tool is heated to the proper temperature—at the proper rate—soaked for the proper time—enveloped in the proper atmosphere—and cooled at the proper speed—it does not make any difference what kind of heat treating equipment is used. If such ideal performance is available from several different types of equipment, the choice can be made on the basis of cost and convenience. Before discussing hardening equipment, it will be worth while to look further into these three elements—temperature, time and atmosphere.

Temperature.—Heat treating instructions always prescribe that the steel should be heated to some definite temperature—or within some temperature range. The ability to do this depends upon the furnace being used, the pyrometer equipment and the skill and care of the hardener. About the best commercial hardening practice to be expected is to stay within a range of 25°F.— for example, 1500° to 1525°F. Working within a total range of 50°F. is only fair performance—and wider variation than this would be considered poor.

The hardening temperature must be controlled for many reasons. If the temperature is too low, the steel will fail to harden properly; and in many cases, toughness can be impaired just as much by too low a temperature as by too high a temperature. For many years it was considered to be a fundamental rule that "tool steel should be hardened at the lowest temperature at which it will fully harden." Today, it is known that this rule is wrong more often than it is right so it is a good rule to forget. Overheating is also objectionable. It increases scale and decarburization, and promotes warpage and distortion. If carried to excess, it causes grain growth, brittleness and frequently cracking.

The impression might be gained from the above statements that every tool steel has a single *best* hardening temperature which should never be varied. This is not strictly true. A steel like WATER-HARD may be deliberately hardened anywhere between 1450° and 1600°F. The higher hardening temperatures produce greater hardness penetration and increase the strength of the tool to resist compressional stress. The lower hardening temperatures decrease the penetration, but build up the resistance to splitting or bursting stresses. Thus, it may be said that there is a "best" hardening temperature for a given tool, when made from a given steel. This is not the same as saying that a steel should always be hardened from the same temperature—regardless of its use.

Time.—Time involves the rate at which the steel is heated up to its maximum temperature, the degree of soaking at temperature and the speed of cooling. Most hardeners use a clock of some sort—quite frequently one having alarm equipment that rings a bell after accurately measured periods of time have elapsed. Time control in minutes—or even seconds—is not too much to expect of a hardener.

The time required to heat a tool to temperature is of considerable importance, and depends upon several factors such as the size of the tool, the method of heating—that is, furnace, lead pot, etc.—the temperature of the furnace when the work is introduced, the maximum temperature of heating, etc. A more complete discussion of these will be found in Chapter 19. It would be well to state here, however, that the heating of a tool takes place in two stages. The first of these is heating up to the critical or absorption point of the steel, and in this stage the temperature of the tool increases in proportion to the amount of heat being added. The second stage is that of heating through the critical. Steel actually absorbs heat when going through the critical range, without increasing in temperature, and it must absorb enough heat to complete its changes in the critical before it again continues to rise in temperature.

To illustrate this, in Fig. 131, pages 228B and C, are four interesting photographs taken through the peep hole of a hardening furnace while a piece of .90% carbon tool steel is being heated through the critical range. They serve to illustrate that it takes *time* for a piece of tool steel to go through its critical transformation. In carbon tool steel, the steel absorbs as much heat in the critical (without changing temperature) as would be needed to heat it about 150°F. That is why the furnace (and the pyrometer tube, shown standing upright at the left of the block) get ahead of the steel.

Back in the days of brittle timbre tool steel it was considered important to heat tools very slowly, particularly those of large section, in the belief that the surface would heat much faster than the inside and thus result in injury to the tool. This is true now only of tools having light projections. In tools of fairly solid design it has been found that, due to the high heat conductivity of steel, there is only a slight lag between center and surface in the first stages of heating, and practically none in the second stage. If the tool is placed directly in the hot furnace the center and surface will come to temperature at the same time. Consequently newer recommendations for the hardening of tough timbre steels call for putting the tools right in a hot furnace running at the hardening temperature and allowing to heat "naturally." This practice has certain distinct advantages, only one of which is better control of decarburization. These statements, of course, do not apply to such steels as high speed, where preheating is necessary on account of the extremely high hardening temperature used.

Atmosphere.—Although hardeners have always recognized that the atmosphere surrounding their tools during hardening has some influence on the results, it has only been within recent years that scientific work has been done along this line and even more recently that hardening furnaces have been constructed with controlled artificial atmospheres. Three general types of furnace atmosphere have long been recognized—**oxidizing, neutral** and **reducing.** This subject is discussed in considerable detail in Chapter 18, page 447. It is sufficient to state that an *oxidizing* furnace atmosphere is created by admitting more air to the furnace than is necessary to burn the fuel. A *reducing* atmosphere is produced by admitting less air than is needed to completely burn the fuel, thus leaving an excess of combustible gases in the furnace. A *neutral* atmosphere results from complete combustion, with no excess of either fuel or air. In order to control the atmosphere with greater accuracy, modern equipment is available which introduces into the furnace gases of known analysis and in definite percentages. These are known as **atmosphere controlled furnaces.**

Several definite facts have now been established concerning the effects of atmosphere on steel in heating, and these can be briefly summarized as follows:

It is known that the *composition* of the steel is important, some types tending to scale or decarburize more than others.

It can be generally stated that an oxidizing atmosphere, while it produces scale on the tools, frequently does so without decarburizing the metal underneath. A reducing atmosphere avoids scale, but sometimes produces excessive decarburization.

In a conventional fuel-fired furnace, the best atmosphere for the **lower temperature range of hardening,** that is up to 1600°F., is a distinctly **oxidizing** one.

For the **higher temperature range**—above about 1700°F.—the opposite is true, and the best atmosphere is a **reducing** one. The exact effect of reducing atmospheres, however, depends upon their exact composition. Water vapor even in a highly reducing atmosphere, as an example, will tend to decarburize. Consequently the fuel and the type of furnace affect the behavior even though the atmosphere maintained is highly reducing.

The amount of **circulation** of the atmosphere in the furnace is important. Stagnant areas in an oxidizing atmosphere tend to become neutral or even reducing, and hence will decarburize. Stagnant areas (such as those inside blind holes in a die) will, in highly reducing atmospheres, tend to become more reducing, and this effect is so pronounced in some cases that they frequently cause excessive carburization.

Since it is known that atmosphere does affect the surface and structure of tools, every effort should be made to keep the atmosphere *uniform.* Duplicate results cannot be secured time after time if the hardener allows the atmosphere of his furnace to vary over wide ranges. In selecting a hardening furnace, the ability to control atmosphere is therefore an important consideration.

Hardening Room Instruments

The tool hardener needs few instruments but these few should be good ones and should be kept accurate. It is indeed poor

economy to spend hours in the tool room working to split thousandths, and then send the tool to a hardening room where the
measuring instruments are inaccurate. For example—manganese oil-hardening, non-shrinkable tool steels will actually
shrink if *under* heated; they will expand if *over* heated; and they
will "stay put" only when quenched from a comparatively
narrow intermediate range. A pyrometer that is 50°F. off
calibration can throw many hours of needless stoning and adjusting back into the tool room. Indeed many tools find their way
into the scrap box, or give a miserable account of themselves in
service, just because the heat treating instruments are inaccurate,
or inadequate.

For a time the only instruments used by the hardener were
pyrometers, thermometers and clocks. To these has recently
been added apparatus for testing the atmosphere of the hardening
furnace. The modern hardener is thus able to now control all
three important variables—temperature, time and atmosphere.

Pyrometers.—For many years, hardeners had to judge the
temperature of their work without the assistance of any instrument. Fortunately, at that time, they had little to work with
other than plain carbon tool steel, and since this steel hardens
from a temperature slightly above its critical point, an excellent
job could be done by experienced men. A chart of incandescent
temperature colors is shown in Fig. 130 on page 228A. These
may be helpful in the absence of a pyrometer, but they are
only approximate at best. Good "eye hardeners" can actually
see carbon tool steel go through its critical range by the lights
and shadows that appear on it. As may be seen from the illustration on pages 228B and C (Fig. 131), this was not done by
simply observing the incandescent color of the metal. With the
advent of alloy tool steels, many of which are hardened several
hundred degrees above their critical and on which the critical
changes are so gradual that they cannot be seen, pyrometers
became absolutely necessary.

While there are various types of pyrometers embodying
different principles, the thermoelectric pyrometer is the one
almost universally used in the hardening room. The principle of
this is quite simple. If two different metals are joined together,
and the joint is locally heated, a small electric voltage will
be generated between the colder parts of the metals. This is

called a **thermocouple,** and is illustrated in Fig. 125. To be more specific, suppose one of the metals is pure iron and the other is a nickel-copper alloy called "Constantan," and both are in the form of wire. We can cut off three or four feet of each kind of wire, twist them together at one end, and then weld the twist to be sure of a perfect contact. When the welded joint is heated, a

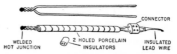

FIG. 125.—Thermocouple.

delicate voltmeter will measure a voltage across the cold ends of the two wires. The voltage increases with the temperature, like this:

IRON-CONSTANTAN COUPLE

Temperature of Welded End	Voltage with Cold End at 75°F.
75°F.	.00000 volts
500°F.	.01321 volts
1000°F.	.02947 volts
1500°F.	.04713 volts
1800°F.	.05785 volts

These voltages are very small, and their measurement requires a meter that will read in thousandths of a volt—in other words, a millivoltmeter. Now all that is necessary is to remove the "millivolt" card from the meter and put in another card calibrated in "degrees Fahrenheit," and we have a pyrometer. The simplest types of pyrometers are made in just this manner. (See Fig. 126.) Strictly speaking, the meter does not measure the temperature of the hot junction—it measures the *difference* in temperature between the hot junction and the cold junction. If the

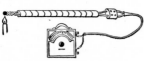

FIG. 126.—A simple millivoltmeter pyrometer.

wires were heated to the same temperature throughout their entire length, the meter would read zero. Therefore it is important that the cold junction be kept at a constant temperature at all times if the simple instrument just described is to read accurately. Modern instruments provide either automatic or manual compensation for temperature changes in the cold junction, and thus eliminate this difficulty.

If copper lead wires were employed between the thermocouple

and the instrument, there would be set up new "couples" where the copper leads were attached to the thermocouple alloys, and these "accidental" couples would develop a voltage of their own. Hence it is common practice to make the lead wires out of the same materials as used in the thermocouple—or some other materials having the same thermoelectric properties. This also has the effect of moving the cold junction of the thermocouple away from the vicinity of the furnace and placing it at the instrument.

Thus far, only iron-constantan thermocouples have been mentioned. These are useful up to about 1800°F., but above this temperature they burn out rapidly. "Chromel-Alumel" is another popular combination useful up to about 2200°F., and

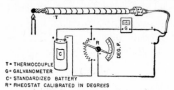

T = THERMOCOUPLE
G = GALVANOMETER
C = STANDARDIZED BATTERY
R = RHEOSTAT CALIBRATED IN DEGREES

Fig. 127.—A much simplified sketch illustrating the principle of a potentiometer. (Not a wiring diagram.)

intermittently somewhat higher. For temperatures up to about 2800°F., pure platinum is used for one wire and the other is an alloy of platinum and rhodium. All of these different thermocouple combinations develop different voltages and therefore the pyrometer instrument is always calibrated for one particular kind of couple—and no other can be used.

Couples do not stay accurate indefinitely and instructions furnished by the makers for their care and protection should be adhered to if maximum life and accuracy are expected.

The lead wires, of course, have a certain amount of electrical resistance depending on their length, and compensation must sometimes be provided in the instrument to take care of this. Some pyrometers avoid this necessity by using a **potentiometer** instead of a millivoltmeter to measure the voltage, as illustrated in Fig. 127. The potentiometer does not draw current from the thermocouple as the voltmeter does. It contains a standardized electric battery with an adjustable voltage, and it uses this battery to "buck" the thermocouple voltage. When these two voltages are exactly equal and opposite, no current can flow through the lead wires, and hence there can be no error due to resistance. All that is necessary is a very delicate "current meter" (called a Galvanometer) to show when the current becomes zero—then the voltage from the standardized battery necessary to exactly buck the thermocouple voltage, can be measured on a rheostat which for convenience is graduated directly in degrees. Potentiometer pyrometers can be installed a long distance from the furnace.

The inherent accuracy of a pyrometer depends somewhat upon the temperature range, but commercial installations can hardly be expected to be closer than 10°F. plus or minus. That is, if the instrument reads 1400°F, the actual temperature may be anywhere between 1390° and 1410°F., and this would be considered good pyrometer performance. At temperatures above 2000°F. the variation is likely to be greater. Errors in a pyrometer may originate in the thermocouple, the lead wires, the instrument, or in the connections and switches which join these three elements together. Therefore in checking the accuracy of a pyrometer, the entire installation should be checked. In other words the hardener should not install a new thermocouple, and just because this one reads the same as the old one, pronounce the instrument correct. Errors in the lead wires, switches, or instrument will not be caught in this manner.

Pyrometers are available in three general types—**indicating, recording** and **control.** Various commercial types are illustrated on pages 224 and 225 (Fig. 128). **Indicating pyrometers** are those which simply show the temperature on their face in the same manner that a clock shows the time of day. **Recording pyrometers** have a chart which is mechanically driven, and on this the temperature is continuously recorded. Such instruments make a permanent record of the temperature throughout the day. **Controllers** not only indicate or record the temperature, but they automatically regulate the temperature of the furnace so that it will stay within a predetermined zone. A modified type of semi-automatic controller operates lights in front of the furnace. Thus a red light may tell the hardener that his furnace is too hot, a green light too cold, and a white light "O.K." With this system the hardener must adjust his own valves to hold the temperature on the white light.

Checking the Pyrometer.—Just as every well equipped *tool room* has master precision gauges to check the accuracy of working gauges, so every well equipped *hardening room* should own a portable master instrument which is kept locked up and used

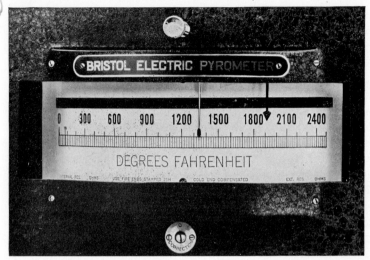

Bristol electric indicating pyrometer.   (*Courtesy of The Bristol Co.*)

Dial type recording pyrometer. (*Courtesy of Leeds and Northrup Co.*)

Potentiometer controller. (*Courtesy of Foxboro Co.*)

FIG. 128.—Modern pyrometers.

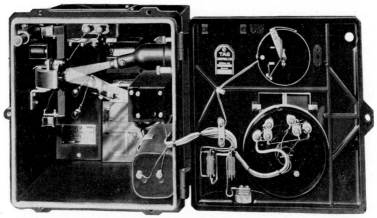

Indicating potentiometer controller actuated by photo electric cell.   (*Courtesy of C. J. Tagliabue Div., Portable Products Corp.*)

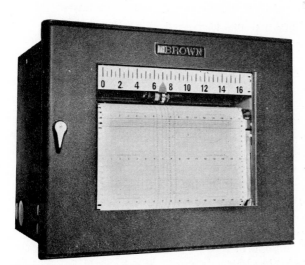

Multiple recording electronic potentiometer pyrometer. (*Courtesy of The Brown Instrument Co.*)

Oil bath thermometer. (*Courtesy of Taylor Instrument Co.*)

FIG. 128.—Modern pyrometers (*Continued*).

periodically to check the service pyrometers. The master instrument itself should be checked by the pyrometer service man whenever opportunity affords.

In the absence of the master instrument, the following simple method for calibrating pyrometers by determining the freezing point of salt, has the merit of accuracy and the advantage of locating a fixed point upon the scale of the instrument near the range generally used in the heat treatment of steels:

Pure salt (sodium chloride) is melted in a clean crucible of fire-clay, iron or nickel, either in the furnace or over a forge fire, and then further heated until a temperature of about 1600° to 1650°F. (871° to 899°C.) is attained. Chemically pure salt is recommended to avoid variations in the freezing point of common salt that would be caused by the presence of impurities. It is also essential that the crucible be clean, because a slight admixture of a foreign substance might noticeably lower or raise the freezing point.

Next, the thermocouple to be calibrated is removed from its protecting tube and its "hot" end is immersed in the salt bath. When this end has attained the temperature of the bath, the crucible is removed from the source of heat and allowed to cool, and while cooling, readings are taken every ten seconds on the instrument. A curve is then plotted by using time and temperatures as co-ordinates, and the temperature of the freezing point of salt, as indicated by this particular thermocouple, is noted—as the point, namely, where the temperature of the bath remains temporarily constant while the salt is freezing. The period during which the temperature is stationary, depends on the size of the bath and the rate of cooling, and is not a factor in the calibration. As the true freezing point of salt is 1474°F. (801°C), the needed correction for the instrument under observation can be readily applied. The diagrams, Figs. 136 and 137, illustrate the calibration of a correct and incorrect pyrometer.

If it is preferred not to use the molten salt method, the hardener can check his pyrometer quite accurately by taking advantage of the visible critical point on a piece of high carbon water-hardening tool steel. If nothing better is available, a piece of a heavy file can be used for the purpose. The piece of tool steel should approach the same cross-section as the protective tube of the thermocouple. Carbon tool steel absorbs about as much heat at the critical point to complete its transformation as would be needed to heat it nearly 150°F. While this critical heat absorption is going on, the steel does not increase appreciably in temperature. The critical point comes at 1355°F., and this furnishes the following method for checking the pyrometer. At a time after the furnace has been in use and the brick work is thoroughly hot, cool the furnace to about 1250°F. to 1300°F. Place the piece of tool steel and the pyrometer tube near the hearth—preferably in such a manner that the pyrometer is *behind* the tool steel and the dividing line between them can be clearly seen. The progress of heating should be observed by slightly raising the door—*not* by looking through the peep hole. When the steel has reached exactly the same temperature as the thermocouple, the dividing line between them will disappear and they will simply look like one piece of metal. Now start heating the furnace slowly and it will be observed that the thermocouple and the steel show exactly the same color until the tool steel reaches its critical point (1355°F.). At this point the steel stops heating, and the thermocouple keeps on getting hotter. By the time the pyrometer is about 10°F. hotter than the tool steel, the eye can easily see the dividing line between them again. The hardener should then immediately look at his instrument and it should read 1365°F. (this is 10° higher than the critical point of the steel). When this difference in color is *first* noted, if the instrument reads 1340°F., it is reading about 25° low. If it reads 1395°, it is 30° high. This simple test is illustrated in Figs. 131 and 133. It does not take long and there is no reason why it cannot be repeated once or twice a week.

There are several other types of device for measuring temperature, for example the optical pyrometer and radiation pyrometer. These are relatively unimportant however, in the heat treatment of tool steel. A quite important type of appliance is that which indicates the critical point by recording a temperature "hump "on the heating curve and another utilizes variation in the rate of expansion of the steel as it heats (Fig. 129). These appliances serve a very useful function, but as mentioned before, the hardener should not attribute to them any more information than they actually give. The proper hardening temperature

"Hump" type. Enlarged insert of pyrometer chart shows critical "hump" on the heating curve. (*Courtesy of Leeds and Northrup Co.*)

Fig. 129.—Furnaces that indicate the critical range.

Laboratory dilatometer furnace which heats, and measures the expansion and contraction of the steel being heated. (*Courtesy of The Bristol Co.*)

may, or may not, be close to the critical point and nothing but trouble may come from heating *all* tool steels "just above the critical" and then quenching them.

Repairs to a pyrometer should be made only by qualified

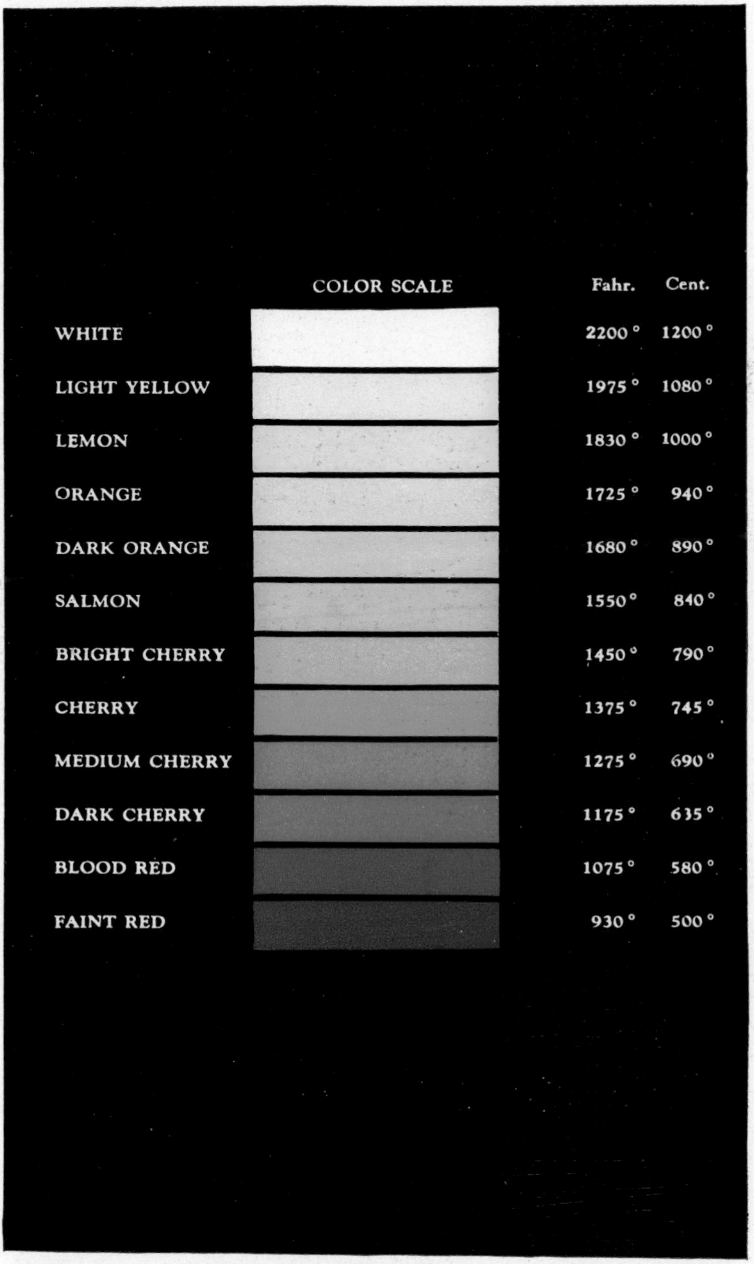

COLOR SCALE		Fahr.	Cent.
WHITE		2200 °	1200 °
LIGHT YELLOW		1975 °	1080 °
LEMON		1830 °	1000 °
ORANGE		1725 °	940 °
DARK ORANGE		1680 °	890 °
SALMON		1550 °	840 °
BRIGHT CHERRY		1450 °	790 °
CHERRY		1375 °	745 °
MEDIUM CHERRY		1275 °	690 °
DARK CHERRY		1175 °	635 °
BLOOD RED		1075 °	580 °
FAINT RED		930 °	500 °

FIG. 130.—Heat colors in moderate diffused daylight with approximate temperature.

(See text page 220)

Pyrometer = 1300°F. Steel is same temperature as the pyrometer.

Pyrometer = 1360°F. Steel stops heating at 1355°F. to complete critical transformation.

FIG. 131—Heating through the critical.

(See text pages 217 and 218)

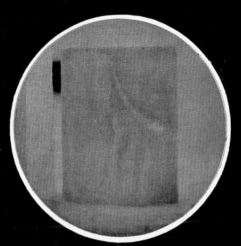

Pyrometer = 1400°F. Pyrometer continues to heat. Steel
still lags behind.

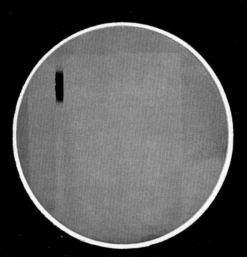

Pyrometer = 1425°F. Critical
transformation complete.
Steel catches up to pyrometer.

Unretouched photographs taken through peep-hole of an electric muffle furnace
—showing block of .90 % carbon tool steel, and pyrometer tube at left of block.

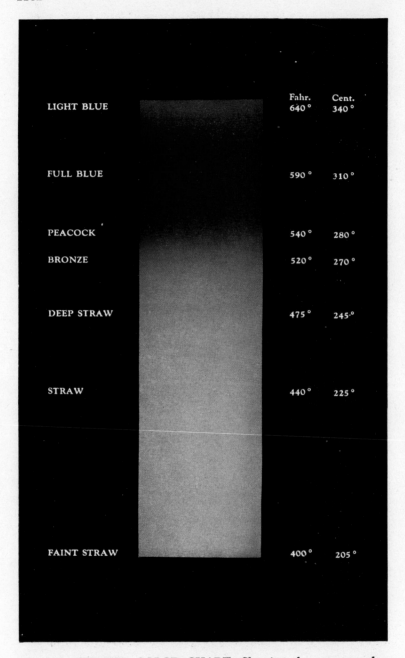

		Fahr.	Cent.
LIGHT BLUE		640°	340°
FULL BLUE		590°	310°
PEACOCK		540°	280°
BRONZE		520°	270°
DEEP STRAW		475°	245-°
STRAW		440°	225°
FAINT STRAW		400°	205°

FIG. 132.—TEMPER COLOR CHART—Showing the temper colors momentarily assumed by plain carbon tool steel just as it reaches the temperatures indicated. Soaking at heat causes colors to progress further. Chart does not apply to alloy tool steel.

(*See text page* 258)

instrument men. The only thing that a hardener is normally licensed to do is to replace the thermocouple, and spare couples should be kept on hand for this purpose. If this does not correct the difficulty, a competent service man should be called.

In concluding this discussion of pyrometers, a word of caution is in order. The hardener should realize that a pyrometer does not show the temperature of the furnace—it simply indicates the temperature of those two twisted wires inside the protective tube.

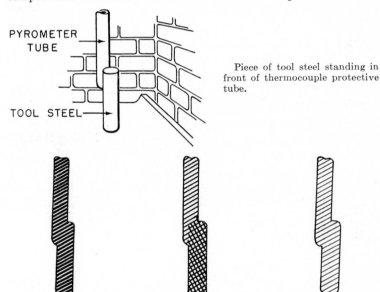

PYROMETER
TUBE

TOOL STEEL

Piece of tool steel standing in front of thermocouple protective tube.

Up to 1355°F., the tool steel and the tube blend together as though they were one piece of metal.

Tool steel stops heating at 1355°F. and soon looks distinctly darker than the tube. (Instrument should read about 1365°F.)

After critical change is complete, the steel catches up to the tube, and their colors blend perfectly again.

Fig. 133.

If the furnace is heating or cooling rapidly—if the temperature within the furnace is non-uniform—if the thermocouple is way up near the roof, far removed from the work—it is anybody's guess what the temperature of the tool may be. Thermocouples should be located close to the hearth and close to the work. If, in this position, they interfere with charging or discharging the furnace, they should be movable so that they can be lowered close to the work while it is being heated. There are probably more errors originating from misplacement of thermocouples than there are from inaccurate instruments.

Thermometers.—Little need be said about these familiar and trustworthy instruments. Glass thermometers are useful in liquid or air tempering furnaces for measuring temperatures up to about 600°F. See page 225 (Fig. 128). It is worth repeating that a thermometer tells only the temperature of the spot where the mercury bulb happens to be—and it is up to the operator to make sure that it is in the right place.

Clocks.—An ordinary clock will serve for many heat treating operations, and an alarm attachment frequently comes in handy. For super-heating high speed steel or heating tools in a salt bath or lead pot, a clock with a sweep second hand can be used. Also, some very convenient "timers" are available—some having alarms and others not. There is a useful type which the hardener turns ahead to the time interval desired; the clock then runs *backward* until the hands get back to zero, indicating that the time has elapsed. Some accurate timing device should be available in every hardening room. Practical applications of time control in the hardening room are discussed in Chapter 19.

Atmosphere Control Apparatus.—The function of atmosphere control equipment is to both analyze and control the atmosphere in the hardening furnace at the operating temperature. In most fuel-fired oven furnaces, the tool is surrounded by the same combustion gases that heat the furnace. In electrically heated or muffle furnaces, gases may be deliberately introduced for purposes of atmosphere control. These artificial atmospheres are generally produced by burning a known percentage of gas and air in a precombustion chamber and then leading the product of this combustion into the furnace chamber.

The combustible materials in practically all fuels are some form of carbon (C), or hydrogen (H), or both. These combine with atmospheric oxygen (O) to form carbon monoxide (CO), carbon dioxide (CO_2), and water (H_2O). There is, of course, plenty of nitrogen (N) present from the atmosphere, but since this is inactive it is ignored. In its most simplified form, gas analysis consists in determining the percentages of CO, CO_2 and O. It may surprise many hardeners to know that a man with no chemical knowledge can, with a little experience, analyze furnace gases for these three components in ten or fifteen minutes.

The oldest and most conventional type of gas analysis equipment is the **Orsat apparatus,** which can be purchased from any good laboratory supply house.   This contrivance looks terribly complicated, but it isn't. Suppose someone were to hand you 100 white marbles and told you that some of them were compressed salt, others were marble, and still others were quartz, and asked you to tell how many there were of each. If you drop the entire assortment into water and wait a little while, there might be only 92 of them left. The eight which dissolved were made of salt—the other two kinds being insoluble in water. Now you could drop the remaining pieces into muriatic acid, and perhaps 18 more

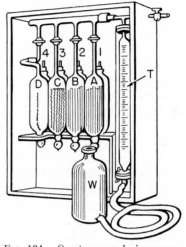

FIG. 134.—Orsat gas analysis apparatus.

would disappear. These would be the ones made of marble. The balance of the pieces would be quartz because it does not dissolve in either water or acid.

This is exactly the principle of a gas analysis apparatus. You withdraw a sample of gas from the heating chamber of the furnace with a convenient apparatus provided for the purpose. Fig. 134 illustrates the Orsat type equipment used in actual analysis of the gas. A portion of the gas is drawn into the long graduated tube "T" at the right hand side of the Orsat apparatus —exactly 100 cubic centimeters of it. The bottle "W" is filled with water and by raising or lowering this in the hand, the gas can be forced out of the graduated tube or sucked in at will. No. 1 pet cock is opened and the gas is compelled to bubble through the chemicals contained in the glass receptacle "A". This dissolves out all of the CO_2. Upon sucking the gas back into the graduated tube you may now have only 95 cubic centimeters left. Thus you know that there was 5% of CO_2 in the gas. By closing pet cock No. 1 and opening No. 2, the gas can now be sent through the second receptacle which removes the oxygen and the

quantity lost can readily be measured. This process is simply
continued until the various components of the gas have been
determined. These are not exact operating instructions, but
they serve to illustrate how the apparatus works and why you do
not have to be a chemist to use it. It is not too much to expect
that such apparatus will become commonplace in progressive
hardening rooms as the appreciation of atmosphere control
becomes more general.

Several pyrometer manufacturers have turned their attention
to the manufacture of **automatic gas analysis equipment.** Some
of these rather elaborate devices actually record on a scroll of
paper variations in the composition of the furnace atmosphere.
Perhaps perfection has not yet been attained in these automatic

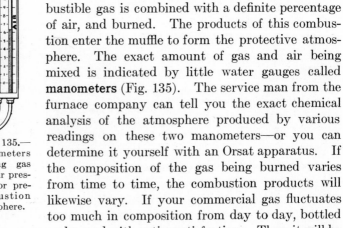
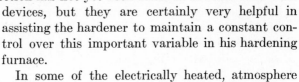
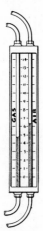

devices, but they are certainly very helpful in
assisting the hardener to maintain a constant control over this important variable in his hardening
furnace.

In some of the electrically heated, atmosphere
controlled furnaces, a definite percentage of combustible gas is combined with a definite percentage
of air, and burned. The products of this combustion enter the muffle to form the protective atmosphere. The exact amount of gas and air being
mixed is indicated by little water gauges called
manometers (Fig. 135). The service man from the
furnace company can tell you the exact chemical
analysis of the atmosphere produced by various
readings on these two manometers—or you can
determine it yourself with an Orsat apparatus. If
the composition of the gas being burned varies
from time to time, the combustion products will
likewise vary. If your commercial gas fluctuates
too much in composition from day to day, bottled

Fig. 135.—
Manometers
showing gas
and air pres-
sure for pre-
combustion
atmosphere.

propane gas can be used with entire satisfaction. Thus, it will be
seen that the hardener has available a considerable choice of
equipment which he can use to keep track of his atmosphere—
reserving actual gas analysis for checking purposes only. The
practical application of atmosphere control in tool steel hardening is discussed in Chapter 18.

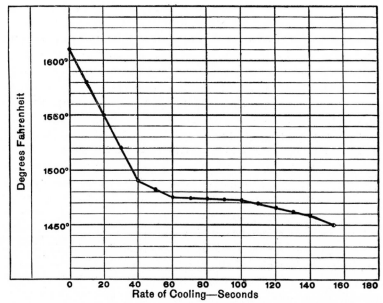

Fig. 136.—Molten salt calibration of a pyrometer that is correct.

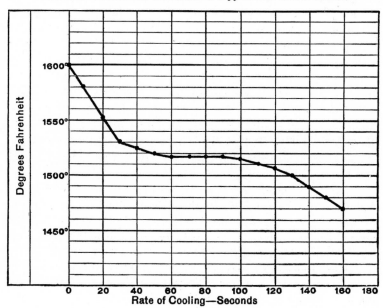

Fig. 137.—Molten salt calibration of a pyrometer that reads 45°F. too high.

Hardening Furnaces

Before launching into a discussion of hardening furnaces, it might be well to make some comments on a subject close to the heart of every tool hardener, namely the hardening room itself—its condition, arrangement, lighting, etc.

The immediate ancestor of the hardening room was the blacksmith shop. There are many hardeners working today who learned their trade as blacksmiths, and can easily remember when there was no such thing as a "hardening room"—all hardening being done in the blacksmith shop, and most of it in a forge fire. This would be unimportant were it not for the fact that quite a number of present day hardening rooms seem to have inherited the "atmosphere" of the blacksmith shop. They are dirty, unlovely places stuck away in some remote corner with very little regard to light, ventilation, comfort, or "inspiration." Any one who has visited the plants of some of the large manufacturers of taps, drills, cutters, etc., cannot fail to be impressed by the clean, neat and "inspiring" appearance of their heat treating departments. These firms, who make tools for a living, say that the hardening room is the very heart of their organization—and this is easy to believe from the care they give it.

In plants where the hardening department has been a sort of neglected step-child, it is no exaggeration to say that the performance in this division could be improved at least 10% by simply removing the junk, giving the whole place a good cleaning, and then applying a couple of coats of paint. A 10% gain may not look like much until you apply the "Good Tools" formula (page 3) and find that it means an average gain of 10% in the efficiency of every tool that goes through the department—and that's something.

While the painters are there, be sure to give some thought to the windows. Direct sunlight should not shine into the hardening room at any time during the day. Such windows should be painted an opaque color (green is frequently used). Theoretically, a hardening room should have uniform light all day long—and the nearer you can come to this ideal, the better your results will be. A north exposure is best if there is a choice. We would not recommend darkening the windows completely and using artificial light; a better and more pleasant condition can be had with subdued daylight. Hardening is still as much an art as a science, and it is well known that art does not thrive in dirty or depressing surroundings.

Fig. 138 illustrates what can be done toward a clean, orderly and efficient hardening room.

Hardening furnaces should be judged by their size, shape, method of heating, atmosphere control, and capacity for turning out work. Their heat insulation for comfort in the hardening room, their economy and convenience of operation, etc., have nothing to do with the metallurgy of hardening but are nevertheless important considerations.

Fig. 138.—Remodeled tool hardening room in a metal working plant, making only production tools for their own shop use.

A furnace should be large enough to uniformly heat the largest tools that are likely to be placed in it. Oven type furnaces should have a hearth roughly three times as wide, and twice as long as the largest piece to be hardened. Thus, to harden a block the size of an ordinary 9″ × 4½″ brick, the hearth should be at least 12″ × 18″. It is better that a furnace be too large than too small—especially if the hardener will take care to place the pyrometer close to his work. The capacity of a furnace is sometimes rated in pounds of work per square foot of hearth area. A capacity of 40 lbs. per sq. ft. is usually considered the average maximum.

Forgetting fuel for a moment, furnaces may be divided into **muffle** type, **semi-muffle** type and **open hearth** type. In the

muffle type (Fig. 139) the tool is placed in a closed refractory retort which is heated from the outside. Combustion gases are not supposed to enter the retort and the tool is therefore surrounded by ordinary air or else some artificial atmosphere introduced for the purpose. Practically all electrically heated oven furnaces have the characteristics of a muffle type furnace.

In a **semi-muffle** type furnace (Fig. 140) there is a refractory tile supported on pillars some inches above the solid bottom of the furnace. This tile joins the front and back walls, but does not touch the side walls. The fuel—usually gas or oil—is burned in the space below the tile, the combustion products rise through the space between the tile and the side walls and vent through

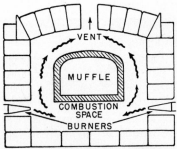

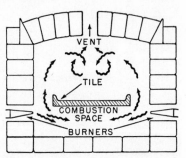

FIG. 139.—Illustrating the principle of the muffle type furnace.

FIG. 140.—The principle of the semi-muffle type furnace.

holes in the roof. In this furnace the atmosphere surrounding the tools consists of combustion products—but the tool does not lie in the direct path of the flame. The roof vents provide the hardener with a rough control over the flame travel. If there are two or three vents, he can partially (or entirely) cover certain vents with a brick and force the flame toward other parts of the furnace. Covering **all** the vents builds up pressure in the furnace and forces the gases to escape around the door. This is not particularly desirable unless the door is kept part-way open for constant introduction or removal of work. In such cases, it prevents room atmosphere from being sucked in the door to cool the furnace and perhaps damage the work.

The **open hearth** oven furnace (Fig. 141) is the least desirable design for tool hardening. It consists essentially in a refractory lined oven containing only one compartment in which the burners operate. Obviously, both temperature and atmosphere can vary tremendously within the oven, depending upon whether the tool lies in the path of the flame or off to one side. There is really little point in giving further attention to this type of equipment when so much better furnaces are available.

In comparing the muffle type with the semi-muffle type for tool hardening, much depends upon whether an artificial atmosphere is to be used. In the absence of such an artificial atmosphere the advantage lies with the semi-muffle type due to the fact that the hardener can exercise a reasonable control of the atmosphere in which his tools are heated. The semi-muffle furnace will average to heat faster than the muffle furnace—this is helpful from a production standpoint, but of doubtful advantage to the steel.

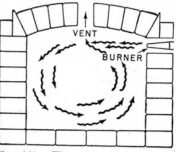

Fig. 141.—The principle of the open hearth oven furnace.

Both decarburization and scale can be better controlled in the semi-muffle type.

Atmosphere control is obtained in two ways, either by proper regulation of the air-fuel ratio or by the introduction in the furnace of a synthetic atmosphere. The first method adapts itself, of course, to fuel-fired furnaces of the open or semi-muffle type, and the products of combustion constitute the atmosphere in which the tools are heated. The second method, which might be termed specialized atmosphere control, can be applied either in the full muffle fuel-fired furnaces, or in electric furnaces. Specially prepared atmospheres of known composition introduced into the furnace muffle independent of the source of heat, constitute the medium in which the tools are heated.

A question frequently asked is, "Which kind of hardening furnace is better—a gas furnace, an oil furnace, an electric furnace, or a liquid bath?" In view of what has already been said, any arbitrary answer to this question would obviously be unfair, because *any* type of furnace constructed *suitably* for the job would be better than another type which was not so constructed. It is worth while therefore to discuss these various methods of heating further.

Oil Fired Furnaces.—These are most commonly found in larger sized installations—with a hearth perhaps 2 ft. × 3 ft. or larger. They have the advantage that the fuel is available in almost any location—they have a rapid heat input, and can turn out a lot of work.

With proper oil burners, manually operated, a reasonable degree of atmosphere control can be effected without special equipment. From an atmosphere standpoint, in general they do not lend themselves well to automatic regulation—although this is not the fault of the fuel. Oil burners are now available in which the air-oil ratio is set, and maintained for all temperatures without readjusting, temperature regulation being obtained by the operation of one valve. Many of these automatically regulated furnaces are fired steadily until the pyrometer reaches the proper temperature, then the regulator shuts off the oil altogether, and the furnace is allowed to "die down" to the point where the regulator again turns on the oil. Obviously no predetermined atmosphere can be maintained under these conditions. Instead of being regulated "on-and-off," there should be two burners— one regulated to heat the furnace slightly hotter than needed and the other regulated to heat the furnace slightly lower than needed. If both burners are adjusted for the proper atmosphere, automatic control can be had by switching from one to the other.

Some oil burners do not "throttle down" as well as gas or electricity so that many oil fired furnaces work best only within a certain temperature range. Fundamentally, there is no reason why oil cannot be used as a satisfactory heating medium in a hardening furnace, as hundreds of excellent installations testify.

When oil fuel is used, some thought must be given to assuring a steady flow to the burners. If the storage tanks are out-of-doors, and a heavy grade of fuel oil is used, trouble will be encountered in securing a free flow during the winter months. Also, those who secure the best results with oil-fired hardening furnaces do *not* buy the cheapest fuel oil they can find; oil containing dirt or solid residues can be just as effective as cold weather in clogging the burners or lines.

A uniformly steady supply of compressed air should be available. The hardening room should preferably have its own blower, and thus avoid fluctuations in the main air lines or embarrassment due to the supply being cut off altogether at a critical moment. The supply of air should be ample to avoid changes in pressure due to other furnaces being cut in or out.

Gas Fired Furnaces.—Gas fired furnaces are usually either of the muffle or semi-muffle type. These furnaces are available in all sizes but not uncommonly give way to oil on the largest installations. Gas is a nice clean fuel and is easy to regulate although in some locations its composition is likely to vary considerably. Gas furnaces frequently have the advantage of multiple burners which help to heat the furnace uniformly, and facilitate atmosphere control. The heat input from gas is adequate to turn out production as fast as is good for the tool steel. If automatically controlled, a continuous atmosphere should be provided as described for the oil furnace.

When natural gas or manufactured gas are not available, liquefied gas in steel tanks can be procured which is very satisfactory when the cost is not prohibitory. There is now available also equipment for gasifying oil in a separate unit, using this gas as fuel.

Electric Furnaces.—These furnaces are becoming quite popular for many obvious reasons. Most of them are heated by means of a resistor element. This may take the form of a coil located in the sides of the heating chamber—or for higher temperature work, a bar type of resistor in the heating space to provide heat by both radiation and convection.

Even the earliest electric furnaces were easy to control from a temperature standpoint. They are clean, easy to operate and lend themselves readily to automatic regulations. The earlier electric furnaces had the universal objection that there was no atmosphere control. They were filled with ordinary outside atmosphere which is, of course, oxidizing and the only thing the hardener could do to change conditions was to throw in a handful of charcoal or some other combustible material in an effort to eliminate the air. This was not very satisfactory. Today, electric furnaces are available for all incandescent temperature ranges with synthetic gaseous atmospheres. In these furnaces we no longer talk about "oxidizing atmospheres" or "reducing atmospheres" but speak of "4% oxygen" or "10% carbon monoxide" and "2% hydrogen." It is through the use of this equipment that our knowledge of the effect of atmospheres has been greatly extended in the past few years. Electric furnaces have a slower heat input than in the fuel fired furnaces and their output of work is likely to be considerably less per dollar of original investment.

If the electric furnaces appear at the moment to sound more attractive in the above description, it is the authors' opinion that this is not due to any fundamental virtue of electric heat. The manufacturers of electric furnaces have been forced more quickly to recognize the fundamental requirements of a modern hardening furnace and have catered to them. There appear to be no insurmountable obstacles to prevent fuel fired furnaces from duplicating the metallurgical progress of the electric furnaces—and still retain their advantages of output and economy.

Specialized Atmosphere Control.—As we have already indicated, synthetic atmospheres can be applied to both fuel-fired and electric furnaces, provided they are of the muffle type. There are now in use various types of atmosphere control embodying different principles. A very popular one is the **gas curtain** in which a continuous curtain of gas of known composition is maintained across the front opening of the muffle. A second type embodies a furnace containing a **carbon block** or carbon muffle in which the steel is heated, and in which the resulting atmosphere is extremely high in carbon monoxide. In other types, various gases are generated or conditioned in units outside the furnace, and led into the muffle. **Carbon monoxide** (CO), **cracked ammonia, nitrogen,** and **hydrocarbon gases** (produced by mixing cracked ammonia and carbon monoxide) are all widely used. In still another type, a proper atmosphere is obtained by **dropping oil** of a suitable type at a determined rate into the furnace. This method adapts itself particularly to the vertical type furnace. A departure from the above methods consists in introducing into the furnace an easily vaporized metal such as **lithium,** which removes the oxygen from the atmosphere by combining with it to form a solid oxide.

There is no general formula which can be applied to determine what type of furnace, or what method of atmosphere control, is best. The buyer of hardening equipment, however, should set out to purchase *temperature, time* and *atmosphere*. The type of furnace that can serve him most economically and conveniently in these particulars is the best choice.

Semi-muffle oven type oil-fired furnace. (*Courtesy of Sunbeam Corp., Industrial Furnace Division.*)

Electric box type furnace. (*Courtesy of General Electric Co.*)

Vertical gas-fired furnace with controlled atmosphere for hardening long slender tools. (*Courtesy of Bellevue Industrial Furnace Co.*)

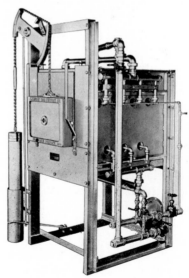

Oven type gas-fired furnace. (*Courtesy of American Gas Furnace Co.*)

Fig. 142.—Modern hardening furnaces.

Figs. 142 and 143, show a variety of commercial heat treating furnaces representing most modern equipment as made by a variety of furnace builders.

Liquid Bath Furnaces.—A pot furnace consists in a refractory lined oven in which is suspended a metal or ceramic pot containing the molten salt or metal. It may be heated by oil, gas or electricity, and if electrically heated may be of either the resistance or electrode type. The latter is confined to salt baths, and has the advantage of providing convection or stirring of the salt.

Large gas-fired oven furnace. (*Courtesy of Surface Combustion Co.*)
Fig. 142.—Modern hardening furnaces (*Continued*).

Selection of the exact type is based entirely on consideration of cost, availability, convenience and control. Metallurgically, it makes no difference which fuel is used. Various types of liquid bath furnaces are illustrated in Fig. 144.

Liquid baths are particularly well adapted for heating tools which are not heated all over—such as drills, taps, reamers, chisels, etc. They heat the tool much more quickly than an oven furnace, and hence time control becomes quite important. Where it is desired to heat a tool more slowly, two molten baths are sometimes used. The tool is preheated in the first bath to a

Atmosphere controlled preheating and superheating "gas curtain" furnaces for hardening high speed steel. (*Courtesy of C. I. Hayes, Inc.*)

Electric hardening furnace with artificial atmosphere (produced by vaporizing oil). (*Courtesy of Leeds and Northrup Co.*)

FIG. 143.—Furnaces with controlled artificial atmosphere.

Gas-fired pot furnace. (*Courtesy of American Gas Furnace Co.*)

Electrically heated pot furnace. (*Courtesy of Hevi Duty Electric Co.*)

Oil-fired pot furnace. (*Courtesy of Sunbeam Corp., Industrial Furnace Division.*)

Salt bath furnace for hardening high speed and other tool steels (*Courtesy of Ajax Electric Co., Inc.*)

Salt bath furnace for hardening high speed steel. (*Courtesy of The Bellis Heat Treating Co.*)

FIG. 144.—Pot furnaces for molten salt or lead.

temperature below its critical point, and is then transferred to the second pot which is maintained at the hardening heat.

Practically all pot hardening furnaces employ either molten lead or molten salts.

A **lead bath** is usually contained in a cast or pressed metal pot and has a useful temperature range between about 750° and 1600°F. Although lead melts at 620°F., some leeway must be allowed to prevent it from solidfying on the tools; and the maximum temperature is limited by volatilization and pot life. Since pots do crack or burn out in time, provision should be made for catching the molten metal in such a way that it will not damage the heating equipment or run out over the floor. Lead vapors are poisonous and the pots should be provided with a ventilating hood.

Hot lead oxidizes in contact with the air and produces a dross which floats on the surface. This dross sticks to the tools as they are being immersed and continues to adhere to them when they are withdrawn and quenched. It not only interferes with the quenching, and is troublesome to remove, but it tends to decarburize the surface of the tool. The most common method for avoiding dross is to keep one or two inches of granulated wood charcoal, or a layer of molten salt, floating on the surface of the pot. Charcoal must be cleaned off and replenished as it is consumed. Proprietary salts are available for this purpose, but a very satisfactory mixture may be made with 50% rock salt (sodium chloride) and a 50% calcium chloride. This mixture should be melted together, then cooled and broken into lumps before placing in the lead pot.

Molten salt makes the best covering for heating water-hardening tool steel; it protects the surface of the tool while it is being removed for quenching and it is thrown off cleanly by the action of the quenching water. Incidentally, tools coated with molten salt are best quenched in running fresh water; otherwise, it would quickly concentrate in a still tank of either water or brine. A charcoal covering is better for oil-hardening tool steel because oil will not "throw" the salt and it is rather annoying to remove after it has solidified on the tool.

Pure, clean lead will not stick to a tool and it will not decarburize the surface. Dirty lead will do both and it is not uncommon to find soft spots on water quenched tools where lumps of lead have adhered. In the interest of first-class hardening, the operator should take every precaution to keep his lead clean and free from dross. Lead baths are rapidly giving way to salt baths for most purposes.

Salt baths may be divided into two classes depending upon the type of salt used. Neutral salts are supposed to heat the steel without either carburizing or decarburizing the surface. Active salts are intended to impregnate the surface of the tools with carbon and nitrogen in order to increase the surface hardness.

The purpose of the **neutral bath** is to heat the steel in the same manner as molten lead—without any chemical effects. The variety of salts recommended for the purpose is legion. A 50:50 mixture of sodium chloride and calcium chloride can be used within the range of about 1000° to 1600°F. There are a great variety of proprietary salts offered for neutral baths and the big problem seems to be to find a salt which will be truly neutral— and stay that way. The salt is contained in either ceramic or metal pots and the same provision should be made for leakage as is recommended for lead pots.

Salt pots are being used also for hardening high speed steel. A group of from two to four pots is used to provide for various degrees of preheat and finally a high temperature bath for superheating.

High speed salt pots have become increasingly popular for hardening some of the molybdenum types of high speed steel. These steels harden around 2200°F. where pot life is not so serious and the use of molten salt seems to be a satisfactory method for avoiding the surface decarburization to which these molybdenum high speed steels are subject.

Active salt baths are relatively unimportant in tool hardening. They usually contain a salt having the properties of cyanide and are intended to inject a thin case of carbon and nitrogen into the surface of the steel. There seems to be little occasion for their use in connection with the Matched Set Tool Steels—which should harden properly without such violent treatment.

One of the interesting uses of cyanide in the tool room is that of drawing (or tempering) high speed tools. If such tools are drawn in a cyanide bath at about 1050°F. for 30 minutes, a slight cyaniding action results which glazes the surface with a very hard film.

One of the precautions in connection with salt bath hardening is to clean all salt off the finished tools—otherwise they will corrode rapidly. A water soluble salt is therefore preferable wherever possible. Another precaution is never to bring nitrate salts in contact with cyanide salts while hot, since serious explosions will surely result.

Induction Heating.—A recent development in hardening practice consists in heating by high frequency induction. Parts are introduced in a coil carrying high frequency current, and heat is generated within the metal itself. The method has the advantages of very rapid heating, freedom from danger of decarburization and ability to confine the heating, and consequently hardening, to the surface alone, when desired. On account of the very rapid heating, extremely careful timing is necessary to properly control temperature. The method has been used primarily for the hardening of parts, but will undoubtedly find future application to the hardening of tools.

Quenching Equipment

Quenching is such an important step in the hardening operation that an entire chapter has been devoted to it beginning page 500. Quenching may be divided into **still bath quenching** and **flush quenching.** In the still bath, the tool is immersed and any motion is communicated by the operator moving the tool around with his tongs. As a general rule, a *slow* up-and-down motion is desirable—but a violent swishing around is quite objectionable.

Still Baths.—These baths may contain fresh water, salt brine, caustic soda solution, or various types of oil. In rare cases, tools are quenched in hot baths of molten salt or molten metal.

A still bath of fresh water is *not* an ideal quenching medium for tool steel. Fresh water has a tendency to form considerable steam on the surface of the hot metal in the first stage of the quench, and this together with any dissolved gas released from the water, tends to form an insulating film on the surface of the work, especially in holes and recesses that are congenial to gas pockets. The hardener can actually *see* this happen in a tank of clear fresh water; red hot spots will persist after most of the tool has become black. Contrary to general opinion, water-hardening steels are *more* likely to crack when quenched in fresh water than they are when quenched in salt brine. They are also more likely to contain soft spots. Fresh water is entirely satisfactory when used as a flush—but it is not as good as brine for still bath quenching.

When common rock salt is dissolved in fresh water it not only inhibits the formation of steam at the metal surface, but also lessens the tendency of the bath to absorb and release atmospheric gases. This allows direct contact of the bath and hot metal surface, and consequently more uniform cooling in the important first stage of the quench. This is the sole and only reason for adding the salt. Many people think that salt brine will quench a tool faster than fresh water. This is not true. The brine "takes hold" and "wets" the tool all over immediately and cools it uniformly. For this reason, the quenching job is likely to be completed faster in brine than in fresh water. Fresh water "takes hold" only in spots where no steam or gas has been deposited—but in these spots it actually cools faster than the brine. This non-uniform quenching—ranging from extreme rapidity down to practically no quench at all—is the thing which sets up tremendous strains in a tool and may cause it to crack.

Some hardeners have come to think of brine as an "emergency quench"—something that acts like a hypodermic "shot in the arm"—to save the day when all else fails. They, therefore, jump to the conclusion that there must be something seriously wrong with a tool steel if brine quenching is recommended as a regular practice. They argue "I've been using fresh water for twenty-five years and am having no trouble; if this new steel requires brine—there must be something the matter with it." The salesman who recommended the brine quench knows perfectly well that *his* steel will harden in fresh water just as well as the other brand will—even as he knows that *both* steels would be better if quenched in brine; and since he would rather *sell* a customer than *reform* him, he lets the matter drop.

It is important to pause and see what is wrong with the hardener's argument. If he has been "using fresh water for twenty-five years," his trouble is all many years behind him. When tools cracked, they quit making that particular tool of water-hardening steel—or changed its design to a safer shape—or did something to relieve the difficulty. No one is going to endure trouble for twenty-five years without doing something about it—

and finally, since all the work in that shop is accommodated to fresh water quenching, they are obviously "having no trouble." If he had started twenty-five years ago using brine, his past trouble would have been much less, and today they would be making a greater number of different kinds of tools from the inexpensive and efficient water-hardening steel. No matter how poor the quality of a steel is—and no matter how poorly it is handled—a shop can finally whittle the use of that steel down to a point where they no longer have trouble. This particular argument is attacked here because no attitude has done more to keep tool steel users "satisfied" and prevent them from embracing newer and better ideas. Brine is definitely better in a still quenching tank than fresh water and the skeptical hardener has only to try it to find out that this is true. At first he will observe little difference, because his practice has been narrowed down to the fresh water limitations. However as time goes on, he will take more and more liberties until he will finally be getting away with things in brine that he knows perfectly well would have caused nothing but trouble in fresh water.

Rock salt can be dissolved in water up to about 26%—that is, 26 lbs. of rock salt in 100 lbs. of finished solution. This solution is called "saturated." Special hydrometers called **salinometers,** similar to those used for testing an automobile storage battery, are available for testing the concentration of brine solutions. These are commonly graduated to read zero for fresh water and 100% for a saturated solution. Table III on page 250 will be found useful in holding any desired concentration.

The more salt added to the water, the less the tendency for steam pockets. Therefore, it might be expected that the best quenching solution would be a saturated solution. However, the more salt there is, the *slower* the solution will quench, and a saturated solution quenches so slowly that a water-hardening steel can scarcely be hardened in it. It is therefore necessary to strike a compromise and the most satisfactory brine bath will contain between 5% and 10% of salt. An excellent bath can be made by adding about three quarters of a pound of rock salt per gallon of water. This will yield approximately 8.3% of salt, and will read about 32 on the salinometer scale. Do not use table salt or any other prepared salt in a quenching bath; rock

TABLE III.—Salt Brine Solution

Salinometer reading	Per cent of salt	Pounds of salt per gal. solution	Degrees Baumé
0	0.00	None	1.00
10	2.65	.22	2.60
20	5.30	.46	5.20
30	8.78	.70	7.80
40	10.60	.95	10.40
50	13.25	1.21	13.00
60	15.90	1.48	15.60
70	18.55	1.76	18.20
80	21.20	2.05	20.80
90	23.85	2.35	23.40
100	26.50	2.66	26.00

NOTE: Salinometers and hydrometers are usually calibrated to test brine solutions at 60° F. Hot solutions will give somewhat *lower* readings—roughly one point on the Salinometer for each 10°F. rise in temperature. For example, a 10% salt solution would read about 37 on the Salinometer at 65°F., and about 35 at 85°F.

salt such as is sold for freezing ice cream is not only the cheapest but the best.

One of the objections to heating water-hardening tool steel in contact with molten salt is the fact that the salt carried into the quenching tank continually changes its concentration. In such cases it is better to use flowing fresh water than to attempt to use brine.

A 5% solution of **caustic soda** in water is one of the fastest and most efficient quenching baths available. It has the objection of being corrosive to the clothing and hands of the workmen. This bath is seldom used and is rarely necessary.

The **temperature** of the water used for quenching tool steel should be neither too hot nor too cold. On cold winter mornings, the bath may become very cold and should be warmed up to about 60°F. with pieces of hot iron. On the other hand, the tank should be large enough to avoid excessive heating during the day's work. The range between 60°F. and 90°F. is good safe practice.

Oil quenching baths are necessary in the tool hardening room to quench high speed steel and other oil-hardening tool steels.

They give a quenching speed slower than water and faster than air. The kinds of oil that have been used are countless, including practically every available type of fish oil, animal oil, vegetable oil and mineral oil—pure and in combination. The essential properties of a good quenching oil are these. It should have a high flash point—about 350°F. or higher—to avoid unnecessary fire hazard. It should have a low viscosity so that it will circulate freely past the tool during quenching, and drain off well when the tool is removed. The oil should not change composition by oxidization or by heating so that its quenching characteristics may remain constant. It should be an oil that is difficult to emulsify; some oils can actually take up water in considerable quantities and cause all sorts of quenching difficulties. Finally, it is preferable to have an oil without a disagreeable odor. These properties are well combined in some of the proprietary brands of prepared quenching oil now on the market.

The temperature of the oil is of importance. If the oil is either extremely cold or extremely hot, the quench will be slowed down, in the first case on account of higher viscosity, and in the second on account of the slower heat carrying ability. The best temperature range for efficient and uniform quenching is about 100°F. to 130°F. Since oil is most frequently contained in a still tank, the tank should be large enough so that the day's work will not heat the oil above this top temperature or not hotter than the bare hand can comfortably touch. Sometimes the oil is circulated through cooling coils to keep the temperature more nearly constant. Even more rarely, facilities are available for using the oil in the form of a flush. After reading Chapter 20, it is hoped that more such apparatus will come into use.

A word should be said about the presence of water in the oil tank. From various sources water may accumulate to an appreciable depth at the bottom of an oil quenching tank. If a deep basket is used into which tools are dropped after quenching, sometimes this basket will reach down to the water and cracked tools will inevitably result.

Hot **molten salt or metal** baths are used in various methods of interrupted quenching already mentioned on page 213. Their purpose is to cool the steel quickly down to some predetermined temperature, automatically interrupt the quench at this point, and permit of a different cooling speed down to room temperature, thus minimizing hardening strains.

Flush Quenching.—Sometimes it is desirable to quench very actively certain surfaces of a tool—and perhaps retard the quench on other surfaces. For example, on a draw ring, it might be desired to have the interior working surface of the ring quenched as rapidly as possible, and the outside rim left soft for toughness and support. Obviously this result could not be secured by quenching the ring all over in a still bath. Although the subject

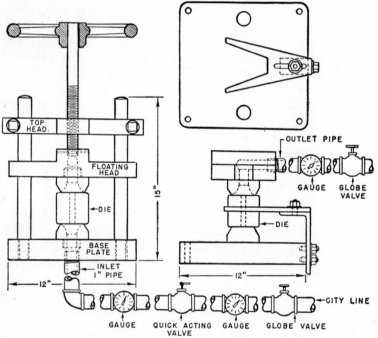

Fig. 145.—Fixture for flushing cold header dies.

of flush quenching will be more completely discussed in Chapter 20, it should be emphasized here that there is justification for spending considerable money to make special flushing fixtures for hardening tools. Tool life can sometimes be increased several fold by flush quenching. This is particularly true of cold forging tools such as are used for upsetting, coining or extruding cold metal. Just to illustrate the care that is warranted in designing flushing fixtures, there is illustrated in Figure 145 a flushing fixture for the internal flushing for cold header dies. Figure

146 shows the cross section of a die hardened in this fixture and the light colored zone around the hole is the only part that is hard. Flushing fixtures are usually employed for water quenching, and fresh water is just as good as brine for the purpose, since the rapid motion of the water prevents any gas pockets from forming. An immersion type pump designed for quenching baths is illustrated in Fig. 147.

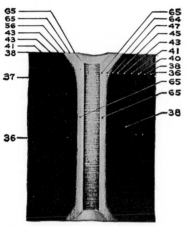

Fig. 146.—Etched section of solid cold header die quenched in fixture shown in Fig. 145. Figures denote Rockwell-C hardness values.

Fig. 147.—Immersion type pump for use in quenching tanks. (*Courtesy of Ingersoll-Rand Co.*)

Air quenching is used for certain types of highly alloyed tool steels as recommended by the steel manufacturers. For still air quenching, the best practice is to place the heated tool on a screen so that the air can circulate freely past it. Accelerated air cooling can be induced by using a common electric fan. This has the advantage of supplying a draft of *dry* air—but, unless specially arranged, the blast will cool one side of the tool faster than the others. Compressed air is also used—especially to concentrate the cooling at some point on the tool. Extreme care must be used to insure the blast being dry. Much water frequently accumulates in a compressed air line and this is likely to crack an air-hardening steel.

A convenient layout for quenching is illustrated in Fig. 148. The large tank is filled with fresh water which serves to cool both the brine and the oil. Water is admitted through a vertical standpipe—sometimes called a "bubbler." With this water flowing, certain types of tools can be quenched in the upstream of the bubbler with little danger of gas pockets. It is important to note the nipple at the bottom of the bubbler pipe. This is to permit the connection of flushing equipment.

The water overflows through a standpipe at the right. Provision must be made to hold the water level at any point desired, because many types of flushing apparatus do not operate beneath

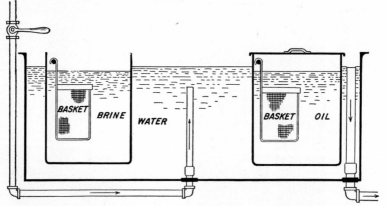

Fig. 148.—A convenient quenching layout for a tool hardening room.

the surface of the water—they must be out in the air. The water level is controlled by using overflow pipes of different lengths. The oil quenching bath should be provided with a cover to extinguish fires which can always occur in a busy hardening room.

The baskets are useful for holding hardened tools during the short interval before they are drawn. Below the surface of the liquid they are protected from sudden temperature changes that might strike them in the air.

Drawing (or Tempering)

As has already been pointed out, tools are drawn to relieve hardening strains and make them tougher. The softening effect is incidental—and usually unwanted. The requirements of good drawing equipment are simple, involving only an apparatus for maintaining a constant and uniform temperature in a relatively low range.

The simplest equipment consists of a pot or tank containing a liquid that can be heated to the desired range.   For temperatures between room temperatures and 550°F., a heavy, high flash oil can be used.   For temperatures between about 450° and 1050°F., molten salts can be used.   Various commercial salts are available for use throughout this range.   To cover the higher temperatures, molten lead can be used since it has an operating range between about 750° and 1600°F.

A glass thermometer can be used within the range of an oil bath, but above 600°F. a pyrometer should be employed.   Liquid drawing baths can be heated by any convenient means providing circulation of the liquid is established to maintain uniform temperature throughout.   All liquid baths have the slight drawback that the liquid must be cleaned from the tools after they are removed.   Lead is best removed with a brush before it solidifies. Salts can be dissolved in hot water, and oil can be removed with kerosene or hot soda solution.   As a general rule, tools should not be quenched after drawing.   There is a temptation to do this as an aid to cleaning off the drawing liquid but it is not good for the tools.   Drawing baths are illustrated in Fig. 149.

Electric tempering ovens of various design are fast becoming popular because they lend themselves to automatic control and the work does not require cleaning afterwards.   Unless the hot air is mechanically circulated, it takes the tools much longer to reach the drawing temperature in an oven—to which there is no metallurgical objection providing ample soaking time is allowed—but it does slow up production.   Some electric furnaces also have the disadvantage that when well loaded with work, they may heat non-uniformly.   The older and cruder furnaces worked almost like an electric toaster—they "toasted" the work on one side and underheated the work that was not in front of the heating element.   Later models have improved this condition by using more heating elements distributed around the chamber.

The most modern electric tempering ovens are using power driven fans to rapidly circulate the air and drive it to all parts of the charge.   Not only do these fans distribute the heat uniformly, but they speed up the heating to approximately that of an oil tempering bath.   Such an oven is shown in Fig. 149.

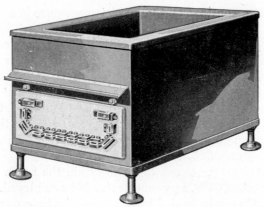

Electrically heated oil drawing bath. (*Courtesy of Hoskins Mfg. Co.*)

Electrically heated air temper-
ing furnace with circulating fan.
(*Courtesy of Westinghouse Electric
Corp.*)

Fuel-fired oil tempering furnace.
(*Courtesy of Sunbeam Corp., Industrial
Furnace Division.*)

Fig. 149.—Modern drawing (or tempering) equipment.

Gas-fired tempering furnace with circulating fan.   (*Courtesy of Lindberg Engineering Co.*)

Installation of electrically heated tempering furnaces equipped with circulating fans.   (*Courtesy of Leeds and Northrup Co.*)

FIG. 149.—Modern drawing (or tempering) equipment (*Continued*).

Recording pyrometers and automatic temperature controls are particularly valuable on tempering furnaces because of the long time cycles, and become essential if they are to be left running unattended during the night. Furthermore, since the eye cannot detect when the couple and the steel are at the same temperature, an *extra* thermocouple imbedded in the work will be found of great assistance in telling when it is up to temperature. The furnace couple, however, must always be kept free for control purposes; otherwise the furnace will overheat and spoil the work. It should be emphasized that the pyrometer does *not* tell you the temperature of the work—it merely records the temperature of the hot junction of the thermocouple.

In conclusion, it should be emphasized that time is just as important as temperature in drawing. An extra hour or so in the drawing bath may be all that is necessary to save a tool from breaking. Many dollars may have already been spent on the tool and it is now practically finished. This is a poor place to economize on time. If sufficient drawing equipment is not available to give each tool as much time as it should receive, more equipment should be provided. The loss of only one expensive tool plus the attendant embarrassment to the production department might easily pay the entire cost of installing an additional drawing unit.

A word should be said about **color drawing.** Back in the days when hardeners did their work by eye and their principal material was carbon tool steel, most tools were drawn to color. A portion of the hardened tool was polished with emery cloth and the tool was then placed near some source of slow heat (frequently another block of steel or iron heated for the purpose) and it was allowed to remain there until certain temper colors—straw, purple or blue—appeared on the polished surface. A temper color chart for carbon tool steel is shown in Fig. 132 on page 228D.

With the coming of alloy tool steels it was learned that these temper colors appeared at very different temperatures depending on the analysis. Also, there is no opportunity by this method, of soaking the tool at the drawing heat—which is so important on expensive tools. Color drawing is still used to a limited extent on tools hardened by a blacksmith and it is sometimes used on other tools where local softening is desired. For example, sometimes a blow torch might be used to soften the shank of the tool or some other portion where full hardness is not desired.

Tongs.—It would be too bad to conclude this chapter without at least a mention of tongs. There are efficient, handy tongs that

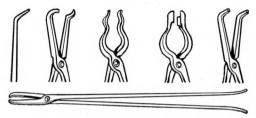

Fig. 150.—Tongs for tool hardening.

pick up the work neatly and hold it securely, and there are clumsy poorly adapted tongs that cover up large areas of the tool that ought to be quenched, cause soft spots, or let the work drop at embarrassing moments. Just another of those little items that make such a big difference.

CHAPTER 11

HARDNESS AND TOUGHNESS TESTING

HARDNESS TESTING

After a tool is finished, the most common non-destructive test is that for hardness. The hardness test is valuable because it indicates much more than just hardness; it is somewhat like a clinical thermometer in the hands of a doctor, and warns that something else may have gone wrong. For example, under the head of toughness testing, it will be learned that the maximum toughness in WATER-HARD corresponds to a Rockwell hardness of about C-63/64. If, upon testing the hardness of a finished tool made of WATER-HARD, it is found to be only C-60, it is fair to assume that the toughness peak has also been missed; and while a hardness of C-60 might be amply *hard* for the tool in question, it might lack the necessary toughness, and break. In fact, in the case just mentioned, when a reading of only C-60 Rockwell is secured, whereas C-63/64 was expected, it is pretty safe to assume that *something* is wrong. It may be a poor job of hardening, the tool may have been drawn too high, there may be a little skin of surface decarburization, or the tool maker may even have gotten hold of a piece of steel of the wrong analysis to start with. Of course, it would be possible to get exactly the hardness expected and still have something wrong, but the fact remains that a hardness tester is just as useful to a hardener as a clinical thermometer is to a medical doctor. There are many methods for determining hardness and several of them will be briefly discussed.

The File Test.—This is the oldest of all hardness tests and it is still one of the most useful. An experienced tool maker or hardener can tell almost as much with a file as a laboratory man can tell with a hardness testing machine. The difference is, the laboratory man can write down his results for future reference and he can talk intelligently to somebody else about them. All the file tester has in his memory is a "feel" which has obvious limitations. Efforts have been made to establish a series of file

260

testing standards—ranging from glass hard down to quite soft. These standards are numbered, and records can then be made by saying that a certain tool appears about as hard as standard sample 8, etc. Such refinements have very little use today because excellent hardness testing equipment is so generally available.

However, the file is still useful and will do certain things better than any testing machine. For example, it can "explore" the degree of surface decarburization. Both the file and the hardness testing machine might indicate that the surface hardness is below normal. Only the file, however, could cut further in and discover that the softness is confined to the surface, and that the material is file hard underneath. A file is also useful for exploring surfaces for soft spots. It can reach down into the inside of holes and uncover things that the hardness tester could not reach.

It should be mentioned that there are all kinds of files. Some files are harder than others and a hard file will take a cut where a softer file might slide over. A fine cut file will make a piece of steel appear softer than a coarse cut file; and of course, a new file cuts better than an old one. Thus, it will be seen that the expression "file-hard" is not a very definite one. In spite of all this, however, there are many tool makers and hardeners who would choose the file in preference to any other equipment— if they were limited to just one means of hardness testing.

The Scleroscope.—This was one of the earliest devices for testing the hardness of hardened tool steel. Both the glass tube variety, Model "C-2," and the dial type, Model "D," are shown in Fig. 151. This instrument drops a diamond pointed weight on the hardened surface and measures the height of the rebound. The harder the steel, the higher the "tup" will jump. In order to get accurate readings, a clean, smooth surface should be prepared, and the foundation supporting the piece being tested should be as solid as possible. This instrument possesses the advantage of being portable and can be carried to the location of a job that would be entirely too big to place on the anvil of any other type of testing machine. It is still the best method available for testing the hardness of large tool steel rolls some of which measure 20″ or 30″ in diameter and weigh several tons.

The Rockwell Hardness Tester.—At the time of this writing, the Rockwell machine is probably the most widely used machine for testing hardened tool steel. One type of this instrument is shown in Fig. 152. The test is made by driving a penetrator into the surface of the metal being tested, by a dead weight acting through a series of levers. A micrometer dial gauge tells the depth to which the penetrator sinks. The softer the metal being tested, the deeper it will penetrate with a given load. The dial

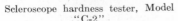

Scleroscope hardness tester, Model "C-2"

Dial recording scleroscope, Model "D"

Fig. 151.—Scleroscopes. (*Courtesy of Shore Instrument and Mfg. Co., Inc.*)

gauge does not read directly in depth of penetration, but carries arbitrary scales showing "Rockwell numbers."

Two types of penetrators are used, a diamond cone known as a "brale," for hard materials such as hardened tool steel, and a hardened steel ball for testing soft materials such as annealed tool steel. In either case a variety of different loadings can be used, each designated by a letter.

The standard loading for hardened tool steel using the diamond brale is 150 kilograms, and the letter designation is "C," so that the readings obtained are on the "Rockwell C Hardness" scale. The hardest tool steel will seldom reach C-70; "file hardness" is in the neighborhood of C-65 and a "spring temper" might show C-45/55.

The standard loading for soft materials using a $\frac{1}{16}''$ diameter ball is 100 kilograms, and the letter

Fig. 152.—Rockwell hardness tester. (*Courtesy of Wilson Mechanical Instrument Co.*)

Fig. 153.—Brinell hardness tester. (*Courtesy of Steel City Testing Laboratory.*)

designation is "B," so that resulting readings are in terms of "Rockwell B Hardness."

For loadings lighter than 60 kilograms, which are often convenient for testing the extreme surface of hardened tools or very thin sections of soft materials, a special type of machine known as the Superficial Hardness Tester is used. When the brale is used as in testing hard materials the letter "N" is used in conjunction with a number indicating the load applied, designating the reading, such as "30N" or "15N." When the $\frac{1}{16}''$ ball is used, the letter "T" is used in conjunction with the load, such as "30T" or "15T."

The Brinell Test.—A Brinell hardness machine is shown in Figure 153. This is a much older test than the Rockwell and it operates very similarly to the Rockwell ball test in principle. In the Brinell machine, a much larger steel ball is used (the standard being 10 millimeters, or about $\frac{2}{5}''$ diameter) and this is forced into the steel under a load of 3000 kilograms (approximately 6500 pounds). Instead of measuring the penetration, the test piece is usually removed from the Brinell machine and the diameter of the impression is measured with a small microscope. The measured diameter is converted by means of a table into "Brinell Hardness Numeral."[1] Brinell machines are now available which read hardness numbers direct on a dial, by automatically determining the depth of the impression as the ball is sunk into the material being tested.

The Brinell machine finds its greatest usefulness on soft and medium hard materials. On hardened tool steel, the impression is so small that it is difficult to read, and after all, the steel ball itself is nothing more than hardened tool steel so that it tends to flatten against a surface which is almost equally hard. In recent years, balls of tungsten carbide had been used to prevent flattening, but this has not been sufficient to enable the method to compete with the Rockwell or Scleroscope on hardened tool steel. Furthermore, the Brinell test is rather gross for many tools.

The Vickers Test.—The Vickers machine is illustrated in Figure 154. This is like a highly refined Brinell hardness test. Instead of using a steel ball, it employs a diamond penetrator in the form of a square pyramid. This is driven in under a constant load and the hardness is measured by determining the diameter of the impression across the corners by means of a microscope. The readings of this test are also converted into Brinell hardness numerals. This instrument appears to avoid

---

[1] The formula used is $H = \dfrac{2W}{\pi D(D - \sqrt{D^2 - d^2})}$; where H = Brinell hardness numeral; W = load in Kgs ; D = dia. of ball in mms.; d = dia. of impression in mms.

the principal objections to the Brinell test as applied to hardened tool steel.

The Micro-hardness Tester.—This instrument, originally known as the "Knoop indentor," is illustrated in Fig. 155. It

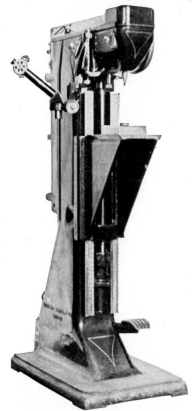

Fig. 154.—Vickers hardness tester.

Fig. 155.—Long Range Model TUKON Tester for determining Knoop hardness numbers. (*Courtesy of Wilson Mechanical Instrument Co., Inc.*)

employs a very narrow diamond penetrator, shaped much like the edge of an axe, but diamond shaped, which is pressed into the surface under a very light load. Hardness is determined by measuring the length of the impression. This impression is so small that hardness can be determined upon individual micro constituents in the metal, hence its name. This is still classed as a laboratory instrument, and it is mentioned here simply as a matter of interest.

On page 551 will be found a conversion table that gives approximate equivalents on the Scleroscope, Rockwell and Brinell hardness scales.

While hardness is not a true indication of **wear resistance,** it is the best available at this writing. It is known that two steels of different analysis may show exactly the same hardness and yet one of them may wear many times longer than the other. This is due to the presence of certain wear resisting alloys in the composition. As a matter of experience, it is known which analysis formulae possess great wear resistance and which ones do not. However, in considering just one steel, its hardness is certainly related in some useful way to its wear resistance. There are many different kinds of wear so that it is unwise to make any definite statement, but it appears to be a fact that the tools used in the metal working industry will generally last longer as the hardness increases—until a point is reached where chipping, crumbling or breaking results.

Hot Hardness Tests.—For certain types of tools such as hot forging dies, it is often desirable to know their hardness at the elevated temperatures encountered in service, as well as the ordinary "room temperature" hardness. All steels become softer as they are heated. Assuming that the drawing temperature used in treating was higher than the temperature reached in service, this softening is only temporary, and the steel regains its hardness when it cools back to room temperature. Hot work steels are so designed that they lose relatively little hardness when heated, and it is on these steels that we are concerned in making hot hardness or "red-hardness" tests.

The easiest way to make a test for red-hardness is to simply heat a specimen of the steel to the desired temperature, and make a Brinell test. This is open to the obvious objections that the specimen will cool somewhat before the test is complete, and furthermore that if the ball itself is not previously heated to the testing temperature, it also will have a chilling effect. Both of these objections have been overcome in what is known as the "mutual indentation test." A modification of this test as developed and practiced in the Carpenter Laboratories is made as follows:

Two cylindrical specimens 10 millimeters in diameter (about ⅖″), both made of the steel to be tested, are placed in contact with each other in a closed chamber and heated to the required temperature. A load is applied just as in the regular Brinell test causing the pieces to flatten along the line of contact, as shown in the sketch in Fig. 156. After removing the pieces from the furnace the amount of flattening or indenting is measured, and converted to a Brinell number. This can be done by comparing the measurements with those of specimens of different known Brinell hardnesses tested in exactly the same way, but at room temperature.

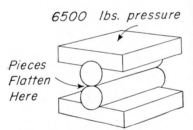

6500 lbs. pressure

Pieces
Flatten
Here

Fig. 156.—Method of loading test specimens in making Brinell red-hardness test.

Fig. 157.—Test machine and specially designed furnace used in making Brinell red-hardness test.

A photograph of the furnace containing the specimens to which the load is being applied in a testing machine, is shown in Fig. 157.

Many conscientious efforts have been made to determine the **tensile strength** of hardened tool steel. It would indeed be valuable to know the tensile strength of hardened tool steel if there were any way to accurately measure it. Unfortunately, the conventional tensile test appears to work only when the material being tested has a certain amount of ductility. If a steel will stretch slightly before it will break, a reasonably accurate tensile figure can usually be secured. However, if the material is so hard that it breaks before it stretches, the specimen will rupture in the test long before the true strength has been obtained.

Those tensile tests which have been successfully made on tool steel involve the use of drawing temperatures which are much higher than are actually used on tools, and the values are therefore questionable as a means of forecasting the probable strength of a tool drawn at the lower temperatures.

More success has been achieved in determining the breaking strength of tool steel by the *static torsion test*. However the values derived from this test represent strength in torsion, and like the hardness tests are only indicative of tensile strength. Torsion testing in general is of most value in determing toughness, and this will be discussed in the following section.

TOUGHNESS TESTING

For many years, toughness testing was in exactly the same position as tensile testing. Many excellent toughness testing machines were available but they seemed able to give useful results only on steels which possess some ductility—namely, those that would bend before they would break, and this excludes a hard tool steel. Toughness, or the ability to resist breaking, is such a vital requirement in a hardened tool steel that the inability to measure it blanked out almost half of the knowledge that the tool maker wanted to secure about his tools. Of course, there was accumulated gradually—and at terrific expense—a certain amount of approximate knowledge by having tools break in service. Gathering experience in this manner is a long and painful process.

In 1933 there was developed in the Research Laboratory of The Carpenter Steel Company an impact testing machine that could really be used on fully hardened tool steel.[1] It has its limitations, and it is far from perfect, but it has succeeded in opening doors to a whole realm of new information. It has revealed things about tool steel that were never even suspected and it has made possible a simplification of heat treatment that is saving industry a tremendous amount of time and money. The torsion impact is a destructive test—useful only in the laboratory to develop fundamental information; it cannot be used in the tool room, like a hardness tester.

[1] By George V. Luerssen and Omar V. Greene (The Carpenter Steel Co.), see—"The Torsion Impact Test"—Proceedings, American Society for Testing Materials, 1933. Also U. S. Patent No. 1,962,604.

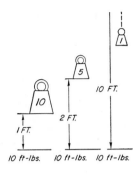

10 ft-lbs.   10 ft-lbs.   10 ft-lbs.

Toughness is measured in "foot pounds." One foot pound is the blow struck by a one pound weight falling one foot. If a five pound weight falls one foot, that is five foot pounds. A one pound weight falling five feet would be the same thing. A ten pound weight falling twenty feet would be 10 × 20 or 200 foot pounds.

A method for measuring the toughness of a piece of steel might be imagined as dropping a weight on it from different heights until it breaks. If the weight is multiplied by the distance it falls, that would measure the toughness of the steel in foot pounds. This would constitute a crude impact or toughness test.

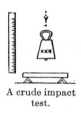

A crude impact test.

A neater way would be to put the piece in a vise or clamp and let a heavy pendulum swing against it. The pendulum could be pulled back a little further each time until the sample broke. Again the foot pounds could be figured by knowing the weight of the pendulum and the vertical distance it fell.

The pendulum principle.

The Izod toughness testing machine is built on this pendulum principle. The steel to be tested is machined into a test piece about ⅜″ square, notched on one side. It can be heat treated any way desired. The machine consists of a vise for holding the test piece and a heavy pendulum that acts as a hammer. The pendulum is pulled back a definite distance and allowed to fall of its own weight. The toughness of the test piece is measured by the

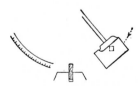

Diagram of Izod test.

Izod test piece.

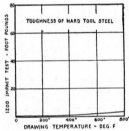

Transverse impact readings are negligible on hard tool steel.

The torsion impact principle.

amount of over-swing of the pendulum. The more brittle the steel, the less it will hinder the pendulum and the greater will be the over-swing.

Another toughness tester called the **Charpy** also works on the pendulum idea, but the test piece is supported at both ends and the knife edge of the pendulum hits it in the middle.

These standard types of impact machine were designed to test tough materials such as gear steel, axle steel, etc., and none of them can be used to accurately measure the toughness of hardened tool steel. A tool steel specimen will snap and show hardly any reading on the scale at all. If a lighter machine is built on the same principle, higher readings are secured but they are extremely variable. This method of breaking the test piece by hitting it on the side seems difficult to adapt to tool steel testing.

The new Carpenter toughness testing machine works on an entirely different principle. The sample is broken by a **torsional** blow. This puts the load on the entire cross section at one time, and the readings are surprisingly high—and extremely accurate. It is much the same action that would be had by seizing one end of a test piece in a vise, attaching a wrench to the other end, and then hitting the handle of the wrench a sharp blow.

The torsion impact test piece is shown in the. group of illustrations at

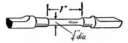

Torsion impact test peice.

Diagram of action of torsion impact test.

the left. The test section is the portion in the middle, measuring $\frac{1}{4}''$ diameter $\times$ 1″ long. Instead of using a monkey wrench and a falling weight, a heavy fly wheel equipped with two lugs is set in rotation at a high speed. The test piece is gripped tightly at one end, and on the other end there is clamped a cross arm. When the fly wheel is up to a definite speed, a clutch is tripped and the lugs of the fly wheel engage the cross arm on the end of the specimen producing a torsional blow violent enough to break the test piece. This slows down the fly wheel and the tougher the specimen the more the fly wheel is slowed down. All that is necessary is to note the speed of the fly wheel just before and just after breaking the piece—and the difference represents the energy consumed in the test. Some clever mathematician has figured out what this means in foot pounds.

It seems hard to believe, but a good tough piece of plain carbon tool steel (WATER-HARD) hardened to C-63 Rockwell will often require more than 100 foot pounds to break. Just think of it—the test section is only $\frac{1}{4}''$ round, it is almost file hard—and it takes the equivalent of a ten pound sledge falling ten feet to break it in torsion.

The original laboratory model of the torsion impact machine shown in Fig. 158 was somewhat crude—but quite accurate. An improved machine containing many refinements—including an integral power drive, a braking mechanism, and a built-in speed indicator or tachometer is now being built by the A. H. Emery Company (see Fig. 159).

To illustrate the utility of the torsion impact test—suppose it was desired to know how different drawing temperatures affect the toughness of a plain carbon tool steel like WATER-HARD. It

FIG. 158.—The original Carpenter torsion impact testing machine. (*The Carpenter Steel Company.*)

FIG. 159.—A modern torsion impact testing machine. (*Courtesy of A. H. Emery Co.*)

is, of course, known that "the higher the draw, the *softer* the steel becomes" and it had always been assumed that "the higher the draw, the *tougher* the steel becomes." What does the torsion impact machine say?

To answer a question like this, it is necessary to machine at least thirty test specimens. These are all hardened in the same furnace at the same time in order that they may be hardened exactly alike. Two of the test pieces are not drawn at all. Two of them are drawn at say 275°F., two more at 325°F., and etc. clear up to 800°F. The samples are run through in pairs to get duplicate toughness tests and thus see how accurately the machine is able to duplicate its own results.

The Rockwell hardness on each test piece is measured and then they are all broken on the torsion machine. The hardness and toughness figures are given in Table IV.

TABLE IV.—TORSION IMPACT TOUGHNESS OF WATER-HARD—BRINE QUENCHED FROM 1450°F.

Drawing temperature 1 hour at heat	Torsion impact foot-pounds	Rockwell hardness C-scale
No draw	24–29	66.8
275°F.	58–61	65.8
325	106–112	65.0
350	121–123	64.0
375	122–122	63.0
400	110–112	62.2
425	59–69–70	61.2
450	53–55	60.2
475	49–51	59.8
525	51–53	57.8
575	63–65	56.0
600	72–74	54.7
650	74–76	52.0
700	78–79	49.6
800	97–99	46.0

It will be noted that the hardness falls off gradually as the drawing temperature increases, just as had been expected. The toughness figures, however, contain some surprises. In the hardened and undrawn condition the specimens are rather brittle showing only about 26 foot pounds. At ascending drawing temperatures the toughness increases as would be expected until it reaches 122 foot pounds corresponding to a 350°F. draw. However, upon drawing above 375°F. the toughness falls off until it amounts to only about 50 foot pounds at 475°F. Above this, the toughness again increases. If the above toughness data are plotted, they yield a curve like the one shown in Fig. 160.

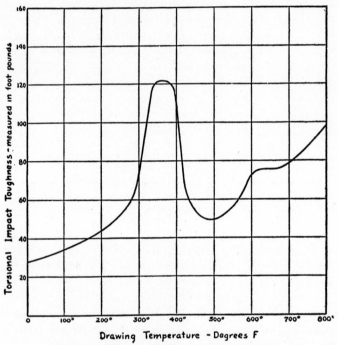

FIG. 160.—WATER-HARD tool steel. Effect of drawing temperature on toughness after hardening at 1450°F.

There is a definite **toughness peak** at 350°/375°F., corresponding to a Rockwell hardness of C-63/64.

It appears that the torsion impact test is most significant on materials which are so hard that they will break before they will bend appreciably. When WATER-HARD is drawn above 500°F., it will bend quite a lot before it will break and it does not therefore seem wise to jump to the conclusion that this steel is tougher drawn at 375°F. than it is when drawn at 700°F. It takes more *energy* to twist off the torsion impact specimen at the lower drawing temperature—there can be no argument about this. However, most people's conception of "toughness" involves the idea that a piece that will bend before breaking is "tougher" than a piece that will break before bending. It is also known that if a tool contains a sharp notch—like a tap for example— it would require a harder blow with a hammer to break it when drawn at 700°F. than when drawn at 375°F. This is because the steel when drawn at 700°F. has greater *ductility*—ability to stretch or bend before breaking. Torsion impact toughness is really a combination of ductility and strength, and perhaps some new word, such as "strength-toughness" or "rigid-toughness" would better describe the significance of the peak on the torsion impact curve. Tool makers who use the Matched Set method do not need to worry about toughness comparison at drawing temperatures higher than 500°F. for a reason that will now be explained.

The Matched Set method says "When WATER-HARD is not tough enough to make a certain tool, switch to WATER-TOUGH." The WATER-TOUGH tool steel described in Chapter 12 will, after heat treatment, show about C-59/60 Rockwell hardness. At this hardness, it is very much tougher than WATER-HARD would be if drawn back to the same hardness figure. When a tool maker buys WATER-HARD, he is buying a steel capable of extreme hardness and good wear resistance. It is a foolish waste of money to harden this steel and then draw it back softer than C-60 Rockwell in an effort to make it tough. By doing this, he is throwing away the hardness and wear resistance that he paid good money to get and is finishing up with a make-shift that is *neither* hard nor satisfactorily tough. In the normal use of the Matched Diagram, WATER-HARD would not be drawn above 400°F. or about C-62 Rockwell; if this were not tough enough, the tool maker would switch immediately to WATER-TOUGH and get a much more efficient tool.

This principle applies all through the Matched Set. The tool maker is justified in drawing a hard, wear resisting steel only until the next tougher steel is able to pick up the job. This comes very close to saying that all Matched Tool Steels should be drawn at the peak of the torsion impact curves—and certainly, many years of practical application have confirmed the wisdom of this course. There have been some exceptions wherein tools drawn 50° or 100° higher have given better service, but the number of these has been small. The next chapter will show the torsion impact curve for the nine steels in the Air-Hardening, Oil-Hardening and Water-Hardening Matched Sets. Definite hardening instructions will also be given so that certainly in a majority of cases the tool maker need try only one hardening temperature and one drawing temperature in order to determine whether he has the right steel. It is not claimed that we yet know all there is to be known about tool steel and its heat treatment and, therefore, it is not recommended that a tool maker adhere blindly to this general rule. However, if these new and

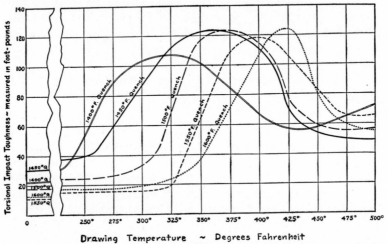

Fig. 161.—WATER-HARD tool steel. Effect of various hardening temperatures on toughness.

simplified methods will even reduce by half the amount of experimenting in the hardening room, they will pay a handsome reward in the form of lower tool costs and higher production.

The torsion impact test gives us the answer to many other questions concerning the toughness of tool steel, and its relation to heat treatment. For example, the test described on page 274 covered only one hardening temperature—1450°F. How would this curve look if the hardening temperature had been higher or lower? To get this information, it is necessary to machine a great many specimens and harden about thirty of them at each different hardening temperature. This provides enough pieces to draw a few of them at each different drawing temperature and thus establish the complete curve. This curve is given in Fig. 161 and it will be noted that the diagram has been spread out more in a horizontal direction so that the curves appear more rounded.

The solid line marked "1450°F. quench" is plotted from the same data previously given in Table IV; the other four curves are new ones.

Note the following things:

1. Each curve shows a toughness peak followed by a valley.

2. Observe how the toughness peak moves to the right as the hardening temperature is raised. This is summarized in Table V.

TABLE V.—WATER-HARD—EFFECT OF HARDENING TEMPERATURE ON LOCATION OF TOUGHNESS PEAK

Hardening Temperature	Drawing Temperature for Max. Toughness
1400°F.	325°F.
1450	350
1500	375
1550	400
1600	425

This table shows that there is a different "best" drawing temperature for each different hardening temperature.

3. The steel does not have as high a peak when quenched at 1400°F. as it does when quenched at 1450°F. The steel becomes fully hard at 1400°F. because the critical point for this steel is only about 1355°F., and for many years 1400°F. was considered the ideal hardening temperature. This was in accordance with the old-fashioned rule to "always harden a high carbon tool steel at the lowest temperature at which it will satisfactorily harden." Practical experience, however, bears out the torsion impact data, because tools made from WATER-HARD have proved less likely to crack in hardening and also tougher in service when they are quenched at 1450°F.

4. Since WATER-HARD is a tough timbre steel and therefore retains a fine grain size at higher hardening temperatures, it will be observed that the toughness peak is just as high for a 1600°F. quench as it is for a 1450°F. quench.

5. It is interesting to compare the toughness values secured right after quenching and before the specimens have been drawn or tempered. These values are tabulated in Table VI.

TABLE VI.—WATER-HARD—EFFECT OF HARDENING TEMPERATURE ON
TOUGHNESS "AS QUENCHED"

Hardening Temperature	Toughness "as Quenched"
1400°F.	22 Ft. Lbs.
1450	29
1500	18
1550	11
1600	13

If a tool is going to crack during heat treatment, it usually does so before it has been drawn. These values therefore give some clue to the relative *safety* of the various hardening temperatures. Again, 1450°F. appears as the best temperature—better even than 1400°F. The "cracking hazard" at 1550° to 1600°F. is more than twice as great as at 1450°F. The reader may wonder why the "toughness peaks" are so nearly alike and yet the "as quenched" values are quite different. This will be more fully described in Chapter 21 but can be briefly explained here. A tool cracks in hardening as a result of internal strains set up by the quench. The higher the hardening temperature, the greater the internal strains will be. These strains are resisted by the strength and toughness of the steel. Even if a tool does not crack in hardening, it comes from the quench in a highly strained condition. Just for sake of illustration, let us assume that WATER-HARD quenched at 1450°F. has a strength and toughness of 100%—and when quenched from 1600°F., it also has 100%. Let us assume that the strains resulting from a 1450°F. quench equal 75%, and the strains resulting from a 1600°F. quench equal 90%. In the "as hardened" condition, 25% of the strength will be available to resist fracture in the first case and only 10% available in the second case. This explains the torsion impact values "as quenched." Now assume that the drawing operation removes the bulk of the quenching strains from both samples—their torsion impact values would then be approximately the same. These may not be true percentages, but they illustrate the principle.

6. Observe on the curves that the toughness peaks become *sharper* as the hardening temperature is raised. After hardening at 1450°F. there is a total range of about 50°F. in which the steel may be drawn and still secure maximum toughness. With a 1600°F. quench, the peak is so abrupt that there is only about 25° within which maximum values can be secured.

Here is another question for the torsion impact machine. It was previously stated that *soaking time* was an important element in the drawing operation. All of the torsion impact data thus far given have been based on samples which were soaked at the drawing temperature for one hour. What would happen if they had been drawn for a longer or shorter time?

To get this information, a large number of torsion impact test pieces must be hardened at the same temperature. In order to see what happens as a result of drawing for only fifteen minutes, a complete series must be drawn at all different temperatures and held at heat for only fifteen minutes. This permits drawing the "fifteen minute curve." Another batch is held for four hours at different heats and these are used to draw the "four hour curve." The procedure is then repeated for eight hours and twenty-four hours. This is a tremendous amount of work but it is all contained in the curves shown in Fig. 162.

The exact toughness values are not given but it can be seen that there is not much difference in the height of the various curves. The Rockwell

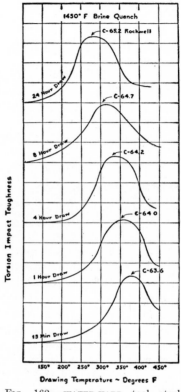

FIG. 162.—WATER-HARD tool steel. Effect of drawing time on toughness.

hardness values corresponding to the toughness peaks have been marked on the diagram. Observations from these curves may be summarized as follows:

1. The hardness values are not the same at all of the peaks. A 24 hour draw at 275°F. will give maximum toughness with a Rockwell hardness of C-65.2. A 15 min. draw at 375°F. produces maximum toughness with a hardness of about C-63.6.

This suggests the general rule for drawing:

Better tools are secured by drawing for a long time at a lower temperature than by drawing for a shorter time at a higher temperature.

2. The toughness peak occurs at a lower drawing temperature when the drawing time is increased. This may be summarized as follows:

TABLE VII.—WATER-HARD—EFFECT OF DRAWING TIME ON LOCATION OF TOUGHNESS PEAK

Drawing Time	Drawing Temperature for Peak Toughness
15 min.	375°F.
1 hr.	350
4 hrs.	325
8 hrs.	300
24 hrs.	275

This result is typical of that secured on other similar tests and establishes the rule—

As the drawing time is increased, the drawing temperature should be lowered.

If any one attempts to follow blindly or thoughtlessly the curves illustrated in Fig. 162, he will get into difficulties. For example, he might say to himself, "The toughness peak for a 15 min. draw is just as high as it is for a 24 hour draw—a Rockwell of C-63 is plenty hard enough for this tool and I can therefore save a lot of time by drawing it for only 15 min." The thing he has overlooked is the fact that these tests are made on a test section ¼″ round and having a perfectly smooth uniform shape. The tool he is going to heat treat may weigh ten pounds or thirty pounds and may contain sharp corners and intricate, unbalanced sections. Obviously, such a tool will be more highly strained in quenching than the torsion impact test specimen would be—and, furthermore, it takes a lot more time to draw the strains out of a piece weighing ten pounds than it does out of a piece weighing one ounce. The hardener must decide upon the necessary drawing time from the size and shape of the tool and the kind of work that it must do. He should not even *look* at the torsion impact data until he has decided in his own mind *how long* that particular tool should be drawn. If he decides that it should be drawn for four hours, he can then look at the torsion impact curves and pick out the drawing temperature that will give him maximum toughness for a four hour draw. If the hardening temperature has been 1450°F., he will draw it at 325°F.

In Chapter 12 complete heat treating instructions are given for WATER-HARD steel and on page 287 will be found a table giving the best drawing temperature for all combinations of hardening temperatures and drawing time. This table was arrived at by making a complete set of curves like the group illustrated in Fig. 162 for all different hardening temperatures between 1400° and 1600°F. This was a tremendous task involving many hundred tests but the hardener will find that the results are well worth the effort made to get them.

The torsion impact machine has been called upon to answer many other questions. For example, long before this machine

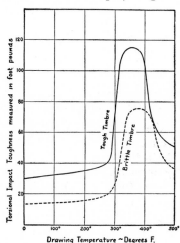

Fig. 163.—Tough timbre vs. brittle timbre. Comparative toughness when brine quenched from 1450°F.

was invented, the expressions "tough timbre" and "brittle timbre" carbon tool steel were in use. If one of them is really tough and the other brittle it should show up on the toughness curves.

In Fig. 163 is shown a comparison between the torsion impact tests on these two types of steel. The analyses of the two bars used were as follows:

	C	Mn	Si	P	S	Alloys
Brittle timbre...............	1.03	.23	.16	.019	.017	Nil.
Tough timbre...............	1.06	.20	.16	.010	.012	Nil.

The analyses of these two steels are so close together that a buyer who was purchasing tool steel on analysis alone could get either one of them and would assume that they were "perfect mates."

Torsion impact tests after hardening from a gas furnace at 1450°F. are shown on the curves. The discrepancy in peak toughness is obvious, but note also the values "as quenched." Before drawing, the brittle timbre steel showed only 14 foot pounds compared to 29 foot pounds for the tough timbre steel. This means that the brittle timbre type is much more likely to crack in hardening than the tough timbre type. The toughness peaks show that the brittle timbre steel is also more likely to fail in service.

A thoughtful reader will think of many questions that he would like to ask the torsion impact machine. To some of these the answers may be available and if he will address a letter to The Carpenter Steel Company, Reading, Penna.—attention of Research Department, the information will be supplied if it is available.

NOTE: In spite of the valuable information the torsion impact test has furnished to assist in the proper heat treatment of individual steels, it is not a safe guide to the comparative toughness of two different steels having entirely different analyses. For example, it will be seen in Chapter 12 that *Stentor* (OIL-HARD) shows the same toughness peak as *Solar* (WATER-TOUGH). This would lead to the conclusion that these two steels, when properly drawn, had the same toughness. Actually, this is not true—*Solar* is very much tougher than *Stentor* in service. This is the same type of difficulty encountered in trying to gauge wear resistance from the measured hardness values. In any one steel, there is certainly a useful relation between hardness and wear resistance—but this relation is entirely lost when comparing two steels of entirely different analysis. For example, *Stentor* (OIL-HARD) shows about the same measured hardness as *Hampden* (OIL-WEAR), and yet *Hampden* will outwear *Stentor* by a large margin. These inconsistencies are continually encountered whenever an attempt is made to go too far in translating test measurements into actual service performance. Therefore, while the torsion impact figures have been of tremendous help in solving the behavior of individual steels, the reader should go slow in using these values to compare the properties of two steels having entirely different type analyses.

CHAPTER 12

PROPERTIES AND HEAT TREATMENT OF TWELVE MATCHED TOOL STEELS[1]

The reader must continually distinguish between the theoretical diamonds on the Matched Diagram named OIL-WEAR, OIL-TOUGH and etc., and the actual "flesh-and-blood" tool steels that are assigned to these diamonds. In order to discuss proper-

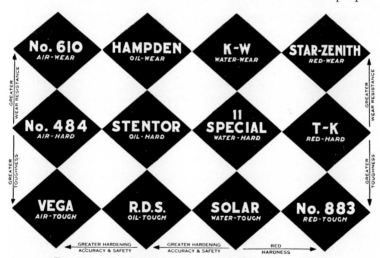

FIG. 164.—The diagram of Carpenter Matched Tool Steels.

ties and give exact heat treating instructions, it is necessary to talk about real steels, and this chapter is therefore devoted to giving such information on the twelve Carpenter Matched Tool

---

[1] The descriptions of the steels that follow are quoted almost verbatim from the Carpenter Manual "Matched Tool Steels." In addition to the educational value of the material contained, it furnishes for the purpose of this book an interesting example of a modern tool steel catalog and illustrates the type of information a tool maker or hardener may expect from the tool steel manufacturer. It also serves to give practical reality to an otherwise theoretical Diagram.

283

Steels. They will be called by their private brand names so that the reader cannot possibly mistake the information as applying to the diamonds themselves.

Brand Name—*NO. 11 SPECIAL*
Matched Set Name—WATER-HARD

Type Analysis:

```
Carbon........................................... 1.05%
Manganese.......................................  .20
Silicon.........................................  .20
Alloys..........................................  None
```

PROPERTIES

Description.—*No. 11 Special* is a high quality, straight carbon, water-hardening tool steel. It is guaranteed to be tough timbre, with a medium hardness penetration.

FIG. 165.— Fracture—*No. 11 Special* hardened.

In sections larger than about $\frac{1}{2}''$, it hardens with a dense, fine grained case, and a tough, unhardened core as in Fig. 165. It owes its hardness and wear resistance to the case, and its toughness to the softer core.

No. 11 Special is 100% acid disc inspected in the billets during manufacture to insure clean sound steel in every bar.

Deformation in Hardening.—Being a water-hardening steel, *No. 11 Special* will not hold its exact size or shape during hardening. However, if we are to judge from the number of tool makers who have switched from oil-hardening tool steel back to *No. 11 Special*, it must be far above the average in this respect.

Decarburization.—*No. 11 Special* has very little tendency to decarburize on the surface when heated for hardening. By using an **oxidizing** furnace atmosphere soft skin can be positively prevented.

Machinability.—*No. 11 Special* is the easiest of all tool steels in the Matched Set to machine. The absence of special alloys and good annealing account for this fact.

Uses of *No. 11 Special*.—**All** tools should be made of *No. 11 Special* unless there is some good reason for making them from some special alloy steel. This is the first rule of the Matched Diagram. Typical uses include:

Drills	Blanking dies	Heading dies
Taps	Striking dies	Jewelers' dies
Reamers	Forming dies	Knockout pins
Punches	Bending dies	Woodworking tools
Stamps	Button dies	Jig bushings
Bushings	Coining dies	Jigs and fixtures
Knurls	Plug gauges	Dowel pins
Mandrels	Cutters	Locating studs
Threading dies	Hand chisels	

NOTE: For specific recommendations see the Tool Steel Selector Chart in Chapter 9.

When to Switch from *No. 11 Special*.—If you want greater wear resistance (at some sacrifice of toughness) use *K-W* (WATER-WEAR).

If you want greater toughness (at some sacrifice of wear resistance) use *Solar* (WATER-TOUGH).

If you want great hardening accuracy or safety, use *Stentor* (OIL-HARD) or *No. 484* (AIR-HARD).

If you want red-hardness for hot forging tools, switch to *T-K* (RED-HARD). For red-hardness in a metal cutting tool, switch to *Star-Zenith* or *Speed Star* High Speed Steel (RED-WEAR).

THE HEAT TREATMENT OF *No. 11 Special*

To Forge.—Heat slowly and uniformly to a maximum temperature of 1950°F., and forge. Cool in air in a dry place.

To Normalize.—Forgings are normalized by heating to 1650°F. and cooling in air.

To Anneal.—Pack in a suitable container with clean cast iron borings, heat uniformly to 1375/1400°F., and cool slowly in the furnace. Average Brinell hardness 180.

To relieve machining strains for greater accuracy in hardening—first, rough machine, then anneal **below the critical** (from 1200°/1250°F.) and cool slowly—then finish machine.

To Harden.—First heat the furnace to 1450°/1500°F., depending on the cross-section of the tool. Coining dies, striking dies, header dies, etc., which are under heavy pressure can be hardened at higher temperatures such as 1500°, 1550° or even 1600°F. to increase the penetration of hardness to prevent sinking. When available, neutral salt baths can also be used for heating for hardening.

Then adjust the atmosphere so that it is definitely **oxidizing.** Excess oxygen between 2% and 4% is preferred. Use the wood block test as described on page 456. Place the cold tool, without preheating, right in the hot furnace and let it heat "naturally" (see page 476) until it uniformly matches the color of the thermocouple in the furnace. Soak an additional 5 minutes per inch of thickness, then quench in brine. Hardening temperatures under 1440°F. are not recommended for this steel.

All water-hardening steels of the Matched Set should be quenched in 5% to 10% salt brine—and may be quenched right down to bath temperature.

No. 11 Special is an easy steel to harden—heat it right up, soak a little, then quench it right down. This saves time and trouble; it is the *safest* procedure, and it gives you better tools.

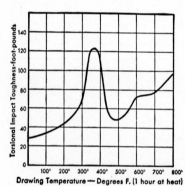

Drawing Temperature — Degrees F. (1 hour at heat)

Fig. 166.—Effect of drawing temperature on toughness. *No. 11 Special* —brine quenched from 1450°F. (drawn 1 hour).

If blind holes, or through holes close to the edge, *must* be packed, pack with steel wool, *not* asbestos or clay.

Hollow impressions on dies should be flushed in quenching. Fresh water is satisfactory as a flush.

In sizes equivalent to about $\frac{3}{16}''$ round or smaller, *No. 11 Special* will become file hard when quenched in oil from about 1500°/1550°F. This practice is recommended on very small parts to reduce warping, deformation and possible cracking.

To Draw.—The real purpose of drawing is to remove internal strains and increase toughness. A procedure should therefore be adopted which will give the best toughness with the least possible sacrifice of hardness. In this book, "one hour draw" means one hour **soak** at temperature. Be sure to allow sufficient time for the tool to reach the proper temperature (see page 492) and then start counting time.

The curve in Fig. 166 shows how various drawing temperatures affect the torsional impact toughness of *No. 11 Special* and the table which follows gives the corresponding Rockwell and Scleroscope hardness values.

The data given show that tools made from *No. 11 Special*—when quenched in water or brine from 1450°F.—will have the maximum combination of hardness and toughness when drawn for one hour at 350°/375°F. For other hardening temperatures or longer drawing times, see Table IX.

TABLE VIII.—EFFECT OF DRAWING TEMPERATURE ON HARDNESS

No. 11 Special—Brine quenched from 1450°F.—drawn 1 hour

Drawing temperature	Rockwell hardness	Equivalent scleroscope
As hardened	C-66/67	96
200°F.	66/67	96
300	64/65	92
350	63/64	90
375	62/63	88
400	61/62	86
500	58/59	82
600	54/55	74
700	50/51	68
800	46/47	62

Effect of Hardening Temperature and Drawing Time.—While most *No. 11 Special* tools should be hardened from 1450°F., certain types of cold forming tools require higher hardening temperatures. Further, exceptionally large or intricate tools should frequently be soaked at the drawing temperature longer than one hour. To find the best drawing temperature for each hardening temperature and each drawing time, refer to Table IX.

TABLE IX.—DRAWING DATA FOR *No. 11 Special*
To secure maximum toughness

Hardening temperature	Drawing time			
	1 hr.,	4 hrs.,	8 hrs.,	24 hrs.,
1450°F.	350°F.	325°F.	300°F.	275°F.
1500	375	350	325	300
1550	400	375	350	325
1600	425	400	375	350

First, find in the left hand column the hardening temperature used; then decide how **long** the tool should be soaked at the drawing heat and use the drawing temperature given in the table.

For example, if you harden a tool at 1500°F. and decide to draw it four hours, draw it at 350°F. If you quench at 1550°F. and are going to draw 1 hour, use 400°F. If you quench at 1450°F. and want to draw 24 hours, use a temperature of 275°F.

Small tools of very simple shape are sometimes drawn less than one hour. A tool drawn for only 15 minutes should receive 25° more drawing heat than is recommended for a one hour draw.

Small tools hardened in oil should be drawn the same as though they had been quenched from a corresponding temperature into water.

You seldom need to bother trying any other drawing temperature than the one you pick from this table.

It is usually not advisable to draw *No. 11 Special* softer than about C-62 Rockwell. If this is not tough enough, it is preferable to switch to *Solar* (WATER-TOUGH) because this steel at about C-60 Rockwell will be much tougher than *No. 11 Special* at the same hardness. This, of course, does not apply to shanks and other parts of tools remote from the "business end" which might need to be softened for special reasons.

Green Label Drill Rod

Green Label Drill Rod is the running mate to *No. 11 Special.* It is a tough timbre, high carbon, water-hardening drill rod con-

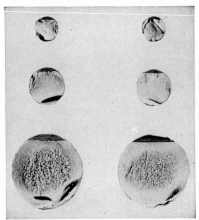

These three hard-　These three hardened at 1450°F.　ened at 1550°F.

FIG. 167.—*Green Label Drill Rod* fractures illustrating tough timbre. (Actual size.)

taining approximately 1.20% carbon—which is slightly higher than *No. 11 Special.*

Polished *Green Label Drill Rod* has a beautiful smooth surface and is distinguished by its roundness and accuracy to size. It is guaranteed free from surface decarburization and will harden file hard right out to the surface.

Special attention is given to machinability in the manufacture of *Green Label Drill Rod.* Experience has shown that the small sizes can be machined easier and with less tendency for bending if they are supplied somewhat harder. Each size range is therefore processed for best machinability.

Green Label Drill Rod is made from tough timbre tool steel and, therefore, has a wide, safe hardening range. Fig. 167 shows three sizes that have been brine quenched from both 1450°F. and 1550°F. Note that the tough timbre prevents the steel from becoming coarse and brittle as a result of this overheating. Observe also the hard, dense case and the tough core in the larger size. This tough core is a valuable reinforcement to the toughness and strength of the tools.

To Harden *Green Label Drill Rod.*—Use exactly the same instructions as given for *No. 11 Special.* Sizes $\frac{3}{16}''$ round and smaller will become file hard when quenched in oil from about 1500°/1550°F. Larger sizes should be quenched in brine.

Green Label Polished Drill Rod is stocked in three-foot lengths in all standard sizes. Unpolished finish, special lengths, or extra close size tolerance can be furnished to order.

Brand Name—*SOLAR*
Matched Set Name—WATER-TOUGH

Type Analysis:

Carbon	.50%
Manganese	.40
Silicon	1.00
Molybdenum	.50

PROPERTIES

Description.—*Solar* is a water-hardening alloy tool steel of extreme toughness. It hardens to about C-62 Rockwell, and when drawn back to about C-59 Rockwell, it is the strongest and toughest tool steel known.

A tensile test on *Solar*, properly treated, will show:

Breaking strength.............. 323,000 pounds per sq. in.
Elongation in 2″................ 4.5%

Even with this great hardness and strength, *Solar* is ductile enough to **stretch** more than 4% before breaking. At C-59 Rockwell, *Solar* will bend before it will break.

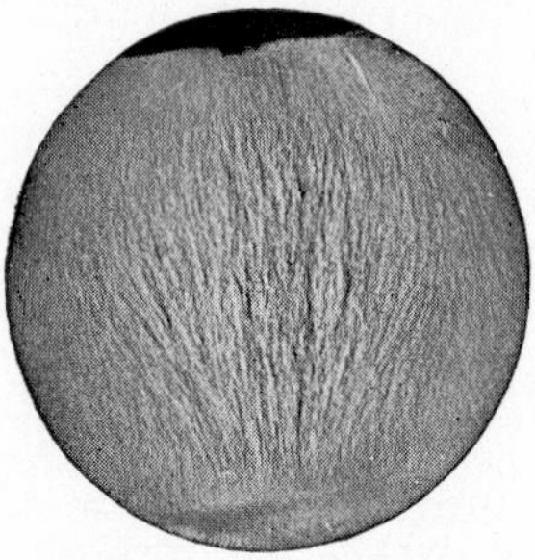

FIG. 168.—*Solar* hardened.

When hardened in medium and large sized pieces, *Solar* acquires a hard case and a tough core. For example, in the 1½″ round piece shown in Fig. 168 there is a fine grained case about ³⁄₁₆″ to ¼″ deep showing C-61/63 Rockwell hardness; and a tough, coarser grained core showing about C-40/45 Rockwell. Sizes under ¾″ round will harden clear through.

Deformation in Hardening.—Since *Solar* hardens deeper than *No. 11 Special* (WATER-HARD), it tends to expand more in hardening. *Solar* will expand in larger sizes where the straight carbon steel would shrink. Also, rectangular blocks of *Solar* will tend to harden with **concave** faces. That is, the flat surfaces will become slightly hollow, whereas *No. 11 Special* would bulge under similar conditions. Holes bored in *Solar* tools will tend to expand or open up in heat treatment. Allowance should be made for this size change. *Solar* is not recommended for tools that must hold size and shape accurately in hardening. This is the field for *R. D. S.* (OIL-TOUGH).

Decarburization.—Because of its high content of silicon and molybdenum, *Solar* is more subject to surface decarburization when heated than any other steel in the Matched Set. This tendency may be felt if the steel is to be hot forged, but it can be avoided altogether in hardening if our instructions regarding furnace atmosphere are followed.

Machinability.—Being an alloy steel, *Solar* does not machine as readily as *No. 11 Special*. It is not as difficult to machine as high speed steel, but might be classed as intermediate between these two.

Uses of *Solar*.—The rule of the Matched Diagram is:—When *No. 11 Special* (WATER-HARD) is not **tough** enough for a job, travel south and use *Solar* (WATER-TOUGH). As a general rule, you do not draw *No. 11 Special* below C-62 Rockwell—if this is not tough enough, use *Solar*.

Solar hardens to about C-61 to C-63 Rockwell and after drawing to C-60, it is very much tougher than *No. 11 Special* (WATER-HARD) would be at this same hardness.

In almost every tool room and shop, there are a vast number of tools or parts that must, above all else, be tough. Along with toughness we want all the hardness and wear resistance we can get, but they must not break. Here are just a few, as reminders—you can fill in the list almost without limit.

Punches	Heavy duty bending tools
Pins (knockout, clutch, indexing)	Heavy duty coining dies
Trimming dies	Shear blades
Crimping dies	Spring collets
Swaging dies	Feed fingers
Jaws	Special knurls
Wrenches	Stamps
Heavy duty forming tools	Circular shear blades

NOTE: For specific recommendations see the Tool Steel Selector Chart in Chapter 9.

If these tools were made of straight carbon tool steel, you would draw them back to a "blue"—and often "blue" isn't half far enough. *Solar* fits into this field like a key into its lock.

Here is another group frequently referred to as "battering tools":

Pneumatic chisels	Pipe cutter wheels	Punches
Hand chisels	Screw drivers	Vanstoning dies
Rivet busters	Rivet sets	Concrete breakers
Beading tools	Sledges	Caulking tools
Track chisels	Drift pins	

NOTE: For specific recommendations see the Tool Steel Selector Chart in Chapter 9.

All of these tools demand a combination of hardness and toughness that can be squeezed out of carbon tool steel only by lowering the percentage of carbon and drawing back entirely too far.

There is not a job in this list that *Solar* has not done—and done well.   For most of them, it is by far the best steel we know of— regardless of price.

When to Switch from *Solar.*

If you want greater hardness and wear resistance than *Solar* can deliver, use *No. 11 Special* (WATER-HARD).

NOTE: Do not make this shift until you are **sure** your trouble is not due to surface decarburization.   Grind or file below the surface and see whether the hardness increases.   If it does—try to do a better job of hardening before switching to *No. 11 Special.*

If *Solar* changes size or warps too much in hardening—or if the shape is so intricate that you do not dare to quench it in water— use *R. D. S.* (OIL-TOUGH) or *Vega* (AIR-TOUGH).

If the tools get hotter than about 300°F., in service, go **east** and select *No. 883* (RED-TOUGH).

THE HEAT TREATMENT OF *Solar*

To Forge.—Forge from a temperature not over 2100°F.   Heat rapidly and avoid unnecessary soaking in order to minimize surface decarburization.   Cool the forgings in air in a dry place.

To Normalize.—Forgings are normalized by heating to 1650°F. and cooling in air.

To Anneal.—Pack in a suitable container with clean cast iron borings.   Heat uniformly to 1375/1425°F., and cool slowly in in the furnace.   Brinell hardness will average 190.

To relieve machining strains for greater accuracy in hardening—first, rough machine, then anneal **below the critical** (from 1200°/1250°F.) and cool slowly—then finish machine.

To Harden.—First heat the furnace to 1550°F.   Then adjust the atmosphere to show between 1.5% and 4% oxygen by means of the wood block test as described on page 456.   This atmosphere will give you *Solar* tools that are hard right out to the skin —don't fail to get your atmosphere right before putting the tools in the furnace.   Neutral salt baths can also be used for heating for hardening.

Without preheating, place the tool right in the hot furnace near the thermocouple, and let it heat "naturally" (see page 476) until it uniformly matches the color of the thermocouple.   Soak about 5 minutes per inch of thickness, and then quench in brine.

All water-hardening steels of the Matched Set should be

quenched in 5% to 10% salt brine, and may be quenched right down to bath temperature.

Solar is an easy steel to harden. Get your atmosphere all set, heat the tool right up, soak a little, then quench it right down. This saves time and trouble; it is the *safest* procedure, and it gives you better tools.

Small tools, measuring under about ½″, can be heated to 1600°F., in the same atmosphere, and quenched in oil.

To Draw.—In this book "one hour draw" means one hour **soak** at temperature. Be sure to allow sufficient time for the tool to reach the proper temperature (see page 492) and then start counting time. The effect of drawing upon the torsional impact toughness and hardness of *Solar* is shown in Fig. 169 and Table X.

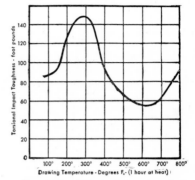

Fig. 169.—Effect of drawing temperature on toughness. *Solar*—brine quenched from 1550°F. (drawn 1 hour).

TABLE X.—EFFECT OF DRAWING TEMPERATURE ON HARDNESS
Solar—Brine quenched from 1550°F.—drawn 1 hour

Drawing temperature	Rockwell hardness	Equivalent scleroscope
As hardened	C-61/63	87
200°F.	61/62	86
250	60/61	85
300	**59/60**	**83**
350	58/59	82
400	57/58	79
500	55/56	76
600	54/55	74
700	52/53	71

For practically **all** water (or brine) quenched tools, we recommend a drawing temperature of 275° to 300°F. for one hour—or longer, according to size. Shanks of pneumatic chisels are drawn at 900°F.

When *Solar* tools are **oil quenched** from 1600°F., they frequently need not be drawn at all and will then show C-59/61

Rockwell. If the shape is intricate, draw at 200° to 250°F. to relieve the hardening strains.

Do not draw *Solar* to **color,** because a straw color begins to appear above 400°F.—which is too hot for most tools.

Brand Name—*K-W*
Matched Set Name—WATER-WEAR

Type Analysis:

Carbon.. 1.30%
Manganese... .30
Silicon... .30
Tungsten.. 3.50

PROPERTIES

Description.—*K-W* is a water-hardening tool steel that will resist wear and abrasion from four to ten times longer than plain carbon tool steel.

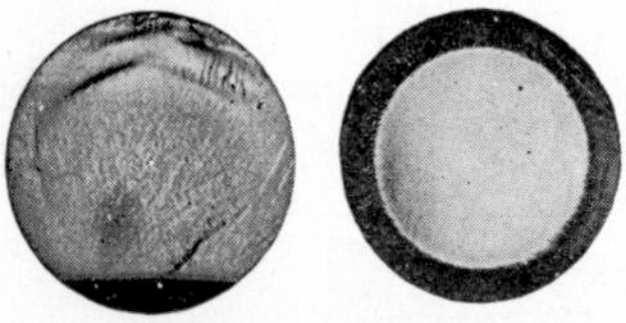

fracture.   etched section.
FIG. 170.—*K-W* hardened in brine from 1550°F.

When hardened, it acquires a peculiar slippery-hard surface which is so difficult to scratch that even an ordinary emery wheel can scarcely cut it. Special wheels are used for grinding *K-W* tools as described on page 298. Because of the "soapy" nature of the hardened surface, K-W tools do not gall or pick up as quickly as other tools.

K-W is a surface hardening steel and hardens with a somewhat thinner case than *No. 11 Special.* The hard case is backed up with a softer, tougher core having a Rockwell hardness of about C-45/50 (Fig. 170). K-W billets are 100% acid disc inspected to insure clean sound metal in the finished bars.

Deformation in Hardening.—Being a shallow hardening, water quenched steel, K-W tends to shrink in hardening. This is a useful property in draw dies which can frequently be shrunk enough in re-hardening to take up the wear, thus allowing them to be re-used for the same size.

K-W is not recommended for tools that must hold size and shape accurately in hardening. For such tools, use *Hampden* (OIL-WEAR), or *No. 610* (AIR-WEAR).

Decarburization.—Tungsten increases the tendency toward surface decarburization in hardening. Also, the higher hardening temperature of *K-W* (1525° to 1600°F.) helps this tendency along. By carefully following our instructions regarding furnace atmosphere, decarburization can be avoided and the tool will come from the quench with a glass hard surface.

Machinability.—*K-W* machines almost as well as *No. 11 Special*. It averages to be a little bit harder.

Uses of *K-W*.—The rule of the Matched Diagram is—use *K-W* for all water-hardening tool steel jobs where you want more wear resistance and greater production than *No. 11 Special* (WATER-HARD) will deliver. Therefore, *K-W* has been successfully used for a wide variety of tools. The following is a typical list selected from letters that our customers have written us about the uses of this steel:

Burnishing tools	Forming dies	Ball header dies
Tube drawing dies	Brass cutting tools	Finishing tools
Wire drawing dies	Reamers	Quills
Draw dies for stainless steel	Sectional blanking dies	Eyelet dies
Extruding dies (cold)	Piercing punches	Small header dies and inserts

NOTE: For specific recommendations see the Tool Steel SelectorChart in Chapter 9.

When to Switch from *K-W*.—If you want greater toughness, use *No. 11 Special* (WATER-HARD).

If you want greater hardening accuracy or safety, use *Hampden* (OIL-WEAR), or *No. 610* (AIR-WEAR). These steels are used for the same wear resisting jobs as *K-W*.

If service temperature gets above 300°F. and softens the *K-W* tools, use *Star-Zenith* or *Speed Star* High Speed Steel (RED-WEAR). These steels likewise possess great wear resistance and will function at temperatures up to 1100°F.

If the shallow hardened case of *K-W* limits its use on heavy coining and compression tools, use *Hampden* (OIL-WEAR) or *No. 610* (AIR-WEAR) which harden very deep.

If hardness or wear resistance seem lacking, the trouble is probably surface decarburization or some other hardening difficulty. There is no more wear resisting steel than *K-W*.

The Heat Treatment of *K-W*

To Forge.—Forge from a temperature not over 1950°F. and allow the forgings to cool in air in a dry place.

To Normalize.—Forgings are normalized by heating to 1675°F. and cooling in air.

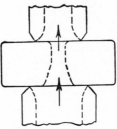

Water nozzles (inlet and outlet) should seat tightly against top and bottom of die to prevent leakage.   Outside of die must be kept dry.   The outlet pipe should restrict the flow of water to create a back pressure in the flush.   This provides positive quenching.

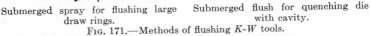

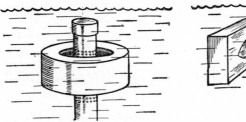

Submerged spray for flushing large   Submerged flush for quenching die
        draw rings.   with cavity.
Fig. 171.—Methods of flushing *K-W* tools.

To Anneal.—Pack in a suitable container with clean cast iron borings, heat uniformly to 1440° to 1460°F. and cool slowly in the furnace.   Average Brinell 235.

To relieve machining strains for greater accuracy in hardening—first, rough machine, then anneal **below the critical** (from 1200°/1250°F.) and cool slowly—then finish machine.

To Harden.—First heat the furnace to 1525° to 1600°F. (according to size and hardness penetration desired).   Then adjust the atmosphere to show 2% to 4% excess oxygen.   Use the wood block test as described on page 456.   Hardened from this atmosphere, there will be no decarburization, and the surface will be "slippery hard" to a brand new file. Neutral salt baths can also be used for heating for hardening.

After the furnace is adjusted to the proper hardening heat—and proper atmosphere—place the tool on the hearth without preheating. Let it heat naturally (see page 476) until it exactly matches the color of the thermocouple, then soak about 5 minutes per inch of thickness and quench in brine.

All water-hardening tool steels of the Matched Set should be quenched in 5% to 10% salt brine, and may be quenched right down to bath temperature.

K-W is an easy steel to harden; get your atmosphere all set, heat the tools right up, soak a little, then quench them right down. This saves time and trouble; it is the *safest* procedure, and it gives you better tools.

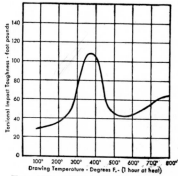

Fig. 172.—Effect of drawing temperature on toughness. K-W-brine quenched from 1550°F. (drawn 1 hour).

To avoid soft spots (due to the shallow hardening nature of this steel) never use fresh water for quenching except in a flush. In a still quenching tank, always use 5% to 10% salt brine. Use flushing fixtures for quenching K-W tools that have hollow impressions—as suggested by the sketches in Fig. 171.

To Draw.—In this book "one hour draw" means one hour **soak** at temperature. Be sure to allow sufficient time for the tool to reach the proper temperature (see page 492) and then start counting time. The effect of different drawing temperatures on the torsional impact

TABLE XI.—EFFECT OF DRAWING TEMPERATURE ON HARDNESS
K-W—Brine quenched from 1550°F.—drawn 1 hour

Drawing temperature	Rockwell hardness	Equivalent scleroscope
As hardened	C-67/68	98
200°F.	66/67	96
300	66/67	96
350	**65/66**	**94**
400	64/65	92
500	62/63	88
600	60/61	85
700	54/55	74

toughness and hardness of *K-W* is shown in Fig. 172 and Table XI.

The data shows that the best combination of hardness and toughness is secured by drawing between 350° and 375°F.

K-W should seldom be drawn hotter than 400°/425°F. If greater toughness is needed, switch to *No. 11 Special* (WATER-HARD).

Draw rings that are hardened in the hole **only** are frequently used without drawing at all.

To Grind.—Because of its extreme wear resistance, *K-W* is difficult to grind with the usual grinding wheels. The following manufacturers of grinding wheels have cooperated to recommend special wheels for *K-W*. These selections are of necessity rather general, and specific problems should be taken up direct with the wheel manufacturers.

NORTON COMPANY, WORCESTER, MASS.

Surface Grinding.—
   Roughing—use wheel 32A60-F12VBEP or 32A60-I8VG
   Finishing—use wheel 32A80-H8VG

Cylindrical Grinding.—
   Roughing—use wheel 32A60-K8VG
   Finishing—use wheel 32A80-J8VG

Internal Grinding.—
   Small wheels—38A120-J9VG
   Large wheels—32A801-K8VG

Lapping.—Refer to Norton Engineering Department.

THE CARBORUNDUM COMPANY, NIAGARA FALLS, N. Y.

Surface Grinding.—Wet or dry; either fast or slow traverse.
   Roughing—use wheel AA46-G7-V10
   Finishing—use wheel AA60-H7-V10

Cylindrical Grinding.—
   Roughing—use wheel DA60-J6-V11
   Finishing—use wheel DA120-J6-V11

Internal Grinding.—
  Wheels 1½″ dia., and smaller—AA80-H6-V10
  Wheels larger than 1½″ dia.—AA60-H6-V10
For wheels and mounted points for portable grinders, and for lapping abrasives—consult Carborundum Abrasive Engineering Division.

Brand Name—*STENTOR*
Matched Set Name—OIL-HARD

Type Analysis:

Carbon... .90%
Manganese..................................... 1.60
Silicon.. .25

PROPERTIES

Description.—*Stentor* is an oil-hardening, non-deforming tool steel. It is safe to harden even in intricate sections and is an excellent tool steel to avoid size change and warpage.

Stentor is made from billets that are 100% acid disc inspected which insures clean sound metal in the finished bars.

Deformation in Hardening.—Oil-hardening steels hold size best only when quenched from the proper hardening temperature. If over heated they tend to show shrinkage after drawing at the recommended temperature.

When properly hardened, *Stentor* will expand slightly—but upon being drawn, it returns very close to its original size. Fig. 173 shows the average size change in *Stentor* per

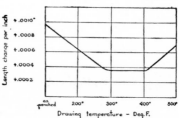

FIG. 173.—Size change of *Stentor*.

inch of length. That is, a piece 1″ long will expand approximately .001″ when hardened, but upon being drawn between 300° and 400°F., it will return within about .0004″ of its original size.

Because *Stentor* is free from alloys like tungsten, chromium, etc., it hardens at a very low temperature (1420° to 1450°F.) which holds warping down to an absolute minimum.

Decarburization.—*Stentor* is no more subject to surface decarburization than *No. 11 Special* (WATER-HARD). This is very important because *Stentor* holds size so accurately that many people do not grind their tools after hardening. The freedom of *Stentor* from soft skin is so unusual in an oil-hardening tool steel that some tool makers do not even know that such a thing is possible. They should try *Stentor*.

Machinability.—Again, because of the absence of complicated, hard-machining alloys *Stentor* is the easiest of all oil-hardening tool steels to machine. It cuts just about the same as water-hardening tool steel.

Uses of *Stentor*.—The rule of the Matched Diagram is—use *Stentor* in place of *No. 11 Special* (WATER-HARD) whenever you want greater **accuracy** or **safety** in hardening.

Since *Stentor* is the oil-hardening running mate of *No. 11 Special*, it is likely to be used for the same type of tools. *Stentor* is most commonly used for:

Blanking dies	Master tools
Forming dies	Spindles
Lamination dies	Master taps
Molding dies	Thread gauges
Trimming dies	Collets
Precision tools	Rolls
Broaches	Stamps
Gauges	

NOTE: For specific recommendations see the Tool Steel Selector Chart in Chapter 9.

When to Switch from *Stentor*.—If the tool does **not** require accurate hardening—if it is **not** likely to crack when hardened in water—use *No. 11 Special* (WATER-HARD).

If you want greater wear resistance—or for working abrasive materials, and if you have some toughness to spare, use *Hampden* (OIL-WEAR).

If *Stentor* is not tough enough to resist chipping or cracking, do not draw higher than 400°F., change to *R.D.S.* (OIL-TOUGH).

If you prefer an air-hardening steel for this same purpose, or if a deeper hardening steel is desired in large sizes, change to *No. 484* (AIR-HARD).

The Heat Treatment of *Stentor*

To Forge.—Forge from a temperature not over 1950°F. and allow the forgings to cool in air in a dry place. If forgings are the equivalent of 4″ square or larger, they should be slow cooled in ashes or in a dying out furnace.

To Normalize.—Forgings are normalized by heating to 1500°F. and cooling in air.

To Anneal.—Pack in a suitable container with clean cast iron borings, heat uniformly to 1330°/1350°F., and cool slowly in the furnace. Average Brinell hardness 200.

NOTE: If a large amount of metal is removed in machining, the resulting machining strains may cause warping in hardening. To avoid this, first rough machine—then anneal **below the critical,** or about 1200° to 1250°F., and cool slowly. Then finish machine. Annealing is much cheaper than stoning.

To Harden.—First set the furnace at the desired hardening temperature 1420° to 1450°F.—depending on size. Then adjust the atmosphere so that it is definitely **oxidizing.** Excess oxygen anywhere between 2% and 12% will do a good job, but 2% to 4% is preferred. Use the wood block test as described on page 456. Neutral salt baths can also be used for heating for hardening.

Without preheating, place the cold tool right in the hot furnace and let it heat "naturally" (see page 476) until it uniformly matches the color of the thermocouple in the furnace. Soak an additional 5 minutes per inch of thickness, then quench in oil.

Quench the tool right down to the temperature of the oil. The basket in the quenching tank is a good place to "store" hardened tools for the few minutes while they are waiting to be drawn.

Stentor is an easy steel to harden—heat it right up, soak a little, then quench it right down. This saves time and trouble—it is the *safest* procedure, and it gives you better tools.

To Draw.—In this book "one hour draw" means one hour **soak** at temperature.　Be sure to allow sufficient time for the tool to reach the proper temperature (see page 492) and then start counting time.

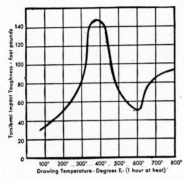

The effect of different drawing temperatures upon the torsional impact toughness and hardness of *Stentor* is shown in Fig. 174 and Table XII.

The best combination of hardness and toughness in *Stentor* tools is secured by drawing at 375° to 400°F.　It is seldom advisable to draw *Stentor* higher than this.　If this is not tough enough, switch to *R. D. S.* (oil-tough).

Fig. 174.—Effect of drawing temperature on toughness of *Stentor*.

TABLE XII.—Effect of Drawing Temperature on Hardness
Stentor—Oil hardened—drawn 1 hour

Drawing temperature	Rockwell hardness	Equivalent scleroscope
As hardened	C-64/65	92
200°F.	64/65	92
300	63/64	90
350	62/63	88
375	**61/62**	**86**
400	60/61	85
500	58/59	82
600	54/55	74
700	50/51	68

Large sized tools should be drawn longer than one hour. Every time you double the drawing time, cut 25° off the temperature—for example:

Drawing Time	Drawing Temperature
1 Hr.	375°F.
2	350
4	325
8	300

Stentor Drill Rod

Stentor Oil-Hardening Drill Rod is supplied with a smooth polished surface and is guaranteed free from surface decarburization.

It is stocked in three-foot lengths in standard sizes. Special lengths, sizes or finishes can be furnished to order.

Brand Name—*R. D. S.*
Matched Set Name—OIL-TOUGH

Type Analysis:

Carbon.. .75%
Manganese.. .35
Silicon... .25
Chromium... 1.00
Nickel.. 1.75

PROPERTIES

Description.—A tool steel containing a large percentage of nickel is so unusual that *R. D. S.* might well be expected to have unusual properties. And so it does. *R. D. S.* possesses approximately the same toughness as *Solar* (WATER-TOUGH) combined with non-deforming properties like *Stentor* (OIL-HARD). From the time when *R. D. S.* was first made available as a member of the Oil-Hardening Matched Set, it has licked so many difficult tooling jobs that tool makers are now wondering why no one ever thought of a **tough** non-deforming tool steel before.

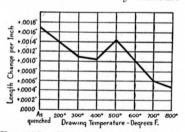

Deformation in Hardening. The chart in Fig. 175 shows typical length changes for *R. D. S.* when quenched in oil from 1525°F. and drawn at various temperatures. A piece

FIG. 175.—Size change of *R. D. S.* ¾" round—oil treated from 1525°F.

of *R. D. S.* 1" long may be expected to expand about .0017" when quenched, and upon drawing to 300° to 400°F., it should return to within about .001" of its original size. Heavier sizes will have less tendency to expand.

Decarburization.—*R. D. S.* has no special tendency to decarburize. If the hardening instructions are carefully followed, the tools should be hard right out to the surface.

Machinability.—*R. D. S.* machines a little tough like *Solar.* It would be rated as intermediate between a plain carbon, water-hardening tool steel and high speed steel.

Uses.—*R. D. S.* is used in three ways—

1. As the tough member of the Oil-Hardening Matched Set, it is used to replace *Stentor* (OIL-HARD) for all tools that require more toughness than *Stentor* possesses. Thus you will find it used for:

Hubs	Thread roller dies
Collets	Forming rolls
Punches	Embossing dies
Blanking dies	Etc.
Forming dies	

2. As the oil-hardening running mate of *Solar* (WATER-TOUGH), *R. D. S.* is used for all tools that would ordinarily be made of *Solar.* Use *R. D. S.* where hardening accuracy or cracking hazards make an oil-hardening steel necessary, such as intricate:

Shear blades	Swaging dies
Punches	Slitting shears
Stamps	Etc.

3. For parts that are not tools at all. There are certain machine parts requiring great strength and toughness combined with hardness and wear resistance such as:

Clutch parts	Spindles
Pawls	Fingers
Dogs	Indexing pins
Stops	Clutch pins
Knuckle pins	Etc.

Since *R. D. S.* is "harder than tempered gear steel and tougher than tool steel," it is ideal for parts of this nature.

NOTE: For specific recommendations on any of the above three groups, see the Tool Steel Selector Chart in Chapter 9.

When to Switch from *R. D. S.*—If size change is not important —if no cracking hazard is involved in hardening, there is no need to use *R. D. S.*—use *Solar* (WATER-TOUGH).

If greater hardness and wear resistance are needed—and you have toughness to spare—use *Stentor* (OIL-HARD).

If even greater freedom from size change is needed, or if very large tools are involved which would not harden sufficiently in *R. D. S.*, switch to *Vega* (AIR-TOUGH).

If the tools get hot in service, switch to a Red-Hard steel— *No. 883* or *T-K.*

THE HEAT TREATMENT OF *R. D. S.*

To Forge.—Forge from a temperature not over 2000°F. and allow the forgings to cool in air in a dry place.

To Normalize.—Forgings are normalized by heating to 1675°F. and cooling in air.

To Anneal.—For parts that have been previously hardened or annealed—pack in a suitable container with clean cast iron borings, heat uniformly to 1400° to 1450°F. and cool slowly in the furnace. Average annealed hardness 200 Brinell.

To relieve machining strains for greater accuracy in hardening —first, rough machine, then anneal **below the critical** (from 1200° to 1250°F) and cool slowly—then finish machine.

To Harden.—First set the furnace at the proper hardening temperature 1500° to 1550°F., depending on size.

Then get a strongly oxidizing atmosphere. *R. D. S.* will harden well from **any** oxidizing atmosphere, but it will throw the scale better in quenching if the atmosphere is about 8% to 10% oxygen. Use the soft coal test described on page 457. Neutral salt baths can also be used for heating for hardening.

Without preheating, place the cold tool right in the hot furnace and let it heat "naturally" (see page 476) until it uniformly matches the color of the thermocouple in the furnace. Soak at temperature 5 minutes per inch of thickness, then quench in oil.

Quench the tool right down to the temperature of the oil. The basket in the quenching tank is a good place to "store" hardened tools for the few minutes while they are waiting to be drawn.

R. D. S. is an easy steel to harden—heat it right up, soak a little, then quench it right down. This saves time and trouble— it is the *safest* procedure, and it gives you better tools.

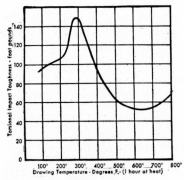

FIG. 176.—Effect of drawing temperature on toughness. *R. D. S.*—oil hardened (drawn 1 hour).

To Draw.—In this book "one hour draw" means one hour **soak** at temperature. Be sure to allow sufficient time for the tool to reach the proper temperature (see page 492) and then start counting time. The effect of different drawing temperatures on the torsional impact toughness and hardness of *R. D. S.* is given in Fig. 176 and Table XIII.

The best drawing temperature to secure the maximum combination of hardness and toughness is 300°F.

TABLE XIII.—EFFECT OF DRAWING TEMPERATURE ON HARDNESS
R. D. S.—Oil hardened—drawn 1 hour

Drawing temperature	Rockwell hardness	Equivalent scleroscope	Drawing temperature	Rockwell hardness	Equivalent scleroscope
As hardened	C-60/61	85	500	52/53	71
200°F.	59/60	83	600	50/51	68
300	**58/59**	**82**	700	47/48	63
400	55/56	76	800	44/45	57

Brand Name—*HAMPDEN*
Matched Set Name—OIL-WEAR

Type Analysis:

Carbon............	2.10%
Manganese........	.25
Silicon............	.25
Chromium.........	12.50
Nickel.............	.50

PROPERTIES

Description.—*Hampden* is an oil-hardening, high carbon, high chromium die steel having extreme wear resistance. It hardens with very little change in size or shape. *Hampden* is a deep hardening steel like high speed tool steel and has a very high compressive strength (Fig. 177).

FIG. 177. — Fracture of 1″ rd. *Hampden* O. T. 1775°F.

Because of its high percentage of chromium, *Hampden* has mild corrosion resisting properties when hardened.

Deformation in Hardening.—*Hampden* is essentially a non-deforming tool steel. Its average behavior is illustrated by the chart (Fig. 178). For example, a piece 1″ long would expand about .0008″ in hardening, but when drawn at 400°F., it returns within .0002″ of its original length. If drawn at 800°F., it will be a shade under size and above this it expands again.

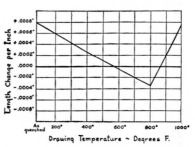

Fig. 178.—Size change of *Hampden*. ¾″ round—oil quenched from 1775°F.

If *Hampden* is over heated in hardening, it will shrink very badly—hence it must never be hardened above 1825°F.

Decarburization.—If hardened in an open furnace *Hampden* **may** acquire a slight soft skin. This is not due to any sensitive elements in the analysis—but results from the high hardening temperature itself. Properly controlled furnace atmospheres or pack hardening are recommended to avoid this.

Machinability.—Due to the very high carbon and chromium, *Hampden* cannot be annealed softer than about 217 to 241 Brinell. At this hardness, it machines about like annealed high speed steel.

Uses of *Hampden.*—*Hampden* is used for tools requiring a combination of hardening accuracy and safety with maximum wear resistance and greatest possible production. On the Matched Diagram, *Hampden* may be approached from two directions:

1. Use *Hampden* to replace *Stentor* (OIL-HARD) for any tools requiring exceptionally long life or for working on abrasive materials—such as:

Slitting cutters	Blanking dies
Master tools	Spindles
Forming dies	Hubs
Lamination dies	Cold rolls

2. *Hampden* is the oil-hardening running mate of *K-W* (WATER-WEAR). Use *Hampden* to replace *K-W* for all tools that must

hold size and shape accurately—or where the shape makes water quenching dangerous, such as:

Thread gauges	Intricate punches
Spinning tools	Blanking dies
Drawing dies	Trimming dies
Extrusion dies	

NOTE: For specific recommendations on either of the above groups see the Tool Steel Selector Chart in Chapter 9.

When to Switch from *Hampden*.—If you want greater toughness, at the sacrifice of wear resistance, switch to *Stentor* (OIL-HARD). A second step would be to go to *R. D. S.* (OIL-TOUGH).

If the tool does **not** require accuracy in hardening, and is safe to quench in water, use *K-W* (WATER-WEAR). *K-W* will usually show even greater wear resistance and longer life than *Hampden*.

If you prefer an **air-hardening,** high carbon, high chromium steel to one which hardens in oil, use *No. 610* (AIR-WEAR). This can be used interchangeably with *Hampden* for almost all purposes for which *Hampden* is recommended. It will, however, not become as hard as *Hampden*.

THE HEAT TREATMENT OF *Hampden*

To Forge.—*Hampden* forges very much like high speed steel. Heat slowly and uniformly to a temperature between 1925° and 2000°F. and forge. Do not continue forging below 1700°F. but reheat as often as necessary. Small, simple forgings can be cooled slowly in lime, but the best practice for large forgings is to place them in a furnace heated to about 1550°F., soak uniformly at this heat, then shut off the heat and cool the job slowly in the furnace. This is **not** an anneal. To anneal, proceed as below.

Normalizing.—Normalizing is not recommended.

To Anneal.—Pack in a suitable container with clean cast iron borings, heat uniformly to 1550° to 1600°F., and cool **very slowly** in the furnace. Average Brinell hardness 235.

To relieve machining strains for greater accuracy in hardening—first, rough machine, then anneal **below the critical** (from 1250°/1300°F.) and cool slowly—then finish machine.

To Harden.—Table XIV shows the effect of different hardening temperatures on *Hampden:*

TABLE XIV.—*Hampden*—EFFECT OF HARDENING TEMPERATURE ON HARDNESS

Oil Quenched from	Rockwell Hardness	Oil Quenched from	Rockwell Hardness
1650°F.	C-61/63	1800°F.	C-65/66
1700	64/65	1850	61/63
1750	65/66	1950	54/56

Note that maximum hardness is secured **only** between 1750° and 1800°F. Also *Hampden* holds size best within this range. If over heated, *Hampden* becomes softer—it shrinks—and it becomes somewhat non-magnetic. Moral—**Don't overheat it.**

The best procedure is to pack the tools in clean cast iron borings, heat uniformly to 1750° to 1800°F., soak thoroughly, then remove the tools from the pack and quench in oil. Atmosphere controlled furnaces or neutral salt baths are also well suited for heating of tools for hardening.

HELPFUL HINT: To prevent the cast iron chips from sticking to the tool, wrap the tool in heavy brown wrapping paper before placing it in the pack. The paper will char and prac-

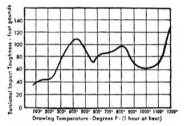

FIG. 179.—Effect of drawing temperature on toughness. *Hampden*—pack hardened from 1775°F. in oil (drawn 1 hour).

tically disappear when the heated tool is removed for quenching—but in the meantime, it will keep the cast iron chips from adhering to the surface of the tool.

NOTE: A cylindrical pipe packed with cast iron borings requires about 30 minutes per inch of diameter to heat to 1775°F. if the furnace is steadily maintained at heat, and the pack is allowed to heat "naturally."

To Draw.—The effect of different drawing temperatures upon the torsional impact toughness and hardness of *Hampden* is shown in Fig. 179 and Table XV.

TABLE XV.—EFFECT OF DRAWING TEMPERATURE ON HARDNESS
Hampden—Pack hardened from 1775°F. in oil—drawn 1 hour '

Drawing temperature	Rockwell hardness	Equivalent scleroscope	Drawing temperature	Rockwell hardness	Equivalent scleroscope
As hardened	C-65/66	94	600°F.	C-59/60	83
200°F	64/66	93	800	58/59	82
300	63/64	90	1000	51/53	70
400	62/63	88	1200	37/39	51

It will be observed that *Hampden* shows **two** toughness peaks—one at 400°F. and the other at 800°F.

To secure maximum hardness and wear resistance with fair toughness, draw at 400°F. To get greater ductility at some sacrifice of hardness, jump directly up to 800°F. There appears to be little gained by drawing *Hampden* anywhere between 425° and 775°F.

Brand Name—*No. 484*
Matched Set Name—AIR-HARD

Type Analysis:

Carbon................	1.00%	Chromium...............	5.00%
Manganese...............	.70	Molybdenum.............	1.00
Silicon.................	.20	Vanadium...............	.20

PROPERTIES

Description.—*No. 484* is an air-hardening steel capable of hardening throughout in heavy sections. It has been added to the Matched Set as a running mate to *Stentor* steel for those applications in which the sections are too heavy to harden in *Stentor*, and those involving extreme accuracy of size and extreme hazards in hardening. It has a good balance between hardness and toughness. *No. 484* is made from billets which are 100% disc inspected.

Deformation in Hardening. *No. 484* has excellent nondeforming qualities when hardened in air from the recommended temperature of 1725° to 1775°F., and properly drawn. Its average behavior is illustrated by the chart in Fig. 180.

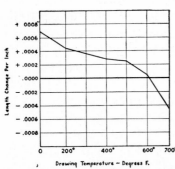

FIG. 180.—Size change of *No. 484*. ¾″ round—air treated from 1750°F.

As indicated, a piece 1″ long will expand about .0007″ when hardened, but when drawn at 400°F., will return to within .0003″ of its original length.

Decarburization.—If hardened in an open furnace *No. 484* may develop a slight soft skin due to the high temperature required in hardening. To avoid this, if controlled atmosphere furnaces are not available, pack hardening is recommended.

Machinability.—*No. 484* does not machine as easily as *Stentor*, but somewhat easier than annealed high speed steel.

Uses of *No. 484*.—Following the rule of the Matched Diagram, use *No. 484* in place of *Stentor* (OIL-HARD) when you want extreme accuracy and safety in hardening, and when the sections are heavy.

Typical uses for *No. 484* include:

Large blanking dies	Trimming dies
Thread roller dies	Forming dies
Long punches	Precision tools
Rolls	Gauges
Master hubs	Coining dies

NOTE: For specific recommendations see the Tool Steel Selector Chart in Chapter 9.

When to Switch from *No. 484*.—If you find you need greater wear resistance, and can do with a little less toughness, use *No. 610* (AIR-WEAR).

If you want greater toughness, and can spare some wear resistance, or if you need even greater hardening penetration than is possible in *No. 484*, use *Vega* (AIR-TOUGH).

If conditions are such that you do not want to harden from the high temperature required for *No. 484*, or if atmosphere controlled furnaces are not available, and you do not want to pack harden, use *Vega*.

If you do not need the extreme accuracy of *No. 484*, and the sections are not heavy, use *Stentor* (OIL-HARD).

THE HEAT TREATMENT OF *No. 484*

To Forge.—*No. 484* forges very much like high speed steel. Heat uniformly to a temperature between 1950° and 2050°F. and forge. Do not continue forging below 1700°F. but reheat as often as necessary. Small, simple forgings can be cooled slowly in lime, but the best practice for large forgings is to place them in a furnace heated to about 1550°F., soak uniformly at this heat, then shut off the heat and cool the job slowly in the furnace. This is *not* an anneal, and after the forging is cold it must be annealed as below.

To Normalize.—Normalizing is not recommended and is not necessary after furnace cooling as described above.

To Anneal.—Pack in clean cast iron borings, heat uniformly to 1550°F. to 1600°F., and cool slowly in the furnace. Average Brinell hardness 223.

To relieve machining strains for greater accuracy in hardening—first, rough machine, then anneal **below the critical** (from 1250°/1300°F.) and cool slowly—then finish machine.

To Harden.—Pack in clean cast iron borings, heat uniformly to 1725°F. to 1775°F., remove tool from pack and cool in still air.

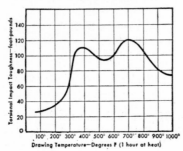

FIG. 181.—Effect of drawing temperature on the toughness of *No. 484* air hardened.

In atmosphere controlled furnaces a highly reducing atmosphere will produce results comparable with pack hardening. Neutral salt baths are also well suited for heating of tools for hardening.

HELPFUL HINT: To prevent the cast iron chips from sticking to the tool, wrap the tool in heavy brown wrapping paper before placing it in the pack. The paper will char and practically disappear when the heated tool is removed for quenching—but in the meantime, it will keep the cast iron chips from adhering to the surface of the tool.

NOTE: A cylindrical pipe packed with cast iron borings requires about 30 minutes per inch of diameter to heat to 1775°F. if the furnace is steadily maintained at heat, and the pack is allowed to heat "naturally."

To Draw.—The effect of different drawing temperatures on the torsional impact toughness and hardness of *No. 484* is shown in Fig. 181 and Table XVI.

TABLE XVI.—EFFECT OF DRAWING TEMPERATURE ON *No. 484*
Pack hardened from 1775°F. (Drawn 1 hour at heat)

Drawing temperature	Rockwell hardness	Equivalent scleroscope	Drawing temperature	Rockwell hardness	Equivalent scleroscope
As hardened	C-63/64	90	600°F.	57/59	78
300°F.	63/64	90	**700**	**57/59**	**78**
350	61/63	88	800	57/59	78
400	**60/62**	**85**	900	57/59	78
450	59/61	83	1000	56/58	76
500	58/60	82			

The best combination of hardness and toughness is obtained by drawing *No. 484* at 400°F. For greater toughness with some sacrifice of hardness, draw at 700°F.

Brand Name—*VEGA*
Matched Set Name—AIR-TOUGH

Type Analysis:

Carbon.. .70%
Manganese.. 2.00
Silicon.. .30
Chromium... 1.00
Molybdenum.. 1.35

PROPERTIES

Description.—Tool makers have long expressed the desire for a non-deforming die steel that would combine the deep hardening characteristics of air-hardening steels with the simplicity of low temperature heat treatment possible in many oil-hardening steels.

Vega is a new type of air-hardening steel developed in the Carpenter laboratories to meet this need. It was found that the hardenability of the manganese-chromium-molybdenum steels is greatly affected by carbon content. Hardenability will increase as the carbon is increased to about .70%. Above this carbon content hardenability, or hardening penetration, again tends to drop off. The analysis of *Vega*

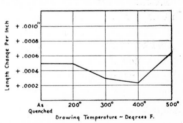

FIG. 182.—Size change of *Vega*. ¾″ round—air treated from 1550°F.

has been so designed that maximum hardenability and toughness are obtained with minimum total percentage of alloys.

Vega is made from billets that are 100% acid disc inspected.

Deformation in Hardening.—*Vega* is outstanding in its non-deforming properties. Its average behavior is shown in Fig. 182. It will be seen that the minimum size change occurs at a drawing temperature of 300° to 400°F. A piece 1″ long will expand about .0005″ when hardened, but when drawn at 400°F, will return to within .0003″ of its original length.

Decarburization.—On account of its relatively low hardening temperature, *Vega* has very little tendency to decarburize. If hardening instructions are followed and proper atmospheres used, the tools should be full-hard right out to the surface.

Machinability.—Because it contains relatively small percentages of the hard-to-machine alloys, *Vega* is one of the easiest air-hardening steels to machine. It will machine much easier than high speed or high carbon, high chromium tool steels.

Uses of *Vega*.—Use *Vega* in place of *R. D. S.* whenever the ultimate in freedom of size change is required, or when the sections are very large. Some of its recommended uses are:

Large blanking dies	Rim rolls
Large forming dies	Master hubs
Trimming dies	Shear blades
Notching dies	Precision tools
Feed fingers	Spindles
Heavy duty punches	Bending tools
Coining dies	Mandrels
Retaining rings	Stripper plates

NOTE: For specific recommendations see the Tool Steel Selector Chart in Chapter 9.

When to Switch from *Vega*.—If extreme accuracy in hardening is not necessary, and if the sections are not extremely heavy, there is no need for *Vega*—use *R. D. S.* (OIL-TOUGH).

If you need slightly higher hardness, and can sacrifice some toughness, use *No. 484* (AIR-HARD).

THE HEAT TREATMENT OF *Vega*

To Forge.—Forge from a temperature of about 2025°F. The finished forgings should be furnace cooled if equipment is available; otherwise bury in dry lime or ashes.

To Normalize.—Normalizing is not recommended for this steel.

To Anneal.—Pack in a suitable container with clean cast iron borings, heat uniformly to 1350°/1375°F. and cool *very slowly* in the furnace (not faster than 20°F. per hour). Resulting Brinell hardness 241 maximum.

To relieve machining strains for greater accuracy in hardening—first, rough machine, then anneal **below the critical** (from 1200°/1250°F.) and cool slowly—then finish machine.

To Harden.—Heat the furnace to a temperature of 1525°F. to 1600°F. depending upon the size of the tool. Adjust the atmosphere so that it is definitely oxidizing. Excess oxygen of 2% to 3% is preferred. Use the wood block test described on page 456. Place the cold tool— without preheating—in the hot furnace and let it heat "naturally" until it uniformly matches the color of the thermocouple in the furnace. Soak for twenty minutes at temperature, and an additional five minutes per inch of thickness, then remove from the furnace and cool in a free circulating air. Sections up to approximately 4″ square will harden to about C-61/63 Rockwell. Sections 8″ square can be hardened as high as C-60 Rockwell. Neutral salt baths can also be used for heating for hardening.

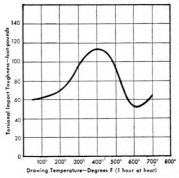

Fig. 183.—Effect of drawing temperature on the toughness of *Vega*—air hardened at 1550°F.

To Draw.—The effect of different drawing temperatures on the torsional impact toughness and hardness of *Vega* is shown in Fig. 183 and Table XVII. The best combination of hardness and toughness is obtained by drawing *Vega* at about 350°F.

TABLE XVII.—Effect of Drawing Temperature on *Vega*
Air hardened at 1550°F. in a 4″ square section.   (Drawn 1 hour at heat)

Drawing temperature	Rockwell hardness	Equivalent scleroscope	Drawing temperature	Rockwell hardness	Equivalent scleroscope
As hardened	C-61/62	87	600°F.	C-55/56	79
200°F.	61/62	87	700	54/55	76
300	60/61	86	800	52/53	73
350	**59/60**	**85**	900	50/51	71
400	58/59	82	1000	48/49	66
500	56/57	82			

Brand Name—*No. 610*
Matched Set Name—AIR-WEAR

Type Analysis:

Carbon	1.50%
Manganese	.30
Silicon	.30
Chromium	12.00
Molybdenum	.80
Vanadium	.90

PROPERTIES

Description.—*No. 610* is an air-hardening, high carbon, high chromium tool steel having extremely high wear resisting properties. Like the other members of the Air-Hardening Matched Set, it is very deep hardening, and will be practically free from size change after proper treatment. The high percentage of chromium gives it mild corrosion resisting properties in the hardened condition.

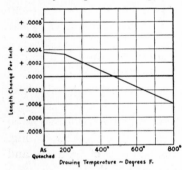

FIG. 184.—Size change of *No. 610*. ¾" round—pack hardened and air cooled from 1850°F.

Deformation in Hardening. The non-deforming properties of *No. 610* are illustrated in Fig. 184. Hardened in air from 1825° to 1875°F. and drawn anywhere between 400° and 700°F., *No. 610* will have minimum size change. If overheated during hardening (1900°F. or higher), it will shrink and become slightly non-magnetic.

Decarburization.—If hardened in an open furnace *No. 610* may acquire a slight soft skin as a result of the high hardening temperature. To avoid this, and also to minimize the formation of scale in treating, properly controlled furnace atmospheres, or pack hardening, are recommended.

Machinability.—Due to its high carbon and chromium contents *No. 610* cannot be annealed softer than about 217 to 241 Brinell. It will consequently machine about the same as annealed high speed steel.

Uses of *No. 610*.—The uses of *No. 610* are much the same as those of *Hampden* (OIL-WEAR), and the two steels can be used interchangeably for most purposes. *Hampden,* however, has the advantage of greater hardness, which may be a governing factor in its selection for certain tools. On the other hand the lower hardness of *No. 610* is accompanied by somewhat greater toughness. Typical applications of *No. 610* are:

Blanking dies	Coining dies	Beading rolls
Forming dies	Forming rolls	Intricate punches
Thread rolling dies	Edging rolls	Extrusion dies
Slitting cutters	Master tools	Drawing dies
Long punches		

NOTE: For specific recommendations see the Tool Steel Selector Chart in Chapter 9.

When to Switch from *No. 610*.—If you do not need the wear resistance of *No. 610*, but still need the hardening accuracy and deep penetration of an air-hardening steel, switch to *No. 484* (AIR-HARD).

If the tool requires slightly greater hardness, and if oil quenching is not objectionable, use *Hampden* (OIL-WEAR).

THE HEAT TREATMENT OF *No. 610*

To Forge.—*No. 610* forges very much like high speed steel. Heat uniformly to a temperature between 1925° and 2000°F. and forge. Do not continue forging below 1700°F. but reheat as often as necessary. Small, simple forgings can be cooled slowly in lime, but the best practice for large forgings is to place them in a furnace heated to about 1550°F., soak uniformly at this temperature, then shut off the heat and cool the job slowly in the furnace. This is *not* an anneal, and after the forging is cold, it must be annealed as below.

To Normalize.—Normalizing is not recommended and is not necessary after furnace cooling as described above.

To Anneal.—Pack in a suitable container with clean cast iron borings, heat uniformly to 1550° to 1600°F., and cool *very slowly* in the furnace. Resulting Brinell hardness 241 maximum.

To relieve machining strains for greater accuracy in hardening—first, rough machine, then anneal **below the critical** (from 1250°/1300°F.) and cool slowly—then finish machine.

To Harden.—Table XVIII shows the effect of different hardening temperatures on the hardness of *No. 610*.

TABLE XVIII.—*No. 610*—EFFECT OF HARDENING TEMPERATURE ON HARDNESS

Air cooled from	Rockwell hardness	Air cooled from	Rockwell hardness
1650°F.	C-58/60	1850°F.	C-62/63
1700	60/61	1950	60/62
1750	61/62	2050	48/49
1800	62/63		

Maximum hardness is secured between 1825° and 1875°F. *No. 610* holds size best when hardened within this range. If overheated, *No. 610*, like *Hampden*, will become softer and will shrink badly. *Don't overheat it.*

The recommended procedure is to pack the tools in clean cast iron borings from 1825° to 1875°F., remove tools from the pack and cool in air. A blast is not necessary. In atmosphere controlled furnaces a highly reducing atmosphere will produce results comparable with pack hardening. Neutral salt baths are also well suited for heating of *No. 610* tools for hardening.

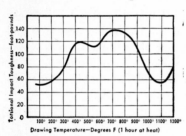

FIG. 185.—Effect of drawing temperature on toughness of *No. 610*— pack hardened 1850°F.—cooled in air.

HELPFUL HINT: To prevent the cast iron chips from sticking to the tool, wrap the tool in heavy brown wrapping paper before placing it in the pack. The paper will char and practically disappear when the heated tool is removed for quenching—but in the meantime, it will keep the cast iron chips from adhering to the surface of the tool.

NOTE: A cylindrical pipe packed with clean cast iron borings requires about 25 minutes per inch of diameter to heat to 1850°F. if the furnace is steadily maintained at heat, and the pack is allowed to heat "naturally."

To Draw.—The effects of different drawing temperatures upon the torsional impact toughness and hardness of *No. 610* are shown in Fig. 185 and Table XIX.

It will be seen that *No. 610*, like *Hampden*, has two toughness peaks, one at 450°F. and the other at 700°F. For the best combination of toughness and hardness draw *No. 610* at 450°F. While this is the best drawing temperature for practically all purposes, greater ductility can be secured by drawing at 700°F. with some sacrifice of hardness.

TABLE XIX.—EFFECT OF DRAWING TEMPERATURE ON HARDNESS OF *No. 610* Pack Hardened from 1850°F. in air. (Drawn 1 hour)

Drawing temperature	Rockwell hardness	Equivalent scleroscope	Drawing temperature	Rockwell hardness	Equivalent scleroscope
As hardened	C-62/63	88	800°F.	C-56/57	77
200°F.	61/62	86	900	58/59	82
400	59/60	83	1000	59/60	83
450	**59/60**	**83**	1100	57/58	80
550	56/57	77	1200	44/45	58
700	**55/56**	**76**			

The hardness curve for *No. 610* shows the same "kickback" or secondary hardening that we find in high speed steel. In *No. 610* this occurs at 1000°F., and if by accident tools have been over-heated in hardening, (causing shrinkage and loss of hardness), they may be salvaged by drawing them at 1000°F. They will regain some of their lost hardness, and will expand close to their former size.

Brand Name—*STAR-ZENITH*—HIGH-SPEED STEEL
Matched Set Name—RED-WEAR

Type Analysis:

Carbon	.72%	Chromium	4.00%
Manganese	.25	Tungsten	18.25
Silicon	.20	Vanadium	1.15

PROPERTIES

Description.—*Star-Zenith* is an 18-4-1 type of high speed steel, that is—18% tungsten, 4% chromium, 1% vanadium. It is manufactured under conditions which insure superior results in service. Close control of chemical limits permits a constant duplication of heat treating results that would not otherwise be possible. Furthermore, *Star-Zenith* is manufactured by methods which give it a strong, keen-cutting edge so important in reamers, form tools, broaches, taps and similar tools.

Deformation in Hardening.—*Star-Zenith* holds size very accurately in hardening. For example, a 1″ cube will lose about .0005″ in hardening from 2300° to 2400°F., and will lose a like amount upon being drawn to 1050° to 1100°F. The hardened and drawn piece will run about .001″ smaller than the annealed block. Cutters and form tools will open up slightly in the hole and shrink slightly on the O. D.

Decarburization.—*Star-Zenith* is particularly free from the tendency to decarburize in hardening. Soft skin is unknown to hardeners who use ordinary care in handling this steel.

Machinability.—The machinability of high speed steel is too well known to require comment. *Star-Zenith* is very carefully and thoroughly annealed to produce the best machinability possible in this type of steel.

Uses of *Star-Zenith*.—It is *Star-Zenith's* job to deliver maximum hardness and wear resistance for tools that get hotter than about 300°F. in service. It does not attempt to compete with tungsten carbide tools for speed, but for cutting steel, cutting in-and-out, and for producing a fine finish, it is frequently superior to either cemented carbide or cobalt high speed steel.

Star-Zenith is the red-hard running mate of *K-W* (water-wear). There is no more wear resisting steel in existence than *K-W*, but it will lose its hardness and efficiency if heated above about 300°F. in service. The rule of the Matched Diagram is to go **east** for red-hardness and here you find *Star-Zenith*.

Star-Zenith is the **only** steel on the Matched Diagram suitable for making metal cutting tools that become hot in service. It is recommended for:

Lathe tools	Broaches	Gear cutters
Planer tools	Milling cutters	Wood knives
Drills	Form cutters	Nut punches
Taps	Thread chasers	Rolls
Reamers	End mills	

NOTE: For specific recommendations see the Tool Steel Selector Chart in Chapter 9.

As the most wear resisting member of the Red-Hard Matched Set, *Star-Zenith* plays a small part in other types of hot working tools. When drawn at temperatures between 1200° and 1400°F., it has some ductility and is useful for certain hot working tools that have flat or convex working surfaces, such as hot shear blades, hot punches, grading roll inserts, flat coining dies, etc. Tools of this nature made of *Star-Zenith* should not be water-cooled during service.

When to Switch from *Star-Zenith*.—If the tool does **not** become heated in service—and red-hardness is not necessary—*K-W*, *Hampden* or *No. 610* will usually do the job more efficiently or more economically.

If greater toughness is needed than can be secured in *Star-Zenith* by drawing it down to C-55 Rockwell, switch to *T-K* (RED-HARD).

THE HEAT TREATMENT OF *Star-Zenith*

To Forge.—Heat **slowly** and **uniformly** to 1950°/2050°F. and forge. Do not work the steel below 1600°F. but reheat as often as necessary. Small, simple forgings can be cooled slowly in lime, but the best practice for large forgings is to place them in a furnace heated to about 1400°/1450°F., soak uniformly at this heat, then shut off the heat and cool the job slowly in the furnace. This is **not** an anneal, and when cold the forging must be annealed as below.

Normalizing.—Normalizing is not recommended.

To Anneal.—Pack in a suitable container with clean cast iron borings, heat uniformly to 1550° to 1600°F., and cool **very** slowly in the furnace. Brinell hardness 241 maximum.

To relieve machining strains for greater accuracy in hardening—first, rough machine, then anneal **below the critical** (from 1250°/1300°F.) and cool slowly—then finish machine.

To Harden.—Preheat slowly and uniformly to 1500° to 1600°F. in a **neutral** atmosphere and soak a reasonable time to heat the section throughout. Transfer to a superheating furnace with a strongly **reducing** atmosphere at 2300° to 2400°F., and quench in oil. Small sizes or delicate sections, or large hot-work dies may be hardened by cooling in still air. Neutral salt baths can also be used for hardening *Star-Zenith*.

The average hardness values to be secured at various hardening temperatures are given in Table XX.

Be sure to quench *Star-Zenith* tools **below** 200°F. before drawing them.

To Draw.—In this book "one hour draw" means one hour **soak** at temperature. Be sure to allow sufficient time for the tool to reach the proper temperature (see page 492) and then start counting time.

It will be noted that Torsion Impact curves are not included for any of the three Red-Hard Steels. These steels are intended for use at elevated temperatures, and thus far our toughness tests have all been made at room temperature. Under these circumstances any such toughness data must be used with certain reservations. Since *Star-Zenith* is used primarily for cutting purposes in which edge toughness is important, toughness tests are probably more significant on this steel than they are in connection with the other two members of the Red-Hard Set. Consequently this subject of room temperature toughness of *Star-Zenith* has been covered in some detail in Chapter 13.

Most metal cutting tools made of *Star-Zenith* High Speed Steel should be drawn at 1025° to 1100°F.

The effect of various hardening and drawing temperatures on the Rockwell hardness of *Star-Zenith* is given in Table XX.

To secure greater toughness on *Star-Zenith* cutting tools, the torsion impact data suggest a draw for 8 hours at 900°F. This will yield about C-64 Rockwell hardness with a greater measured toughness (at room temperature) than a two hour draw at 1050° to 1100°F.

Many tool makers have found it good practice to give high speed tools a **double** draw. The tools are drawn for two hours at 1050°F., cooled back to room temperature, then redrawn for two hours more at a slightly lower temperature (1000° to 1025°F.). This procedure increases the toughness.

Star-Zenith responds well to a cyanide treatment after grinding. The finished tools are heated to 950° to 1000°F. in a cyanide bath for 30 minutes to one hour in order to produce maximum hardness on the ground surface. For some types of service, this treatment has greatly increased tool life.

Hot forming tools made of *Star-Zenith* should be drawn to about C-55 Rockwell so that they will have a slight degree of ductility. If this is not tough enough, switch to *T-K* (RED-HARD) which hardens to about C-55 Rockwell and will be much tougher than the *Star-Zenith* at this hardness. Such hot forming tools,

TABLE XX.—EFFECT OF HARDENING AND DRAWING TEMPERATURES ON
THE HARDNESS OF *Star-Zenith*
(Average Values—Rockwell C Scale)

Drawing temperature two hours at heat	Hardening temperature—quenched in oil				
	2100°F.	2200°F.	2300°F.	2350°F.	2400°F.
As hardened	C-61	C-63	C-65	C-65	C-64
100°F.	61	63.5	65	65	64
200°F.	61	64	65	65	64
300°F.	61	64	64	64	63
400°F.	60.5	63	64	64	63
500°F.	59	61.5	62	63	62
600°F.	58	60	61	62	62
700°F.	58	60	61	62	62
800°F.	58	60	61	62	62
900°F.	58	60	62	62.5	62
1000°F.	58	60	63	64	64
1050°F.	58	60	63	64	64
1100°F.	57	60	61	62	63
1200°F.	50	53	56	57	59
1300°F.	41	43	44	45	49

when made of *Star-Zenith* are usually air-hardened, and from a lower temperature than cutting tools—namely 2100° to 2300°F.

TREATED TOOL HOLDER BITS

Star-Zenith high speed steel is furnished in the form of standard tool-holder bits with 30 degree angle ends. Each piece is hardened, ready to be ground and put to work. The cutting edge should be ground at least $\frac{1}{64}''$ below the surface of the bit.

These are not "trick" bits; they are not made to cut at abnormally fast speeds or high temperature. They combine **good** red-hardness, **good** toughness and the ability to hold a **keen** edge for finishing. They are ideal tool bits for general shop use— cutting all kinds of metal—on all kinds of operations—either roughing or finishing.

Star-Zenith tool bits are furnished from stock in 5-pound boxes; one size or assorted sizes in a box.

STANDARD SIZES, READY TO SHIP

$\frac{1}{4}$ inch square	$2\frac{1}{2}$ inches long
$\frac{5}{16}$ " "	$2\frac{1}{2}$ " "
$\frac{3}{8}$ " "	3 " "
$\frac{7}{16}$ " "	$3\frac{1}{2}$ " "
$\frac{1}{2}$ " "	4 " "
$\frac{5}{8}$ " "	$4\frac{1}{2}$ " "
$\frac{3}{4}$ " "	5 " "
$\frac{7}{8}$ " "	6 " "
1 " "	7 " "

HIGH SPEED DRILL ROD

Star-Zenith High Speed Drill Rod is stocked in 3-foot lengths in standard sizes. Special lengths, sizes or finishes should be submitted for quotations.

Brand Name—*SPEED STAR*
Matched Set Name—RED-WEAR

Type Analysis:

Carbon	.82%
Manganese	.25
Silicon	.25
Chromium	4.25
Molybdenum	5.00
Tungsten	6.25
Vanadium	1.90

Although *Speed Star* does not appear on the Matched Set Diagram, this steel is included here because of its wide acceptance for all-around high speed cutting tools. For many of these, *Speed Star*, when properly treated, may be used interchangeably with *Star-Zenith*, and will perform equally well.

PROPERTIES

Description.—*Speed Star* is a fine grained "Moly" high speed steel, manufactured under the same close control as *Star-Zenith*. It has certain advantages over *Star-Zenith*, some of which are lower cost, less weight per cubic inch, lower hardening temperature and somewhat easier machining.

Deformation in Hardening.—*Speed Star* changes size only slightly on hardening. A 1″ cube will lose about .0005″ in hardening at 2225°F., and will lose a like amount when drawn at 1050°F. Cutters and form tools will open up slightly in the hole, and shrink slightly on the O. D.

Decarburization.—While it is more susceptible to decarburization in hardening than *Star-Zenith*, means of preventing this are now well known, and if proper control of atmosphere is maintained, *Speed Star* will present no difficulty with decarburization.

Machinability.—*Speed Star* is carefully annealed to produce the best machinability possible in this type of steel. It will machine somewhat easier than *Star-Zenith*.

Uses of Speed Star.—The uses of *Speed Star* parallel those of *Star-Zenith* and include such tools as:

Lathe tools	Milling cutters
Planer tools	Form cutters
Drills	Thread chasers
Taps	End mills
Reamers	Gear cutters
Broaches	Wood knives

Note: For specific recommendations see the Tool Steel Selector Chart in Chapter 9.

When to Switch from *Speed Star*.—If the tool does *not* become heated in service—and red-hardness is not necessary—*K-W* (water-wear) or *Hampden* (oil-wear) will usually do the job more economically.

If greater toughness is needed than is possible with *Speed Star* by drawing it down to C-55 Rockwell, switch to *T-K* (red-hard).

The Heat Treatment of *Speed Star*

To Forge.—Preheat very slowly to 1500°/1600°F., then increase the furnace temperature to full heat of 1950°/2050°F. Do not forge under 1800°F., but reheat as often as necessary. Small simple forgings may be cooled slowly in lime or ashes, but the best practice for large forgings is to place them in a furnace heated to about 1400°/1450°F., soak uniformly at this heat, then shut off the heat and let the forgings cool in the furnace.

This, incidentally, is not an anneal, and when the forgings are cool they should be properly annealed.

To Normalize.—Normalizing is not recommended.

To Anneal.—Pack in a suitable container with clean cast iron borings, heat uniformly to 1550°/1600°F. and cool slowly in the furnace. Average Brinell hardness 235.

To relieve machining strains for greater accuracy in hardening—first, rough machine, then anneal **below the critical** (from 1250°/1300°F.) and cool slowly—then finish machine.

To Harden.—Preheat to 1475°/1500°F. with a 5%/8% CO reducing atmosphere. Then transfer to a superheating furnace with a temperature maintained at 2150°/2275°F. and a reducing atmosphere of 9%/12% CO. Exercising the usual control of temperature and atmosphere there should be no difficulty with decarburization. **These atmospheres have been successful in producing a clean surface free from soft skin and showing a Rockwell hardness of C-64/65.**

Best results will be obtained by using standard equipment for analyzing the furnace atmosphere—however, if such equipment is not available, fairly close control of the recommended atmospheres can be obtained in a gas-fired furnace by observing the flame in the furnace through the peep hole.

In the preheating furnace adjust your fuel mixture until you see a flame rolling *in the furnace*. This is sometimes called a "lazy flame."

In the superheating furnace adjust your fuel mixture until you get a half blue, half yellow flame at *the port holes*, possibly slightly more yellow than blue.

Neutral salt baths can also be used for hardening *Speed Star*.

Quench in oil, and be sure that tools are cooled below 200°F. before drawing (cool enough to hold in your hand). Small sizes, that is under about 1″ diameter, or delicate sections may be hardened by cooling in still air.

To Draw.—In this book "one hour draw" means one hour **soak** at temperature. Be sure to allow sufficient time for the tool to reach the proper temperature (see page 492) and then start counting time. Toughness data determined at room temperature are not included here, but are discussed in Chapter 13.

Tools should be drawn immediately after the completion of the quench. For best results with most tools a range of 1025° to 1050°F. is recommended.

The effect of various hardening and drawing temperatures on the Rockwell hardness of *Speed Star* is given in Table XXI.

TABLE XXI.—EFFECT OF HARDENING AND DRAWING TEMPERATURE ON THE HARDNESS OF *Speed Star*
(Average Values—Rockwell C Scale)

Drawing temperature two hours at heat	Hardening temperature quenched in oil		
	2150°F.	2200°F.	2275°F.
As Hardened	C-65	C-65	C-64
300°F.	64	65	64
400	63	63	62
500	61	61	61
600	61	61	61
700	61	61	61
800	61	62	62
900	62	63	62
950	63	64	64
1000	64	65	65
1050	64	65	65
1100	63	64	64
1150	61	62	62

To secure greater toughness on *Speed Star*, the torsion impact data suggest a draw for about 8 hours, at 800°/900°F.

Many tool makers have found it good practice to give high speed tools a **double** draw. The tools are drawn for two hours at 1050°F., cooled back to room temperature, then redrawn for two hours more at a slightly lower temperature (1000° to 1025°F.) This procedure increases the toughness.

TREATED TOOL HOLDER BITS

Speed Star high speed steel is furnished in the form of standard tool holder bits with 30-degree angle ends. Each piece is hardened, ready to be ground and put to work. The cutting edges should be ground at least $1/64''$ below the surface of the bit.

Speed Star tool bits are furnished from stock in 5 lb. boxes; one size or assorted sizes in a box.

STANDARD SIZES, READY TO SHIP

$1/4''$ square	$2\frac{1}{2}''$ long	$7/16''$ square	$3\frac{1}{2}''$ long	$3/4''$ square	$5''$ long
$5/16''$ "	$2\frac{1}{2}''$ "	$1/2''$ "	$4''$ "	$7/8''$ "	$6''$ "
$3/8''$ "	$3''$ "	$5/8''$ "	$4\frac{1}{2}''$ "	$1''$ "	$7''$ "

Brand Name—*T-K*
Matched Set Name—RED-HARD

Type Analysis:

Carbon.. .35%
Manganese.. .30
Silicon.. .30
Chromium... 3.50
Tungsten... 9.00
Vanadium... .40

PROPERTIES

Description.—In the first edition of "Tool Steel Simplified," *D. Y. O.* occupied the RED-HARD diamond in the Matched Set. In line with the principle set forth in the preface of this book, an improved steel, *T-K*, has now been assigned to this diamond. *T-K* has the advantages of both greater hardness and greater toughness, and of more universal application to hot work tools.

T-K is a hot work steel for use in applications where high compressive strength, red-hardness and wear resistance at elevated temperatures are required. The relatively low carbon serves to balance these properties with sufficient toughness to make a good general purpose hot working die steel.

Deformation in Hardening.—*T-K* can be hardened in oil or air, and in either case will hold size and shape very accurately. No difficulty need be anticipated in this direction in hot working tools for which this steel is used.

Decarburization.—By following the recommended procedure in heat treating, *T-K* can be hardened with a smooth, clean surface and a minimum of decarburization.

Machinability.—*T-K* will machine easier than annealed high speed steel.

Cooling in Service.—Because *T-K* is a tungsten bearing hot work steel, water cooling in service is not recommended. Air cooling may be employed without danger of cracking or heat checking.

Uses of *T-K*.—The principal field for this steel is in hot compression tools. It does not become hard enough for metal cutting tools—and it lacks the extreme toughness needed in tools subjected to sharp hammer blows. It is particularly adapted to tools requiring high red-hardness, good resistance to abrasion and wear, and fair toughness. Some typical examples are:

Hot shear blades	Bending dies
Hot gripper dies	Punch and die inserts
Dummy blocks	Hot compression tools not subject
Hot extrusion dies	to sharp hammer blows
Die casting dies	Hot punches for drawing or pierc-
Forging dies	ing

NOTE: For specific recommendations see the Tool Steel Selector Chart in Chapter 9.

When to Switch from *T-K*.—If the tools do not become heated over 300°F. in service, some steel from the Cold Working Matched Set will probably serve better.

If greater red-hardness and wear resistance are needed, switch to *Star-Zenith* or *Speed Star* (RED-WEAR). Either of these can be drawn back in order to meet the hardness of *T-K*.

If greater toughness is needed, and if this cannot successfully be obtained at a higher drawing temperature without softening the *T-K* too much, switch to *No. 883* (RED-TOUGH). Also if greater freedom from heat checking is essential, use *No. 883*.

THE HEAT TREATMENT OF *T-K*

To Forge.—Heat slowly and uniformly to a temperature between 2000° and 2050°F. and forge. Do not work the steel below 1600°F., but reheat as often as necessary. Small, simple forgings may be cooled slowly in line, but the best practice for large forgings is to place them in a furnace heated to about 1550°F., soak uniformly at this temperature, then shut off the heat and cool the job slowly in the furnace. This is *not* an anneal, and when the forging is cool it must be annealed as below.

To Normalize.—Normalizing is not recommended.

To Anneal.—Pack in a suitable container with clean cast iron borings, heat uniformly to 1550°/1600°F. and cool very slowly in the furnace. Resulting annealed hardness 228 Brinell maximum.

To relieve machining strains for greater accuracy in hardening—first, rough machine, then anneal **below the critical** (from 1250°/1300°F.) and cool slowly—then finish machine.

To Harden.—*T-K* tools should first be preheated uniformly to 1500°/1550°F. and thoroughly soaked at this temperature until they are well heated throughout. After preheating, transfer

the tools to a superheating furnace at 2150°/2200°F.   Use a 6%
to 12% CO reducing furnace atmosphere.   When heated
uniformly to this temperature, quench in air or oil.   Neutral salt
baths can also be used for heating for hardening.

To Draw.—All *T-K* tools should be drawn at least one hour.
Be sure to allow sufficient time for the tool to reach the proper
temperature before starting to count time.

The effect of different drawing temperatures on the hardness
of *T-K* is shown in Table XXII.

TABLE XXII.—EFFECT OF DRAWING TEMPERATURES ON HARDNESS OF *T-K*
Hardened from 2175°F.
Drawn one hour at heat

Drawing temperature	Rockwell hardness	Drawing temperature	Rockwell hardness
As hardened	C-52/54	1100°F.	C-51/53
800°F.	52/54	1150	51/52
900	52/54	1200	46/48
950	53/54	1250	41/42
1000	54/55	1300	37/38
1050	54/55		

NOTE: These hardness tests were made on a section measuring $1\frac{1}{4}''$
square $\times$ 6'' long.   Hardness values will vary slightly with the mass of
the section.

Some tool makers have found it good practice to double draw
T-K hot work tools.

It should be observed that *T-K* tools can be left harder for any
given service if the forger will take the time to warm the tools
thoroughly before putting them to work.   Cold dies are likely to
break on the first piece forged but it is a pity to require the
hardener to draw the tools back tough enough to withstand these
first few blows, thus sacrificing the hardness and wear resistance
that will be urgently needed when the dies have warmed up in use.

Hot work tools should never be drawn at a temperature lower
than the working temperature at which they will be used.

Red-Hardness of *T-K*.—Since the hot work steels are used at
elevated temperatures, it is helpful to know the hardness at
various temperatures, following a standard heat treatment.
Table XXIII shows hot Brinell hardnesses at various temperatures determined by the mutual indentation method described
in Chapter 11.

TABLE XXIII.—BRINELL HARDNESS OF *T-K* AT VARIOUS TEMPERATURES
ON SPECIMENS OIL TREATED AT 2175°F. AND DRAWN AT 1000°F.
TO A HARDNESS OF C-54 ROCKWELL

Testing temperature	Hot Brinell number
800°F.	494
850	492
900	488
950	480
1000	467
1050	430
1100	383
1150	329
1200	272
1250	214
1300	160

Brand Name—*NO. 883*
Matched Set Name—RED-TOUGH

Type Analysis:

Carbon	.40%
Manganese	.35
Silicon	1.10
Chromium	5.00
Vanadium	.90
Molybdenum	1.35

PROPERTIES

Description.—In the first edition of "Tool Steel Simplified," *Excelo* occupied the RED-TOUGH diamond in the Matched Set. In line with the principle set forth in the preface of this book, an improved steel, *No. 883*, has now been assigned to this diamond. *No. 883* has the advantage of greater red-hardness, and is applicable to a wider field of uses than the previous steel assigned to this diamond.

No. 883 is a 5.00% chromium hot work steel designed particularly for applications requiring extreme toughness combined with good red-hardness. It will give an extra margin of safety in tools subject to heavy hammer blows, and in those tools containing deep recesses or sharp corners.

Deformation in Hardening.—Because *No. 883* will harden in either oil or air, it holds size and shape exceptionally well.

Decarburization.—With reasonable care in heat treating, *No. 883* can be hardened free from decarburization.

Machinability.—*No. 883* machines decidedly better than annealed high speed steel.

NOTE: *No. 883* is often supplied already heat treated to a Brinell hardness of 275/325. In this condition it can be machined and used without further heat treatment.

Cooling in Service.—If necessary, hot work tools made from *No. 883* can be water-cooled in service without danger of cracking or heat checking.

Uses of *No. 883*.—*No. 883* is used for hot working tools requiring the greatest possible toughness. Typical applications include:

> Forging dies
> Heavy duty compression tools
> Bulldozer dies
> Hot forging tools with deep recesses or sharp corners
> Die casting dies
> Aluminum extrusion dies
> Bolt dies
> Hot piercing and forming punches
> Vanstoning dies

NOTE: For specific recommendations see the Tool Steel Selector Chart in Chapter 9.

When to Switch from *No. 883*.—If tools do not become hot in service, the use of a red-hard steel is not advised. One of the steels of the Cold Working Matched Set will usually do a satisfactory job.

To obtain greater red-hardness and wear resistance at elevated temperatures at the expense of some freedom from heat checking, change to *T-K* (RED-HARD). This change becomes increasingly necessary as the tool temperature increases.

THE HEAT TREATMENT OF *No. 883*

To Forge.—Heat slowly and uniformly to a temperature between 2000°F. and 2075°F. and forge. Do not work the steel below 1650°F., but reheat as often as necessary. Small, simple forgings may be cooled slowly in lime, but the best practice for large forgings is to place them in a furnace heated to about 1550°F., soak uniformly at this temperature, then shut off the heat and cool the job slowly in the furnace. This is *not* an anneal, and when the forging is cool, it must be annealed as below.

To Normalize.—Normalizing is not recommended and is not necessary after furnace cooling as described above.

To Anneal.—Pack in a suitable container with clean cast iron borings, heat uniformly to 1550/1600°F., and cool *very slowly* in the furnace. Brinell hardness 223 maximum.

To relieve machining strains for greater accuracy in hardening—first, rough machine, then anneal **below the critical** (from 1250°/1300°F.) and cool slowly—then finish machine.

To Harden.—*No. 883* can be hardened without danger of decarburization in controlled atmosphere furnaces—or in other furnaces if the atmosphere is adjusted for 1% to 3% excess oxygen. *No. 883* may be air treated or oil treated. For air treating, heat the furnace to 1850°/1875°F., then place the cold tool right in the hot furnace near the thermocouple. Let the tool heat "naturally" until it uniformly matches the color of the thermocouple, soak an additional five minutes per inch of thickness and cool in air. A blast is not necessary. Neutral salt baths can also be used for heating for hardening.

When oil treating *No. 883* follow the same heating procedure recommended above, but drop the temperature to 1825°/1850°F.

To Draw.—The effect of drawing temperatures on the hardness of *No. 883* is shown in Table XXIV.

TABLE XXIV.—EFFECT OF DRAWING TEMPERATURES ON HARDNESS OF
No. 883
AIR hardened from 1875°F.
OIL hardened from 1850°F.
(Drawn 1 hour at heat)

Drawing temperature	Rockwell hardness oil or air treated	Drawing temperature	Rockwell hardness oil or air treated
As hardened	C-55/56	1100°F.	C-49/50
800°F.	55/56	1150	42/43
900	55/56	1200	39/40
950	55/56	1250	33/34
1000	55/56	1300	29/30
1050	54/55		

NOTE: These hardness tests were made on a section measuring 1⅝" round × 6" long. Hardness values will vary slightly depending upon size of section.

It should be pointed out that practically full quenched hardness is maintained up to a drawing temperature of 950°/1000°F. There is, therefore, no reason to draw *No. 883* lower than this range. For greater toughness draw at higher temperatures. Hot work tools should never be drawn at a temperature lower than the working temperature at which they will be used.

It is important to mention that *No. 883* tools can be left harder for any given service if the forger will take the time to warm the tools thoroughly before putting them to work. Cold dies are likely to break on the first piece forged, but it is a pity to require the hardener to draw the tools back tough enough to withstand these first few blows, thus sacrificing the hardness and wear resistance that will be urgently needed when the dies have warmed up in use.

Red-Hardness of *No. 883*.—Hot Brinell hardnesses at various temperatures determined by the mutual indentation method described in Chapter 11 are given in Table XXV. Test specimens were air quenched from 1875°F., and drawn for one hour at 1050°F. to Rockwell hardness of C-55/56. It is important to note that while the hardness of *No. 883* is actually higher than that of *T-K* at room temperature up to about 800°F., at higher temperatures, where many hot work tools operate, it will be seen that *T-K* is the harder of the two steels.

TABLE XXV.—BRINELL RED-HARDNESS OF *No. 883* AT VARIOUS TEMPERATURES ON SPECIMENS AIR QUENCHED FROM 1875°F., DRAWN ONE HOUR AT 1050°F. TO A HARDNESS OF C-55/56 ROCKWELL

Testing temperature	Hot Brinell number
800°F.	505
850	496
900	480
950	455
1000	428
1050	363
1100	268
1150	192
1200	137
1250	82
1300	46

NOTE: Hot Brinell tests on *No. 883* when oil treated from 1850°F. show practically the same red-hardness values.

CHAPTER 13

HIGH SPEED AND HOT WORK STEELS

Red-Hard Steels.—The steels commonly known as "red-hard steels," which include both high speed and the so-called hot work varieties, differ from other general classes of tool steels in one particular—they have the ability when properly hardened to

Fig. 186.—Uses of Red-Hard Steels. Above, high speed lathe tool. Below, hot forging dies.

develop a high degree of hardness when drawn to a relatively high temperature, and to keep this hardness at high operating temperatures. This one characteristic, however, is sufficient to throw them into an entirely separate field from cold working steels, both in use and heat treatment. Their unique and somewhat spectacular ability to retain hardness at high temperatures adapts them to usages far beyond the capabilities of the other tool steels. The heat treatments necessary to obtain these properties differ greatly from what might be termed orthodox treatments. For these reasons it is desirable to discuss them as a separate group, and therefore the present chapter has been set aside for that purpose.

Necessity for Red-Hard Steels.—In Chapter 6 (page 105) the necessity for such steels was discussed and it was pointed out that certain tools become heated in service beyond temperatures at which ordinary steels would function. Such tools fall under two groups; first, cutting tools in which the cutting edges of the tool become hot as a result of frictional heat; and second, forging or forming tools in which the face or body of the tool is heated by contact with the work (Fig. 186). The first group calls for steels capable of a very high degree of hardness, and the property of maintaining a keen edge at high cutting speeds. Such steels are called "high speed tool steels." The second group calls for steels of great toughness, capable of withstanding the shock of impact in forging, and the repeated and sometimes abrupt, heating and cooling encountered in service. Such steels are commonly referred to as "hot work steels." The present chapter is subdivided to discuss these two groups.

HIGH SPEED TOOL STEELS

The purpose of this section might be summarized by saying that it attempts to present in as clear, concise and practical manner as possible information for the tool maker and hardener to assist them in getting the very best performance from high speed steel. It seems appropriate in introducing this subject to list some typical tools commonly made from high speed steel:

Lathe tools	Milling cutters
Planer tools	Form cutters
Drills	Thread chasers
Taps	End mills
Reamers	Gear cutters
Broaches	Wood knives

In our introduction to this book the four requirements necessary to produce a good tool were stated to be like the links of a chain, rather than the strands of a cable—each being essential to the success of the tool. While all of the four elements, design, tool making, tool steel, and heat treatment, were shown to be equally indispensable, in the present instance we shall assume that the first three have been properly taken care of. We shall therefore comment on the first three only briefly, and concentrate principally on the fourth.

It would be difficult to overemphasize the importance of proper heat treatment of high speed steel. On account of the very character of the high speed hardening operation, however, it has been difficult in the past to study the different variables affecting the finally hardened tool. Consequently much erroneous information on the treatment of high speed steel has found its way into the literature. It is of extreme importance to the hardener to have his information accurate, and with this thought in mind the Carpenter Research Laboratory several years ago set out to study by modern methods all the possible variables in the hardening of high speed steel.[1] The results of this long research form much of the foundation for the information which follows.

Composition.—The first step toward an understanding of good heat treating of high speed steels is to learn something about the steels themselves. Only the two most widely used standardized types of high speed steel will be discussed in detail. These are popularly known as "18-4-1" and "6-6-2" and have the following type compositions:

	Tungsten high speed 18-4-1[1]	Molybdenum high speed 6-6-2[2]
Carbon....................	.72%	.82%
Manganese................	.25	.25
Silicon....................	.20	.25
Chromium................	4.00	4.25
Tungsten.................	18.25	6.25
Vanadium................	1.15	1.90
Molybdenum.............	....	5.00

[1] The figures "18-4-1" refer to the approximate tungsten, chromium and vanadium contents.

[2] The figures "6-6-2" refer to the approximate tungsten, molybdenum and vanadium contents. It will be noted that the composition described here, which is now the most generally adopted, might be more accurately called 6-5-2. However, since this general class of tungsten-molybdenum high speed steels is commonly referred to as "6-6-2," that designation will be adhered to in these pages.

[1] Surface Carbon Chemistry and Grain Size of 18-4-1 High Speed Steel— by Walter A. Schlegel (The Carpenter Steel Company). ASM 1941, Vol. 29, page 541.

Let us dissect these two compositions, and thus learn the reasons for their behavior. We have already been told (Chapter 3) something about the effects of various elements in steel. Tungsten has the effect of producing red-hardness. It does so by forming certain compounds with carbon (carbides) which, when taken in solution in heat treatment, become very stable, and resist being again thrown out of solution by heating to temperatures as high as 1100°F. This stability is obtained, however, only by treating from a very high temperature such as 2350°F. The addition of 18% tungsten along with about .65% carbon will furnish enough of this carbide material for stability with a considerable excess to spare. Tungsten, however, is not an element which adds much hardenability to steel, and it is necessary therefore to add hardening power. This is provided by the addition of about 4% chromium, which incidentally contributes also to red-hardness. We now have a fairly good high speed steel, but we could add considerably to its wear resistance if it were possible to increase the carbon. To do so, however, would decrease toughness to a degree which in most tools would be quite detrimental. Consequently a toughening agent must be used, and we find that by adding about 1% vanadium the carbon can be increased to .70 or .75% with safety. Vanadium, like chromium, also adds some red-hardness. The resulting 18-4-1 composition is one which thus contains the necessary percentages of the various elements to produce the best degree of red-hardness, hardenability and wear resistance, along with a high degree of toughness.

Molybdenum also possesses the property of imparting red-hardness, although it differs from tungsten in this respect in two ways—first, it forms more carbide for each percent added; and second, these carbides are more easily soluble, at a lower temperature, and with a greater tendency to again come out of solution. The advantages of both elements are best employed in a combination of 6.25% tungsten and 5.00% molybdenum which imparts the same degree of red-hardness as 18.00% tungsten. With this combination a somewhat higher carbon content is necessary to provide wear resistance. An addition of about 4.00% chromium provides hardenability as in the 18-4-1 analysis, but the vanadium is raised to 1.90% to compensate for the higher carbon. We thus see the reasons for the 6-6-2 composition, which like 18-4-1 combines the best in red-hardness, hardenability and wear resistance, with suitable toughness for cutting tools.[1]

These two steels are so similar in their application, structure and properties, and the procedures and precautions in their heat treatment so parallel, that there is little need to discuss them individually. The main differences in procedures have only to do with treating temperatures and atmospheres. For simplicity the two steels will therefore be discussed as "high speed steel" and a division under the two types will be made only in discussing those topics which compel such division.[2]

Manufacture, Forging, Annealing.—While the matter of providing high speed steel of proper composition, soundness and structure, is distinctly the responsibility of the steel maker, still a few brief comments on its manufacture might be of assistance to the user. Almost all high speed steel is now melted electrically, either in arc or in high frequency induction furnaces. The first requisite in good melting practice is close control of composition, and this is accomplished only by careful chemical control of operations. The second requisite is a sound workable ingot, which is obtained by the use of molds of suitable size and design and by the proper observance of pouring temperature, speed, and many other details. While many of these details are still associated with the *art* of steel making, much of the guess work has now been taken out of the process by the use of modern analytical methods, pyrometers, stop watches, etc. Thus the *science* as well as the art of steel making is now taking a large part in the manufacture of high speed steel.

[1] The old saying that "necessity is the mother of invention" is well illustrated in this steel. During the Second World War tungsten became a scarce "strategic" element, and it became necessary to find a more plentiful element to replace it. Considerable work on molybdenum over a period of years had demonstrated its value in high speed steel, and it remained only to determine how much of the tungsten content in high speed steel could be replaced by molybdenum and still preserve high cutting efficiency and ease in handling. The "6-6-2" analysis made both of these possible with a considerable saving of tungsten.

[2] Reference to Chapter 12 will show that the Carpenter brand corresponding to 18-4-1 is *Star-Zenith* (RED-WEAR), and that corresponding to 6-6-2 is *Speed Star*. Since all the original data presented in this section were developed in The Carpenter Steel Company Laboratory, they were obtained on these two brands.

When a high speed ingot freezes, the carbide constituents form a rigid skeleton-type structure, which can only be broken up by hot work. These constituents also tend to gather together, particularly in the axis and top of the ingot, to form what is known as "segregation." By suitable design of molds and proper control of temperature, pouring rate, etc., ingots free from objectionable segregation can be produced. When these factors are not so controlled, and marked ingot segregation does occur, it can be dispersed to some extent by special forging practices.

On account of the general rigidity of the original ingot structure, the first hot work operations on high speed steel can best be done under the hammer. The resulting billet after preparation, may then be either hammered or rolled into bars. Since high speed steel is a distinctly red-hard steel, all hot working operations are correspondingly difficult, and should be carried out under careful temperature control. The annealing operation also must be conducted carefully, and under good time and temperature supervision. Since both are operations which the steel treater might have occasion to use in the course of his work, they will be dealt with in more detail.

For average purposes the best forging temperature for 18-4-1 is 2000°/2100°F., and for 6-6-2, 1950°/2050°F. Preheating before raising to the high temperature is desirable in the case of large sections. If the steel to be forged is already hard, it should be annealed before heating for forging. The time of soaking for good forging is of importance, and usually longer holding at the forging temperature will result in softer working. High speed steel should not be forged after the temperature has dropped below 1600°F., and it is good practice to discontinue work when the temperature has reached about 1700°F., and reheat if further working is necessary.

The atmosphere for forging should be slightly oxidizing, with a free oxygen content of about 3 to 8%. Such atmosphere provides free scaling and at the same time protects against decarburization. The molybdenum bearing steels such as 6-6-2, are more subject to decarburization, and it is often advisable in the forging of these steels to coat with borax or some high temperature paint to reduce both scalage and decarburization during heating.

Because high speed steels are air-hardening, slow cooling after forging is quite necessary. If a cooling furnace is not available, it is recommended that forgings be cooled in dry ashes, lime or other insulating material, but they should not be removed before they reach a temperature of about 400°F. Such cooling is in no case considered an anneal, and is only for the purpose of preventing cracking during cooling.

When maximum softness is desired, the best annealing temperature for high speed steel is in the range of 1550°/1600°F. The steel should be thoroughly heated to temperature and then cooled slowly with the furnace at a rate of about 20° to 30°F. per hour. While is is only necessary that slow cooling continue down to a temperature of about 1300°F., it is usually preferable to cool to a lower temperature before removing the charge from the furnace. The Brinell hardness of properly annealed high speed steel should be in the range of 217 to 241 Brinell. An average microstructure of a properly annealed bar of high speed steel as it reaches the user is shown in Fig. 187.

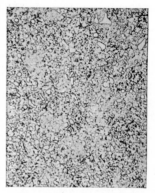

Fig. 187.—Annealed microstructure of 18-4-1 high speed steel at 500 magnifications.

Machining of Tools.—It might be well to point out here some pitfalls in the machining of high speed tools which affect their ultimate service. A bar of high speed steel as it is received from the manufacturer has a thin skin of surface decarburization or bark. This must be entirely removed in order to make a successful tool. Though some of this bark may be left only on portions of the tool which are not to do actual cutting, its presence even there is objectionable since it tends to cause distortion in hardening. A rectangular tool, for instance, which has the bark removed only on three sides is very likely to go out of straight. Surface stresses due to the presence of bark are frequently sufficient to cause cracks during the quench. Sharp corners and sharp angles are always dangerous, and wherever possible should be relieved. Deep stamp marks, or punch marks not entirely removed, also offer points for the beginning of failure, and should be avoided. If excessive machining stresses are introduced in making the tool, these can be relieved by annealing at about 1250°F. Freedom from decarburization or bark, and freedom from stress are much to be desired in the machined tool, and when these are realized the hardener will encounter the minimum hazard in hardening the tool.

Mechanism of Hardening.—To better grasp the discussion which follows, let us see what happens to high speed steel as it is carried through the hardening cycle. If we examine a section of annealed high speed steel under the microscope, we find that it has a structure similar to Fig. 187. Here the round white particles are tungsten carbides, and these are imbedded in a soft "matrix" or background of iron containing certain other of the elements in solution. The annealed steel is soft for the reason that the matrix is soft. The carbides are hard, but they act much like stones in a plowed field. They add little to the difficulty of plowing, since they are easily pushed aside. Carbides in a soft steel matrix behave much the same way in machining.

Upon heating, no change takes place in this structure until the critical temperature is reached at about 1530°F. Here several important things happen. The matrix recrystallizes, and becomes non-magnetic. For convenience the name "austenite" has been given this non-magnetic form of iron. There is nothing more mysterious about this name than there is in calling a solution of salt in water "brine." It is just a convenient term. A second important thing which happens is that the carbide begins to go into solution; and still a third thing, the steel, which up to this time has steadily expanded with heating, suddenly contracts. (See page 501.)

If we were hardening a piece of plain carbon steel, we would now heat about 100°F. above the critical temperature and quench. By so doing we would accomplish all that would be desired, namely to fully harden the steel. However, in the case of high speed steel, we want not only hardness but red-hardness as well and this is obtained by dissolving and keeping in solution as much of the carbide as possible. To accomplish this it is necessary to heat to a much higher temperature, almost 1000°F. above the critical. It is important, however, not to heat too high, since upon overheating the austenite grains grow in size, with resulting brittleness in the finished tool. The desired temperature is one which takes into solution the maximum amount of carbide with the minimum amount of grain growth.

At this point we have a matrix of austenite holding in solution a large quantity of carbides, and imbedded in this matrix a considerable quantity of still undissolved carbide. The next step in our cycle is to cool this at a rate faster than its critical quenching speed in order to harden it (Chapter 4, page 62). The critical quenching speed of high speed steel being low permits hardening in either oil or air. The "gate temperature" of high speed steel corresponding to the knee of the S curve (Chapter 20, page 505) is about 1300°F. Consequently we air or oil cool past 1300°F. and enter the "twilight" temperature zone in which the steel has made its promise to harden, but has not yet gone through its hardening transformation. In this zone it is ductile, and can be bent or straightened because it is still largely austenite. On further cooling no appreciable change takes place until it reaches about 430°F. At this point the austenite matrix begins to change or transform rapidly into "martensite,"[1] the hard needlelike

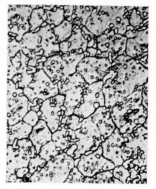

Fig. 188.—18-4-1 high speed steel hardened at 2350° F. and not drawn. 500 magnifications.

constituent. This change continues as the temperature falls and is accompanied by an expansion of the steel. When the steel has reached room temperature, about 80% of the austenite has transformed to martensite, so that if cooling is stopped at that point, as it usually is, there will still be present about 20% of "retained austenite." The resulting Rockwell hardness will be about C-65, and the structure will be similar to Fig. 188.

If we now reheat this hardened structure to a series of temperatures and again cool to room temperature, we find a slight progressive drop in hardness as the reheating temperature is

[1] A discussion of the various metallographic constituents will be found in Chapter 1, page 38.

increased to about 650°F., where the hardness has fallen to about C-62. This is due primarily to the tempering of part of the martensite. As we draw above 800°F., however, we find that the steel again increases in ultimate hardness, up to a drawing temperature of about 1050°F. This "secondary hardening," as it is called, results from the fact that the retained austenite, which originally failed to transform, now transforms to martensite during cooling from the drawing temperature. After so drawing at 1050°F. the structure will look like Fig. 189. Drawing above 1050°F. will result in softening due to the rapid precipitation of carbide from solution. Note that our sequence of events in drawing is first, to temper the martensite present, and then to transform the retained austenite to form more martensite. It is obvious therefore that this new martensite, which actually does not form until it cools below about 450°F. from the drawing temperatures, does not get the benefit of a drawing operation by simply this one heating to 1050°F. In order to draw this new martensite it is necessary to cool back to about room temperature, and again reheat to 1000°/1050°F., and again cool to room temperature. This explains why double drawing is often recommended.

Fig. 189.—18-4-1. Oil quenched from 2350°F. Drawn for 2 hours at 1050°F. 500 magnifications.

In the above discussion we have followed a *recommended* cycle of operations. Let us see what would happen if in some respects, particularly those having to do with cooling, we had not followed this procedure to the letter. Suppose instead of cooling to room temperature we had taken the steel out of the quenching bath at 500°F., and put it directly into the draw. It is obvious that since there had been no opportunity for the austenite to transform, the steel would go into the drawing bath in the *unhardened* condition. To heat to a drawing temperature of 1050°F. would therefore be simply "going through the motions" since the steel would never really harden until it was finally cooled to room temperature. But when it did, it would be in the hardened but still undrawn condition. If the interruption in quenching had come at a lower temperature such as 250°F. where part of the austenite had transformed to martensite, only that part would temper upon reheating, and the result would be a mixed structure of drawn and undrawn martensite as shown in Fig. 190. Such structures tend to be quite brittle. The necessity for cooling tools to near room temperature before drawing must now be obvious. It should be remarked parenthetically that structures like that shown in Fig. 190 may occur in properly drawn high speed from other causes, such as abnormally high carbon content in the original bar or as the result of carburizing in hardening.

Fig. 190.—Microstructure of high speed steel—quench interrupted too soon—500 magnifications.

Suppose instead of simply quenching to room temperature in the usual way we had continued to cool, as we might in some agent such as dry ice. In that case austenite would continue to transform, and if the steel were cooled to −160°F., it would practically all be transformed to martensite and there would then be no retained austenite. At the same time, however, considerable internal stress would be set up, which combined with the loss of "cushioning effect" of the retained austenite, would make this procedure hazardous. "Cold treatment" or "deep freezing" are practiced to assist in austenite transformation, but are usually applied after a preliminary draw in order to avoid these hazards.

Operations in Heat Treating.—Because of the unusually high temperatures encountered, it is common practice in the hardening of high speed steel to use two furnaces, a low temperature furnace for preheating and a high temperature furnace of special construction for superheating. The preheating furnace is of ordinary construction, and may be any of the types described in Chapter 10. The superheating furnace may be electric or either gas or oil-fired, and its selection should be based on its ability to reach and maintain the desired temperature and the desired atmosphere. Salt baths are often preferred for their easy control of decarburization and close control of time and temperature cycles. Salt baths may be either fuel-fired or electrode heated, and the pots used may be either alloy or ceramic. It is common practice to use a preheating and superheating pot, and in addition, a third pot of low temperature salt for the quench.

Preheating in Furnaces.—There is still a difference of opinion on the proper temperature for preheating high speed steel, some recommending heating below the critical, others in the critical, and still others above the critical, the latter claiming the advantage of less superheating and consequently less danger to light sections in the high heat furnace. The important consideration is preventing decarburization and scaling, and any preheating temperature which will do so under the particular limitations of the furnace is justifiable. The atmosphere, however, should be reducing, preferably 4% to 8% carbon monoxide, and should circulate freely around the work. Reducing atmospheres have the advantage of neither scaling nor decarburizing the tools at preheating temperatures. The preheating temperature recommended for 18-4-1 is 1500°/1600°F., and for 6-6-2, 1475°/1500°F. The time of preheating need only be sufficient to heat the tools uniformly to temperature.

Superheating in Furnaces.—The three important things to consider in superheating are **temperature, time** and **atmosphere.** The **superheating temperatures** used for 18-4-1 range from 2200°F. to 2400°F., and for 6-6-2, 2150° to 2275°F. The exact temperature greatly influences the hardness, red-hardness, toughness and grain size, and in practice the temperature selected is one which will give the most favorable combination of these properties for the particular tool under consideration. The effect of hardening temperature on the various properties will now be discussed in some detail.

In Fig. 191 are shown curves which give graphically the hardness of both types of high speed steel, each quenched at two temperatures, one at the high side of the range, the other at the low side of the range, and then drawn at various temperatures. It is important to note the "secondary hardening" effect in Fig. 191, and particularly how this effect increases when the quenching temperature is raised. This is entirely in accord with our previous discussion of the subject, and is the result of a greater percentage of retained austenite resulting from the higher quench, and consequently a greater amount of martensite forming during the draw. Note in Table XXVI that **red-hardness** also increases with the higher quenching temperature.

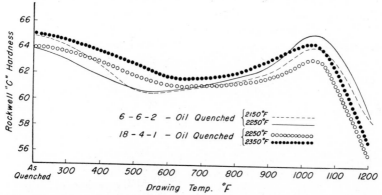

Fig. 191.—Effect of quenching and drawing temperatures on the hardness of 6-6-2 and 18-4-1 high speed steels.

TABLE XXVI.—RED-HARDNESS BRINELL OF 18-4-1 AND 6-6-2 QUENCHED AT TWO TEMPERATURES, DRAWN AT 1050°F. AND TESTED AT 1200°F. BY MUTUAL INDENTATION METHOD

	Red-Hardness Brinell at 1200°F.
6-6-2 Oil quenched from 2150°F., drawn at 1050°F.	348
Oil quenched from 2250°F., drawn at 1050°F.	399
18-4-1 Oil quenched from 2250°F., drawn at 1050°F.	355
Oil quenched from 2350°F., drawn at 1050°F.	390

These results tell us unmistakably that the higher quenching temperatures are preferable from the standpoint of both hardness and red-hardness, and if these were the only considerations, our instructions might read "heat to the highest temperature possible." But we have another factor to consider, and one of considerable importance where cutting tools are concerned, that of toughness. Toughness is governed both by the grain size of the steel resulting from the temperature used in hardening, and by the drawing temperature. The second of these should properly be taken up under the subject of drawing, and discussion of it will therefore be reserved for that section. With reference to grain size, in Fig. 192 is shown a series of photographs of struc-

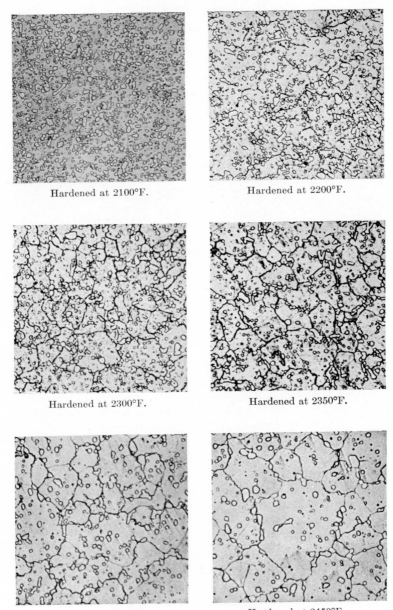

Hardened at 2100°F.

Hardened at 2200°F.

Hardened at 2300°F.

Hardened at 2350°F.

Hardened at 2400°F.

Hardened at 2450°F.

FIG. 192.—Microstructure of 18-4-1 high speed steel hardened from the various temperatures shown. (All magnified 500 times.)

tures taken at 500 magnifications of 18-4-1 steel hardened at different temperatures from 2100° to 2450°F. and not drawn. Note the following points about these structures:

1. With increases in hardening temperature, more and more carbides dissolve in the material that surrounds them. So dissolved, they communicate to the steel their own hardness, resistance to wear, and ability to withstand, without softening, heat generated in cutting.

2. With the higher hardening temperatures, the carbides lose their roundness and become somewhat more angular in shape. This increase in angularity at about 2400°F. is associated with a loss in toughness. It denotes an increased brittleness in the steel with a greater tendency toward crumbling of fine cutting edges.

3. With higher hardening temperatures, the size of the grains increases. At 2200°F., the grain boundaries begin to become visible. (The edges of the grains are evidenced by solid black lines in the photographs.) At 2350°F. they are sharply defined. At 2450°F. they have become very large and coarse. As the size of the grain increases, the tightness with which it is interlocked with neighboring grains is decreased. So "grain growth," as it is called, is associated with a decrease in the toughness of the steel. Brittleness is increased and cutting edges show an increased tendency to crumble. This tendency becomes sufficiently marked to cause tool troubles on keen edged tools at hardening temperatures above 2350°F.

It is frequently more convenient to have some quantitative measure of the grain size of high speed steel than simply to compare actual microphotographs. Such a measure is available in the so-called "intercept grain count." In this method of grain size rating an image of the magnified section is projected on the ground glass of the microscope at 1000 magnifications, and the number of grains cut, or "intercepted" by a 5″ long line drawn at random across the field, is counted. A sufficient number of such fields are taken to obtain a reliable average. The average number of grains cut by this 5″ line is taken as the grain count. For instance if the number of grains cut is 10, the grain size is rated at 10. If 12 grains are cut, the grain size is rated as 12. In high speed steel, an intercept grain size of 6 to 8 is considered

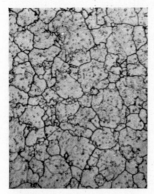

coarse grained; 8 to 12 is average; and 12 or higher is considered fine grained. In Fig. 192 the section of 18-4-1 hardened at 2350°F. shows an intercept grain size of about 12.

It is obvious that for 18-4-1 a quenching temperature of 2350°F. provides the best combination of red-hardness, hardness and grain size. In 6-6-2 this temperature is 2225°F. Fig. 193 shows a section of 6-6-2 quenched at this temperature. Comparison with Fig. 192 will show that this is entirely similar to the 18-4-1 structure at 2350°F.

Fig. 193.—6-6-2. Oil quenched from 2225°F. (not drawn). ×500.

To summarize the effect of hardening temperature, an increase in hardening temperature will—

a. Increase the tool's hardness after tempering.
b. Increase its permissible drawing temperature.
c. Increase its red-hardness or resistance to heat generated in cutting.
d. Increase its wear resistance.

But any appreciable grain growth will—

a. Decrease its toughness.
b. Decrease the resistance of the tool to crumbling of the cutting edges.
c. Be associated with increased scalage in hardening.

Thus for multipoint tools where toughness and keenness of the cutting edge are essential, temperatures which will preserve a fine-grained structure are desirable. Where these two steels are used for roughing, however, such as in heavy lathe or planer tools, they can be hardened at higher temperatures, since the paramount requirement here is red-hardness, and the toughness and keenness of the cutting edge is not so important.

The length of **time at superheat** is a factor worthy of some discussion. The time in the high-heat furnace should always be sufficient to insure the tools being heated throughout before quenching. In the case of tools having a heavy body and relatively light cutting edges or projections, it is not good practice to quench before the body of the tool is up to the temperature of the teeth. Only sufficient time is necessary, however, to insure the tool being uniform, and any extra soaking time will not be beneficial.

We have heard much to the effect that soaking high speed tools in a superheating furnace not only damages the surfaces, but causes rapid growth in grain size. Because of all the warnings in regard to soaking, it has been almost universal practice to

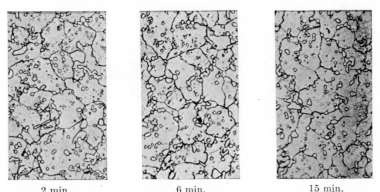

2 min.   6 min.   15 min.

FIG. 194.—How soaking actually affects grain size—18-4-1 high speed steel held at 2350°F. for the times shown—×500. Hardened at 2350°F.

soak high speed steels for the shortest possible length of time, in many cases not even waiting long enough for them to become uniformly heated, for fear cutting edges would get a little soaking and consequently become brittle. The supposition has been that the heat treatment of high speed tools is really bounded by two "fences." The "temperature fence" at 2350°F. in the case of the 18-4-1 type represents the highest temperature to which the steel can be heated without danger of grain growth. We would gladly heat it higher to get extra cutting efficiency if we dared, so we work just as close to the fence as we possibly can. The other fence is the "time fence," and represents the indispensable minimum needed to bring the tool up to temperature. Anything beyond that represents soaking time. We have been told that on the other side of this fence, we run into grain growth, so we work to the upper right-hand corner of the two imaginary fences in order to get the greatest possible cutting efficiency with the smallest grain size.

This supposition led us to investigate thoroughly the effect of soaking time on 18-4-1 steel. Our investigation, checked by independent outside authorities, showed that only **long continued** oversoaking will cause grain growth in the course of time. Contrary to accepted beliefs such growth is **not** rapid. Fig. 194 shows what actually happens to grain size when 18-4-1 is soaked.

Thus it is safe to say that during the time it takes to bring the heavy sections of a tool up to heat, the increase in grain size

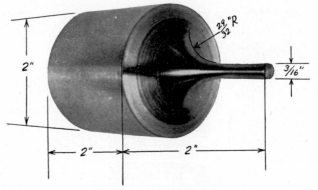

Fig. 195.—Non-uniform section 18-4-1 specimen. Preheated at 1550°F. Superheated at 2350°F. Tip reached heat in 1½ min. Body reached heat in 10 min. Whole piece soaked 5 min. Tip soaked 13½ min.

occurring in thin sections or cutting edges of the tool will be negligible. This statement holds true even for quite badly out-of-balance tools.

After this point in the investigation had been reached it became necessary to find out *how much leeway* these new facts would give the tool maker. The first move was to make up the specimen of 18-4-1 steel shown in Fig. 195. Notice that the body measures 2″ in diameter by 2″ long while the point has been turned down to ³⁄₁₆″ in diameter. It was preheated at 1550°F., then transferred to a superheating furnace at 2350°F. Upon carefully watching the specimen, it was seen that the tip reached the furnace temperature in 1½ minutes, but the heavy body was not up to heat until ten minutes had elapsed. After both the base and the tip were at heat, the whole specimen was given an

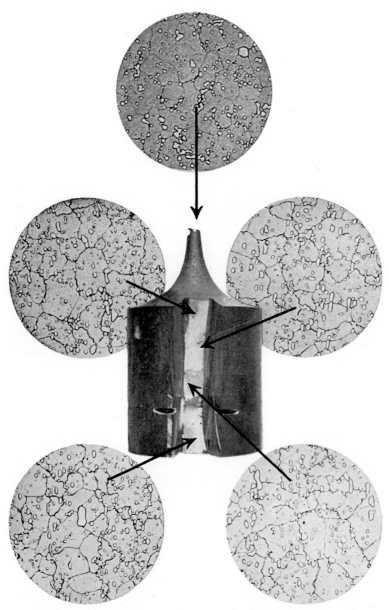

Fig. 196.—Micrographs from various sections of the shape shown in Fig. 195, including the tip, reveal the same grain size throughout.   All ×500.

additional five-minute soak. Consequently, the tip was soaked 13½ minutes. This specimen was then quenched in oil. Micrographs were prepared from a portion broken from the tip and from a slice cut from the heavy body with a flexible grinding wheel. The micrographs given in Fig. 196 show this structure at the tip and at four different points in the heavy section. You will see that the grain size is the same throughout.

The conclusion drawn from this work is that even though the disparity in the sections of some tools might result in excessive soaking of the lighter portions, with 18-4-1 steel there is little

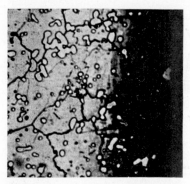 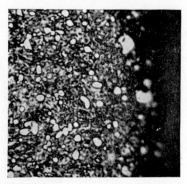

Fig. 197.—As quenched.   Fig. 198.—Drawn at 1050°F.
Figs. 197-198—Surface sections of 18-4-1 high speed steel, oil treated at 2350°F., neutral atmosphere.   ×1000.

need for alarm, since the longer soaking does not appreciably increase the grain size.

While the above discussion has been confined to 18-4-1, the statements regarding soaking temperature apply equally to 6-6-2 for temperatures up to about 2225°F.

Effects of Furnace Atmospheres.—We now come to one of the most important as well as one of the most discussed questions in the successful hardening of high speed steel in furnaces, that of *furnace atmosphere.* Many tools are no better than their surfaces, since it is the surface metal which does the cutting. If the furnace atmosphere is such that it ruins the surface of the tool, it will consequently ruin the entire tool. An understanding of the effects of atmosphere is therefore quite essential to the hardener.

In approaching this subject, it will again be necessary to gather our evidence from structures as they appear under the microscope. If we harden a piece of 18-4-1 in oil from 2350°F. and examine the structures "as quenched," we see the familiar grain structure shown in Fig. 197. After tempering or drawing the steel between 1000° and 1100°F., this structure appears as in Fig. 198. It will be seen that the steel after drawing now etches quite darkly and the grain boundaries are practically invisible. The white particles of undissolved tungsten carbides stand out in bold relief.

In both Fig. 197 and Fig. 198, the micrographs have been taken close to an edge where the original hardened surface is visible. Note the thin layer of adhering oxide which does not come off during the quench. This oxide film may vary from .0002″ to .0030″ depending upon time, temperature and atmosphere.

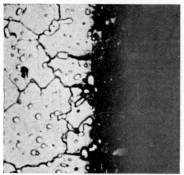 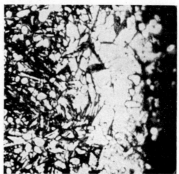

Fig. 199.—As quenched.   Fig. 200.—Drawn at 1050°F.
Figs. 199-200.—Sections of 18-4-1 high speed steel showing carburized surface. Oil treated at 2350°F.   ×1000.

(This is the material that is largely removed by sand blasting.) In Figs. 197 and 198, notice that the surface of the steel is perfectly normal, neither carburized nor decarburized.

A carburized surface of hardened 18-4-1 high speed steel is illustrated in Figs. 199 and 200. In the "as quenched" condition, there is nothing unusual in the structure. However, after drawing at 1050°F., a peculiar needle-like structure immediately becomes visible. From these illustrations it is evident that carburized surfaces must be studied *after drawing*.

A decarburized surface is shown in Fig. 201 in the "as quenched" condition, and in Fig. 202 after tempering at 1050°F.

It is possible to estimate approximately how much carbon has been deposited on the surface from the microstructures shown in Figs. 203 to 208. However, in preparing the samples carbon

DECARBURIZATION

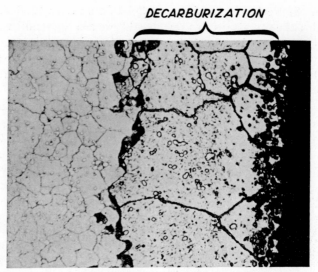

FIG. 201.—Section of 18-4-1 high speed steel showing decarburized surface. Oil treated 2350°F. as quenched. ×500.

DECARBURIZATION

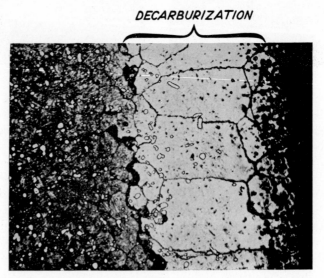

FIG. 202.—Section of 18-4-1 high speed steel showing decarburized surface. Oil treated 2350°F. Drawn 1050°F. ×1000.

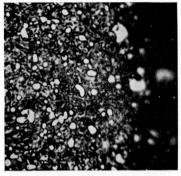

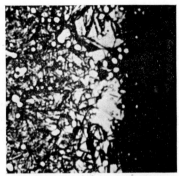

FIG. 203.—Surface .72% C. (not carburized).

FIG. 206.—Carburized surface .84% C.

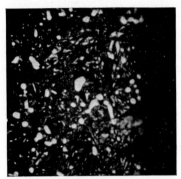

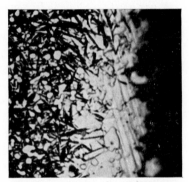

FIG. 204.—Carburized surface .76% C.

FIG. 207.—Carburized surface .87% C.

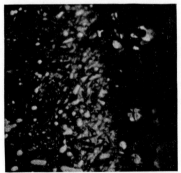

FIG. 205.—Carburized surface .81% C.

FIG. 208.—Carburized surface .91% C.

FIGS. 203–208.—Various degrees of carburization possible by heat treating a .72% C. 18-4-1 high speed steel. All oil treated 2350°F. and drawn at 1050°F. Surface carbon before treating .72%. Surface carbon after treating as indicated—all ×1000.

content was actually determined by chemical analysis. A portion of each specimen was annealed in a lead pot of 1400°F. After all of the scale and oxide was carefully removed, .0025″ on a side was milled off and analyzed for carbon. Actual carbon contents of some of these surface layers are shown later in Fig. 210.

A study of the effect of various furnace atmospheres[1] produced in various furnaces, upon the surface condition, using the method just described, has revealed some interesting facts. These may be summarized in the following statements:

For normal superheating at about 2350°F., 18-4-1 high speed steel will not decarburize, but will slightly carburize in

A gas-curtain electric furnace, regardless of atmosphere all the way from 9% oxygen (O_2) to 16% carbon monoxide (CO),

A semi-muffle, gas-fired furnace, from 3% oxygen to 7.8% carbon monoxide (which happens to be the maximum variation possible in the particular furnace tested),

An oil-fired furnace, regardless of atmosphere from 10% oxygen, which is so raw that the temperature cannot be maintained, to 3.5% carbon monoxide, which is so smoky that it drives you out of the shop,

Carbonaceous blocks or muffles, which produce an atmosphere over 30% carbon monoxide and carburize more actively than any of the furnaces or atmospheres previously mentioned.

In fact, it is difficult to produce a decarburized skin on 18-4-1 high speed steel with any of the above furnace atmospheres—unless the atmosphere cannot reach the surface of the tools. For example, in a blind hole, or on the side of the tool resting on the hearth, it is not uncommon to find spotty decarburization because these areas are not freely washed by the furnace atmosphere. But surfaces which are exposed to the free circulation of the furnace atmosphere will not decarburize. For this reason, all statements made here regarding the effect of furnace atmosphere are based on a **moving** or **flowing** atmosphere that continually bathes the surface of the steel. We are thus forced to the conclusion that most decarburization trouble is probably the result of stagnant atmospheres. These may result from contact

[1] For a complete discussion of furnace atmosphere refer to Chapter 18.

of the work with the furnace floor, or contact between tools in the furnace. Any arrangement of the work which interferes with free circulation of atmosphere around the surfaces may lead to decarburization. On the other hand, in the very high carbon monoxide atmospheres such as those obtained in carbon muffles, stagnant atmospheres are known to have just the opposite effect, and to cause extreme carburization. The use of screens to separate tools or to raise them off the floor of the furnace is often helpful in preventing either occurrence.

We are also led to suspect that many of the "soft skins" on high speed steel which were previously interpreted as decarburization, actually were the result of **carburization.** The higher carbon surface retains on the quench much more austenite than the underlying layers. This high carbon austenite is known to

Fig. 209.—Alligator skin.

be quite resistant to break-down during the draw, and often persists on the surface as essentially undrawn austenite. In that form it is of course softer than martensite, and not as hard to a file.

Thus far, nothing has been said about the importance of furnace atmosphere for its effect on the **appearance** of the **surface** of high speed tools. An experienced hardener knows that an oxidizing atmosphere will produce an "alligator-skin" surface, such as is shown in Fig. 209. He also knows how *long* he can hold a tool in a given atmosphere, at a given temperature, before the surface becomes badly damaged. Furthermore, the degree of damage that might ruin a thread chaser would not necessarily be objectionable in a tool holder bit. Whether or not an oxidizing atmosphere is permissible will therefore depend upon the kind of tool. Since most tools made of 18-4-1 are of types requiring smooth surfaces, the general recommendation is for a reducing atmosphere, this offering the best protection.

Reducing atmospheres will usually cause carburization to the

extent of 2 to 10 points (.02 to .10%) of carbon in a zone .0025″
deep at the surface.   Fig. 210 shows graphically the pick-up
in surface carbon on 18-4-1 high speed steel heated at 2350°F.
in various atmospheres in a gas curtain furnace.   The pieces
quenched were 1″ diameter by 3″ long, and had been preheated at

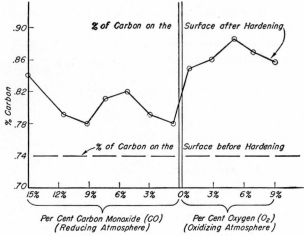

Fig. 210.—The effect of reducing and oxidizing atmospheres on surface carbon of
18-4-1 high speed steel heat treated at 2350°F.

1550°F. in a 2% carbon monoxide atmosphere.   After hardening
they were annealed in lead at 1450°F., and surface turnings
.0025″ deep were taken for the analyses shown.

The content of 15% carbon monoxide represents the highest
percentage obtainable in the gas curtain furnace.   Atmospheres

Fig. 211.—Wrinkled surface on hardened tool of 18-4-1 high speed steel.

containing between 17% and 25% carbon monoxide, produced
by generating carbon monoxide and introducing it into the furnace, have been found in some cases to cause decarburization.
The higher carbon monoxide atmospheres, however, such as are
obtained in carbon muffles where the content may go over 30%
are definitely carburizing.

While a light skin of carburization is usually of advantage in adding some wear resistance to the cutting edge, heavy carburization of course should be avoided.   Fig. 211 illustrates what might happen to surfaces when the atmosphere becomes excessively reducing.   This wrinkled condition may occur in any type of furnace or in carbon blocks, and is not the fault of the furnace, but rather the manner in which the work is placed in the furnace. In the present case the wrinkled surface was the bottom face of a tool so placed that it was not exposed to a free circulation of the furnace atmosphere.   The high carbon monoxide atmosphere lay

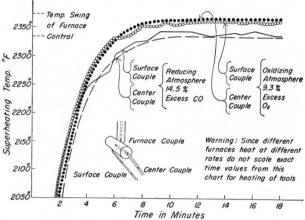

FIG. 212.—Effect of atmosphere on heating rate of 18-4-1 high speed steel.

stagnant against this face, with the result that the surface metal became excessively high in carbon—sufficiently high to actually lower the melting point of the metal and slightly fuse the surface.   Such wrinkles can be prevented by blocking the tool up off the hearth, although in so doing care should be taken to properly support the tool in the furnace so as not to cause sagging and warping during heating.

The character of the furnace atmosphere has some effect on the manner in which the tools heat, and particularly on their tendency to heat higher or lower than the controlled furnace temperatures.[1]   While this effect is small it is worthy of note, and is illustrated in Fig. 212.   The specimens used in obtaining

[1] The effect of furnace atmosphere on the heating behavior of high speed steel was first pointed out by J. P. Gill.   For a more complete discussion see "High Speed Steel, Carbide Segregate and Grain Size," Campbell Memorial Lecture by J. P. Gill, Trans. ASM 1936, Vol. 24, Page 735.

these data were 18-4-1 high speed steel, and measured $1\frac{1}{2}''$ diameter $\times 3''$ long. A thermocouple was buried in the exact center, and another attached to the surface as shown in the illustration. These specimens were preheated in a 2% carbon monoxide atmosphere at 1530°F. They were then transferred to the superheating furnace maintained at 2350°F. The set of heating curves shown in solid and broken lines were obtained in a strongly reducing atmosphere showing 14.5% excess carbon monoxide. The set of heating curves shown by solid and open

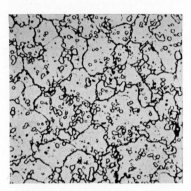 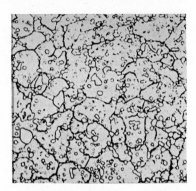

Oxidizing atmosphere. $\times 500$.   Reducing atmosphere. $\times 500$.

Fig. 213.—Microstructure of 18-4-1 high speed steel heated in two different atmospheres as indicated in Fig. 212, and quenched.

circles were obtained in an atmosphere which was very oxidizing, containing 9.3% oxygen.

It will be seen that in both atmospheres samples reach maximum temperature in about 10 minutes, so that atmosphere is seen to have no appreciable effect on heating rate. However, the curves indicate that this maximum differs depending upon the kind of atmosphere, and that the steel does tend to "overheat" slightly in a strongly oxidizing atmosphere and "underheat" slightly in a strongly reducing one. Actually the curves in Fig. 212 show the maximum variation from the controlled furnace temperature to be about 15°F. Microstructures of both specimens after quenching are shown in Fig. 213. They indicate no difference in grain size as a result of either the different atmosphere used or the slightly different maximum temperature resulting.

The superheating of 6-6-2 presents some surface problems not encountered in the heating of 18-4-1. On account of its molybdenum content, oxidizing atmospheres must be avoided. The effect of furnace atmosphere on 6-6-2 is shown in Fig. 214, which was constructed much like Fig. 210. It is apparent that the best furnace atmosphere is from 9% to 12% carbon monoxide. As in the case of 18-4-1, it is important to avoid stagnant atmospheres, and there should always be good circulation around the tools. On account of the close control of atmosphere required, many operators have taken advantage of easier control of salt baths and are hardening their 6-6-2 tools in such installations.

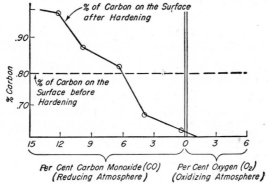

Fig. 214.—Effect of atmosphere on surface carbon of 6-6-2 high speed steel, heat treated at 2225°F.

The remarks under 18-4-1 regarding the effect of atmosphere on rate of heating and grain size apply equally well to 6-6-2. With the exception of the difference in their hardening temperatures, and in their reactions to furnace atmospheres, the two steels behave very much alike.

Heating in Salt Baths.—Heating in salt baths offers some advantages in the hardening of both 18-4-1 and 6-6-2. Heating in salt baths is comparatively rapid, temperature control can be very accurate, and the tools are kept protected by the salt so that both scalage and decarburization can be avoided. Salt bath hardening fits well into production high speed hardening where operations are continuous and in some instances, automatic. It presents some disadvantages, however, to the hardener who has only a few tools to harden at a time, since it does not lend itself well to intermittent operation.

As we have already stated, three pots are commonly used, the preheat, the high heat and the quench. The principal constituent of the preheating bath usually is a chloride salt having an operating temperature range of 1400°/1600°F. A mixture of 85% potassium chloride and 15% sodium carbonate makes a good preheating salt bath. The superheat bath is usually a barium salt such as barium chloride. Mixtures of borax and boric acid are also successfully used. Quenching baths are usually chloride-carbonate mixtures having a useful temperature range of about 900° to 1300°F. A 50% mixture of potassium chloride and sodium carbonate is quite suitable. Many quenching salts have additions of sodium cyanide, to impart a slight cyanided surface to the tool.

The temperatures employed when heating both 18-4-1 and 6-6-2 in salt baths are exactly the same as those recommended for hardening in furnaces. The time of heating in salt baths will of course be shorter than in furnaces, on account of the faster transmission of heat by actual contact. The ultimate effects such as hardness and grain size are exactly the same. With properly controlled salt baths general experience seems to indicate slight carburization to a depth of about .005″. Typical surface and interior carbon tests of high speed steel treated from a boric acid-borax superheat bath are given in Table XXVII.

TABLE XXVII.—INTERIOR AND SURFACE CARBONS OF HIGH SPEED STEEL
TREATED FROM A BORIC ACID-BORAX SUPERHEATING BATH

Type of steel	Interior carbon	Surface carbon to depth of .0025″
18-4-1	.72	.80
6-6-2	.82	.89

It might be well to mention a few precautions in connection with the successful operation of salt baths. In transferring tools from one salt to the next, some salt or "drag out" is always carried over to contaminate the second pot. The high temperature pot is the one most affected, and it is advisable that this contain some of the same type of salt as the preheat. As it becomes enriched in the lower temperature salt it can then be rectified by the addition of the higher temperature salt.

Close chemical control of the composition of the salts is advisable, and they should be kept clean by removing any sludge which tends to accumulate. Finally, salt should be removed from the undrawn tools to prevent rusting. This can be done by immersion in hot water, provided the quenching salts selected are water soluble.

Quenching.—The principles of quenching have been discussed earlier in this chapter, where we learned that the first step is cooling through the gate temperature of 1300°F. at a sufficiently rapid rate to insure ultimate hardening. 18-4-1 high speed steel has a very low critical quenching rate, and consequently even very large sections will harden fully in air. 6-6-2 will harden in air in sections up to about 1″ square cross section, so that the larger sizes must be quenched either in oil or in a heated bath. The martensite point of both steels, that is, the temperature at which the austenite starts to transform to martensite in cooling, is about 430°F.

These facts give rise to four possible types of quenching for the two steels. These are—

1. Oil quenching to near room temperature.
2. Air cooling to near room temperature.
3. Quenching in oil to a black temperature, then air cooling.
4. Quenching in a liquid bath maintained at 1000°/1200°F., holding a sufficient time to equalize, then air or oil cooling to about room temperature.

Oil quenching direct to near room temperature has the advantage of simplicity, and is the most commonly used method. On the other hand, it results in the greatest development of internal stress, and consequently the greatest cracking and distortion hazard. Particularly on intricate tools, and long slender tools requiring straightness, some type of delayed quench is preferable.

Air cooling to near room temperature avoids much of the stress hazard and metallurgically is the most desirable type of quench. It has the disadvantage, however, that the scale developing during cooling is not thrown off as it is in the oil quench, and thus introduces the problem of cleaning. As we have already said it is not applicable to 6-6-2 in sections over one inch square.

Oil quenching to a black, then air cooling, is becoming quite widely used. To be uniformly successful the operation should be timed for each size of tool, so that the temperature at which the tool leaves the quench may be regulated. It has the advantage of "throwing" the scale during quenching. It has a second advantage of allowing a certain amount of straightening to be done just after the tool has been taken out of the oil bath. At this stage the steel is still relatively soft, and straightening operations can be continued down to about 600°F. It has the third advantage, of course, that the martensite change starting at about 430°F. proceeds slowly, and is consequently accompanied by the minimum amount of stress.

Quenching in a liquid bath followed by air cooling embodies all the advantages of the previous method, with the additional advantage of closer temperature control. This method is quite universally used where heating is done in salt baths, since it fits so perfectly into the equipment. One of the earliest methods of interrupted quenching was that of quenching from a furnace into molten lead held at about 1000°F.—and this method is still being used in some hardening rooms.

The exact choice of method depends upon the type of tool and the equipment available. Provided only the critical quenching rate is exceeded in cooling, the method itself will have no effect on the final hardness and grain size. The one necessary precaution in all methods, however, is to make sure tools have reached about 150°F. before they are sent to the tempering operation.

Tempering.—Either oven furnaces or liquid baths may be used to temper high speed steel. The important requirements are that they be capable of reaching and holding accurately temperatures up to about 1100°F. If furnaces are used, those having circulating atmospheres are preferred since they heat both quickly and uniformly. Liquid baths may be either salt or lead pots. They heat quite rapidly, and consequently tools should be definitely preheated; otherwise the sudden expansion upon being introduced into the drawing bath may cause cracking.

We have already discussed the mechanism of tempering, page 343, and have traced the various structural changes in the steel as the drawing temperature is increased to 1100°F. The hardness behavior accompanying these structural changes is shown in Fig. 191, in which it is shown that the highest secondary hardening effect is obtained by tempering at about 1050°F. It now remains to inquire how drawing temperature affects that other important property, toughness.

The toughness of high speed steel can be most conveniently studied by the torsion impact test described in Chapter 11. On account of certain specific requirements in high speed tools, however, two additional specialized tests have been devised, the **static torsion test,** and the **edge toughness test.** Since these are so specifically applied to high speed steel they are being described here, rather than elsewhere in the book.

The **static torsion test** is best described by referring to Fig. 215 which shows in simplified form the type of test machine used in the Carpenter laboratory. The specimen itself is the same as the torsion impact specimen described in Chapter 11. It has a test length of 1″, and a test diameter of .250″. The specimen (C) is gripped at one end by a fixed chuck (D), and on the other end by a rotating chuck (E). The rotating chuck in turn is connected to the large torque wheel (A). A cord and weight pan (B) are fastened to the periphery of the torque wheel. The deflection scale (F) is fastened near one

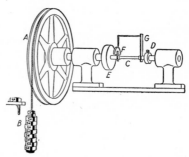

Fig. 215.—The Carpenter static torsion testing machine.

end of the specimen and a pointer (G) near the other. Weights are added in small increments to the pan (B) causing a twist in the specimen which is read on the deflection scale (F).

In making a test, the amount of deflection for each increase in load is recorded up to failure. By plotting the loads and the corresponding degrees of twist, we obtain a chart as shown in Fig. 216. The chart in Fig. 216 shows the curves of two such tests, with one curve superimposed on the other. Curve No.1 represents a specimen of 6-6-2 oil quenched from 2200°F. and drawn at 700°F., and curve No. 2 represents the same steel and quenching temperature but drawn at 1050°F. Notice the lower ductility or degree of twist and the increased strength when the specimen is drawn at 1050°F. as compared to the large degree of twist or ductility and lower strength of the specimen when drawn at 700°F. Both specimens have the same number of degrees of twist for given loads up to a certain point. After that point is passed the degrees of twist increase disproportionately. The point at which this takes place is called the elastic limit.

The static torsion test thus gives us three values; torsional elastic limit, torsional breaking strength, and angle of twist, or ductility. This last figure corresponds to elongation in a tensile test bar. Here is an important distinction to make between the static torsion test and the torsion impact test. In the torsion

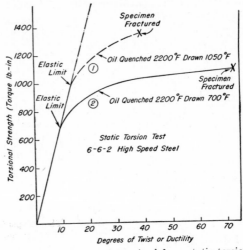

Fig. 216.—"Stress-Strain" curves determined from static torsion test on 6-6-2 high speed steel.

impact test the value obtained is really the product of the load required to break the specimens, and the distance through which the specimens twisted in breaking. Note that the result is expressed in feet × lbs., or ft. lbs., and that this product is **toughness.** In the static torsion test we determine *separately* the load required to fracture the piece, and the angle through which the specimen twists before it breaks. It is often helpful to know the value of *ductility alone* without having it multiplied by the strength, as in the torsion impact test, and it is for this reason primarily that static tests are made. In addition, the static test gives elastic limit values, which are of interest since they show how far the steel can be twisted without being permanently deformed.

Questions have been raised as to just how torsional toughness values could be interpreted in terms of actual tools—particularly if the operations do not involve twisting forces. Single point tools, form tools and broaches are examples of tools that are not subject to twisting loads. The **edge toughness test** was devised therefore in an effort to obtain values which would indicate directly the toughness of a cutting edge. The specimen used for the test is shown in Fig. 217. It measures $1\frac{1}{8}''$ wide $\times$ $\frac{3}{8}''$ thick and 2″ in length, with the knife edge machined to a 45° angle. After suitable heat treatment, the beveled edge of the specimen is carefully ground before it is tested.

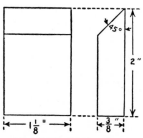

Fig. 217.—Knife edge impact test specimen showing dimensions.

The machine itself is shown in Fig. 218. The specimen (A) is fastened rigidly in the vise (B) which is closed by tightening two heavy bolts. The specimen is held at a slight angle so that the striking pin (C) just touches the very edge and does not come in

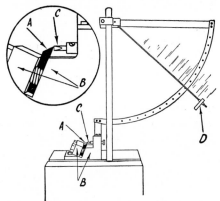

Fig. 218.—The Carpenter knife edge impact testing machine. The diagram in inset shows a specimen in place during a test.

contact with the *body* of the specimen. When the pendulum (D) is released from a predetermined height, it strikes the head of the pin (C) which then transmits the blow to the knife edge of the specimen. A close-up of a specimen in place during a test is shown in the inset in Fig. 218.

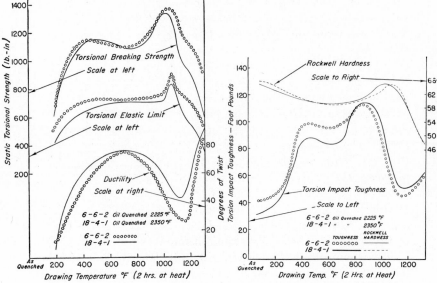

Static torsion tests on 18-4-1 and 6-6-2 high speed steels drawn at various temperatures.

Rockwell hardness and torsion impact on 18-4-1 and 6-6-2 high speed steels drawn at various temperatures.

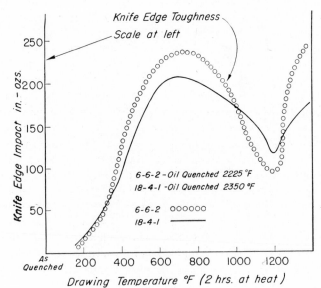

Knife edge toughness on 18-4-1 and 6-6-2 high speed steels drawn at various temperatures.

FIG. 219.

The energy of the falling pendulum (*D*)—in inch-pounds—is known for any height. Naturally the greater the height from which the pendulum falls the greater the energy developed. Again it is the weight and distance through which it moves that determines the strength of the blow. When the pendulum is dropped from moderate heights the edge of the specimen merely dents; from greater heights, the edge fractures. To find the edge toughness of the specimen we gradually increase the height from which the pendulum falls until the specimen fractures. After each impact the specimen is moved in the vise so that a new portion of the edge is always exposed for the next blow. Finally a height is reached when the edge of the specimen no longer dents but breaks and shells out. The greatest height from which the pendulum can be dropped without causing fracture is the end point of the test.

In Fig. 219 are summarized average values determined by the three types of test, with corresponding hardness values for comparison, showing the behavior of 18-4-1 and 6-6-2 over a wide range of drawing temperature.

Because the various toughness tests discussed are made at room temperature, the criticism is often heard that they do not necessarily indicate the toughness of the tool at its operating temperature. It is true that the toughness at elevated temperature is not the same as that at room temperature. But it is also true that the edges of most tools get their most severe shock when they are cold. The precaution is seldom taken to warm up a high speed tool before putting it in use, so that obviously it must start cutting when still cold. Furthermore in many multipoint tools such as milling cutters and hobs, each individual tooth is subjected to intermittent cutting, and the extreme edge of the tool is therefore relatively cold when it picks up the cut. It is safe to say that in all tools in which keen cutting edges are essential, toughness tests made at room temperatures are indicative. On lathe and planer tools taking heavy cuts, keenness of edge is not so important, and here considerable toughness at room temperature can be sacrificed for the greater red-hardness obtained by hardening from higher temperatures. On such tools the value of impact data at room temperature is somewhat questionable.

Several things are worthy of note in Fig. 219:

(1) Both steels behave very much alike through the entire drawing range.

(2) Torsional breaking strength and torsional elastic limit for drawing temperatures over 400°F. follow closely the hardness curve. Since hardness and strength are so closely related, this would be expected.

(3) Both torsional ductility and knife edge toughness have their peaks at temperatures corresponding to the low point in the hardness curve—the point at which quenched martensite has been partly drawn but at which retained austenite is still present.

(4) The torsion impact curve obviously shows a combination of ductility and torsional strength, or we might say the product of the properties discussed in (2) and (3). In this sense the torsion impact test picks out the highest combined value of ductility and strength, and this occurs at about 900°F. as indicated by the torsion impact curve.

To translate the above discussion into terms of tools themselves those tools in which toughness is the outstanding requirement and hardness is not so important, and in which the operating temperature does not exceed 900°F., may well be drawn at 900°F. High speed steel punches afford an example. For those tools requiring greater hardness, but at the same time extreme toughness, some drawing temperature between 900°F. and the full secondary hardening temperature may be selected to best fit the particular tool. Where extreme hardness is the governing factor, tools should of course be drawn at the full secondary hardening temperature, or about 1050°F.

A word should be said about **time of drawing.** Time is always counted from the point at which the tools are fully up to temperature. When we say a one hour draw, we mean one hour after the entire tool is up to the drawing temperature. Time is an important factor in controlling the changes we have discussed, and for safety a drawing time of at least two hours is always recommended. All the foregoing discussion has therefore been based on that drawing time. Large tools are sometimes drawn as long as four hours.

Increasing the drawing time has the effect of shifting both the torsion impact curve and the hardness curve leftward toward the lower temperature side. This is illustrated in Fig. 220 which shows the behavior of 18-4-1 high speed steel drawn for 1 hour and for 8 hours.

The **rate of cooling** from the drawing temperature is important for the reason that while heating to the tempering temperature predisposes the austenite to transform to martensite, the actual change itself occurs during cooling. Consequently rapid cooling from the drawing temperature should be avoided, since it tends

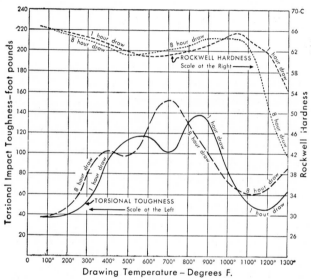

Fig. 220.—18-4-1 high speed steel—effect of drawing time on hardness and torsion impact toughness. All tests preheated 1600°F. Superheated 2350°F. and quenched in oil.

not only to prevent some of the transformation, but to set up stresses as well. While air cooling is not too fast, furnace cooling is preferred. Tools should never be quenched from the draw.

Double tempering of high speed steel has been found effective in increasing toughness of tools as indicated by actual service records, without sacrifice of hardness. As we said earlier in this chapter under "Mechanism of Hardening," the purpose of the second draw is to temper the martensite resulting from the transformation of retained austenite on the first draw. Frequently three or four temperings are used to make this transformation more complete. Multiple tempering is most effective only when drawing to the full secondary hardening temperature.

Cold treating or **deep freezing** of tools is conducted either in a refrigerating unit especially designed for the purpose, or in a gasoline or acetone bath cooled by the addition of dry ice. Four methods have been suggested.

(1) To cold treat directly after quenching.

(2) To draw at 300° to 400°F. before cold treating.

(3) To give the tools a full single draw (1050°F.) before cold treating.

(4) To give the tools a full double draw before cold treating.

If it is decided to cold treat, (3) and (4) represent the safest methods. However, when high speed tools are properly treated it is seldom that any benefit is derived from cold treating. Its primary advantage is really to correct deficiencies in treatment such as overheating in hardening or severe surface carburization both of which result in excessive amounts of retained austenite, or failure to properly transform austenite during the draw. At the present writing it would appear better practice to control these operations so as to prevent these deficiencies than to attempt to correct them by cold treatment.

Nitriding or **cyaniding** of high speed tools has for its purpose obtaining an extremely hard surface of a very limited depth to improve wearing qualities of such tools as reamers, taps, etc. A suitable bath for cyaniding can be made up of 45% sodium cyanide and 55% potassium cyanide. The process consists in immersing the tools (which have been previously hardened, tempered and ground) at a temperature of about 900° to 1100°F. for 20 minutes to 1 hour. The usual depth of the resulting case will be .0005″ to .003″, and since the actual depth depends primarily on the time tools are held in the cyanide bath, it is preferable to preheat the tools to the temperature of the bath before immersing them, so that time at temperature can be controlled exactly.

Straightening of long slender tools such as reamers, broaches, etc., is often necessary, and as we have seen earlier in this chapter, this can be done on the quench, after tools have been cooled below about 1200°F. and before they have cooled to 600°F. If tools must be straightened subsequently, however, as much as possible of this straightening should be done at the full tempering temperature. Straightening under presses should be done with gradually applied loading.

Rehardening of high speed tools is sometimes necessary for various reasons, and this is particularly hazardous on account of the coarse crystalline structure known as "fish scale" which almost invariably occurs when hardened high speed steel is again heated to the hardening temperature. This structure, however, can be prevented by a suitable anneal before the second harden-

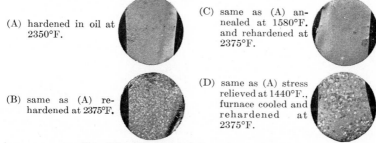

(A) hardened in oil at 2350°F.

(C) same as (A) annealed at 1580°F. and rehardened at 2375°F.

(B) same as (A) rehardened at 2375°F.

(D) same as (A) stress relieved at 1440°F., furnace cooled and rehardened at 2375°F.

FIG. 221.—Fractures of 18-4-1 high speed steel.

ing. It has been found in this connection that a "stress relieving" anneal at 1440°F. is not always sufficient, and that a full anneal is the only sure way of preventing this objectionable structure in rehardening. Fig. 221 shows a series of fractures of 18-4-1 high speed steel illustrating this structure and its correction. It is always recommended that hardened tools of either 18-4-1 or 6-6-2 be fully annealed before rehardening.

Other Types of High Speed Tool Steel.—While the two types of high speed steel just described are the ones most generally used, and represent the greatest tonnage consumed, there are a number of other very important types regularly made and marketed. Some of these, such as the 8% molybdenum-1.50% tungsten and the 18-4-2 types, parallel in usage the 18-4-1 and 6-6-2. Others, such as the high cobalt boron types, are used for special purposes. While the 18-4-1 and 6-6-2 might do a very creditable job in these special applications, (such as heavy roughing cuts), where the quantity of special work is great, it is often good economy to use a steel especially adapted to that particular job.

A list of the recognized types of high speed tool steels now on the market, together with their uses is shown on page 376.

TUNGSTEN STEELS

W	Cr	V	Co	Uses
18%	4%	1%	....	General high speed use.
18	4	2	....	General high speed use.
18	4	3.5	....	Tools which must be very abrasion resistant.
18	4	1	4%	Principally single point tools for heavy cuts.
18	4	2	8	" " " " " " "
22	4.5	1.5	12	Principally single point tools for heavy cuts on hard material.
14	4	2	....	Heavy lathe and planer tools.
14	4	2	5	Principally single point tools; hogging hard tough materials.

MOLYBDENUM STEELS

Mo	W	Cr	V	Co	Uses
5%	6.25%	4%	2%	....	General high speed use.
8	1.5	4	1	....	General high speed use, such as twist drills, taps, reamers, wood knives, etc.
5	6	4	3	....	Fine edge tools.
4.5	5.5	4.5	4	....	Tools which must be very abrasion resistant.
5	4	4.5	1.5	12%	Principally single point tools for roughing.
8	.....	4	2	....	General high speed use.
8	.....	4	1 (Boron added)	2.5	Principally single point tools for heavy roughing cuts.
8	1.5	4	1	4	Principally single point tools for heavy cuts.
8	2	4	1	5	" " " " " "
8.5	2	4	2	8	" " " " " "
6	6	4	2	8	" " " " " "
8	.....	4	1.5 (Boron added)	8	" " " " " "

Cemented Carbides.—No chapter on high speed steel would be complete without mention of the so-called cemented carbides. These materials are characterized by hardnesses far in excess of the hardest steel, but they have considerably less toughness. For this reason they are usually applied in the form of inserts held in a steel shank or body, the carbide being the cutting edge or wearing surface of the tool.

The composition of these materials is either straight tungsten carbide, or combinations of tungsten carbide with carbides of tantalum, titanium and columbium. In the manufacture of tools or inserts, powders of these carbides are mixed with a binder, usually cobalt powder, pressed into the desired shape, and sintered at a high temperature to form a strong compact mass of the exact size required.

The applications of carbide tools fall into two rather distinct classes of use, the first constituting tools in which for some special reason extreme abrasion resistance is required. In this field come such tools as wire drawing dies for heavy drafts at high speeds; rolls for rolling hard or abrasive materials; and certain blanking dies operating on long runs and on abrasive materials. The second class is that of cutting tools. This is rather a broad field, and includes both the cutting of materials which on account of their hardness are beyond the capability of high speed steel, and the cutting of softer materials under special conditions, such as extremely high speeds. For the first class of applications usually straight tungsten carbide tools are satisfactory. For the second class, that of cutting tools, the straight tungsten carbide is usually satisfactory in cutting cast iron, non-metallic materials and nonferrous alloys. For steel cutting, however, the mixed carbides appear to be preferable.

The selection of a suitable *shank steel* is quite important in the manufacture of carbide tools. The inserts or tips are usually brazed to the shanks in a hydrogen atmosphere furnace, or by induction or torch heating. In any case the shank steel must be one which will come through these heat treatments with the necessary strength and toughness to properly function in the finished tool. While soft carbon steels have been used, the trend of shank material is quite strongly toward alloy steels, the exact type depending upon the final hardness desired. Hydrogen brazing is usually conducted at a temperature of 1850°/1900°F. and the entire tool is heated to this temperature, and cooled in air. On lathe and planer tools extremely hard shanks are not necessary, and the shank steel selected for these is preferably one which will remain tough, and harden only slightly on the brazing treatment. On many tools, however, such as drills and reamers, in which the shank is subjected to considerable chip abrasion, a steel capable of air-hardening from the brazing temperature is necessary. The steel selected should be one which will satisfactorily harden at the brazing temperature employed.

The matter of deciding between high speed steel and carbide tipped cutting tools involves many factors having to do with specific conditions in each tool room or production plant. Carbide tools usually justify their higher first cost on long production runs and on machine tools capable of very high speeds. Under certain conditions, and on certain materials, the general use of the more simple single point tools also is economical. On the opposite side of the ledger is the greater flexibility of high speed steel when the user is making his own tools, greater ease in grinding high speed steel, and greater edge toughness. Both materials have their fields of use, and each individual user must weigh the advantages and disadvantages of each in light of conditions in his particular plant.

Hard Cast Alloys.—By using considerably higher percentages of alloying elements than those employed in high speed steel, alloys can be made having very high red-hardness and wear resistance; but such alloys cannot be successfully hot worked, and must be used in the cast condition. On certain applications where cast tools are permissible, the so-called hard cast alloys have found some use.

There is a great variety of these materials, but in general their range of composition is 2%/3% carbon, 5%/15% tungsten, 15%/30% chromium and 40%/60% cobalt, with possible additions of boron, molybdenum, columbium, titanium, nickel and tantalum. They are used to some extent for tipping tools in much the same manner as the sintered carbides. One of the applications of such alloys is the hard facing of tools and parts subject to extreme wear, such as the edges of shear knives, roll guides, etc., in which the alloy is fusion welded to the part, and subsequently ground to the desired final shape.

HOT WORK STEELS

The Hot Work Problem.—While there are various processes for shaping or forming hot metals, such as punching, shearing, bending, upsetting, swaging, piercing, drawing, extruding and molding, they all involve in a varying degree the same general problems. To perform successfully, tools must possess at **elevated temperatures** the proper combination of strength, wear resistance and toughness to resist the **mechanical stresses** exerted upon them. The problem of hot working tools can thus be logically broken down under two headings,

(*a*) The character of the mechanical stresses, and
(*b*) The character of the thermal conditions encountered in service.

Mechanical Stresses.—The element of **shock** or **impact** is important in many hot work tools. In fact all tools used in hammers are subjected to such stresses. Where tools consist simply of flat dies, the effects of impact are distributed evenly over the surface and are therefore not serious. However, in recessed dies, and particularly those with relatively sharp corners, the impact stresses tend to concentrate in the corners or projections, and in such dies maximum toughness is essential, even though it must be obtained at the expense of other desirable properties.

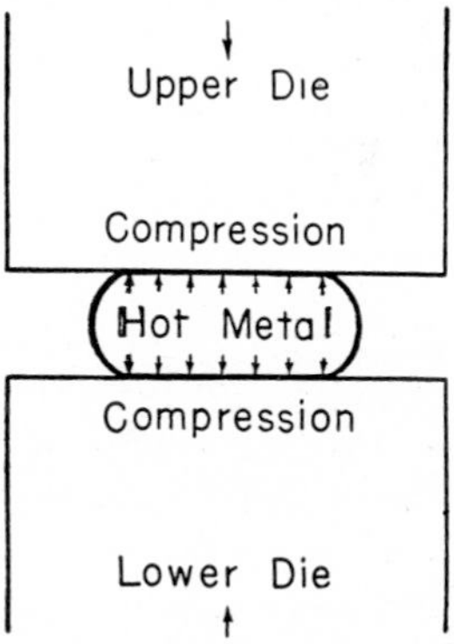

FIG. 222.—Illustrating compressive stresses in flat dies.

Compression is a type of stress which tends to upset the die itself as illustrated in Fig. 222. Compression is resisted by the hardness and strength of the die steel at the temperature of operation. For resistance to compression, therefore, the highest degree of red-hardness is desirable.

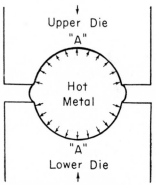

FIG. 223.—Illustrating splitting stresses in die containing an impression.

Splitting stresses are those which tend to break the die or tool apart, as illustrated in Fig. 223. Here we have compression against the faces of the impression at all points, but the net result is a splitting or bursting action at the points marked "A." The tendency at these points is for the skin of the die to stretch. It is under tension just like the walls of an inflated balloon.

Splitting stresses are resisted by toughness, and it is necessary therefore to put hot work steels into service at a considerably lower hardness than is the practice for cutting tools. The initial hardness of the tool is further decreased when it becomes heated in service, so that most hot die steels are in a condition where they have sufficient ductility to deform before they break. Since **ductility** is the important factor here, torsion impact values are not applicable, and transverse tests in which elongation is measured are much more significant. Such tests show that ductility increases as the drawing temperature is raised and hardness falls off.

Friction wears the tool out by both abrasion and galling. While the rapidity of wear or "washing" depends upon many operating factors such as abrasiveness of the metal being worked, temperature, lubricant, etc., proper selection of steel can materially help us to minimize this effect. The most desirable steel to resist frictional wear is one with both high red-hardness and with a structure containing a surplus of hard carbide constitutents of the same nature as those present in high speed steel.

Thermal Service.—The **operating temperature** is taken to be the maximum temperature which the face of the die or tool reaches in service. This is always higher than the average temperature of the tool. In such tools as extrusion dies and hot compression dies where the hot metal is in continuous contact with the die for appreciable times, the difference is quite great, since local heating is intense. In forging dies where contact is intermittent, heat dissipation tends to equalize the temperature. To withstand such service, qualities of both red-hardness and high resistance to softening by drawing action resulting from repeated heating, are desirable.

The amount of **thermal shock** in service is of extreme importance. By thermal shock is meant repeated and abrupt heating and cooling encountered in certain tools. There are some operations, as for example piercing, in which the temperatures are so high, and the contact time so long, that the tool would quickly heat to above its annealing temperature if it were not cooled. No steel would remain hard under such service, and it is necessary therefore to cool such tools after each piece is made, usually in water. Since the most intense heating is on the extreme surface, this repeated heating and cooling has the effect of rapidly expanding and contracting the surface layer. To withstand such service the steel must be very ductile through the entire temperature range encountered in service, otherwise the surface of the tool will develop **heat checks.** (See Fig. 224.) Steels of very high red-hardness are most susceptible to heat checking, so the selection of a steel to withstand supplemental cooling is a matter of nice compromise.

Fig. 224.—Heat checks on nose of hot piercing mandrel.

Our discussion thus far might be summarized by saying that the conditions imposed by service make desirable in any hot work steel some or all of the following properties:

a. Resistance to Mechanical Stresses of
   1. Shock (Impact)
   2. Compression
   3. Splitting
   4. Frictional wear
b. Resistance to Thermal Service involving
   5. High operating temperatures
   6. Thermal shock.

We shall now discuss hot work steels in their relation to the above qualifications.

Types of Hot Work Steels.—There are two general types of hot work steels:

(1) those in which the principal element for red-hardness is tungsten (or molybdenum), and
(2) those in which the principal element for red-hardness is chromium.

Type (1) might be further subdivided into a further type, that in which tungsten and chromium are used in approximately equal percentages. Such steels, however, have properties quite similar to (1).

The steels of type (1) are characterized by high red-hardness, but are in general susceptible to heat checking. Of the desirable properties listed above they possess particularly 2, 4 and 5, and would be logical candidates for the Red-Hard diamond in Fig. 225. Steels of type (2) have less red-hardness than the high tungsten steels, but are tougher and much less susceptible to heat checking. Therefore they possess particularly properties 1, 3 and 6, and would fit into the Red-Tough diamond of Fig. 225. While there are a great number of compositions falling under each

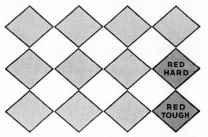

Fig. 225.—Position of hot work steels in Matched Set Diagram.

of these two classes, each having a set of properties which adapt it best to some specific application, experience has shown that there is one composition in each class which most nearly meets the requirements of average hot work applications. These two popular types, which appear to most satisfactorily fill the Red-Hard and Red-Tough diamonds, have the following type compositions:[1]

	9% Tungsten Type (RED-HARD)	5% Chrome Type (RED-TOUGH)
Carbon............	.35%	.40%
Manganese........	.30	.35
Silicon............	.30	1.10
Chromium........	3.50	5.00
Tungsten.........	9.00	......
Vanadium.........	.40	.90
Molybdenum......	......	1.35

[1] Reference to Chapter 12 will show that the Carpenter brand corresponding to 9% tungsten is *T-K* (RED-HARD), and that corresponding to 5% chrome is *No. 883* (RED-TOUGH). Since all the original data presented in this section were determined in The Carpenter Steel Company Laboratory, they were obtained on these two brands.

It will be noted that the 9% tungsten composition contains considerably less carbon than 18-4-1 high speed steel. While 18-4-1 has very good red-hard qualities, which would be quite desirable in a hot work steel, it does not have appreciable toughness nor resistance to even mild thermal shock unless it is drawn at an extremely high temperature. It is preferable in a hot work steel to obtain these properties by reducing the carbon. In doing so, however, it is necessary also to reduce the tungsten and vanadium, since these both reduce hardenability by locking up too much carbon in an inert form. The resulting composition represents the best combination of hardness and red-hardness with a considerable degree of toughness and resistance to thermal shock.

In the 5% chrome composition again the carbon is kept low to add toughness and resist thermal shock. Red-hardness is derived principally from the chromium, but also from the molybdenum and vanadium. The combination of high chromium with silicon, molybdenum and vanadium, produces an extremely tough steel through the entire service temperature range, and consequently one which will resist not only impact, but thermal shock as well.

Heat Treatment of 9% Tungsten Hot Work Steel.—For forging, the 9% tungsten type should be heated to an initial temperature of 2000°/2050°F., preferably in a slightly oxidizing atmosphere. Working should be stopped before the temperature drops to 1600°F., and the steel should be reheated as often as necessary. Small simple forgings may be cooled slowly in lime, but the best practice for large forgings is to place them in a furnace heated to about 1550°F., soak uniformly at this temperature, and then shut off the heat and cool slowly in the furnace. This is **not** an anneal, and when the forging is cool it should be annealed. Normalizing of forgings is not recommended.

The best annealing procedure is to pack in a suitable container with cast iron borings, heat uniformly to 1550°/1600°F. and cool very slowly in the furnace. Resulting Brinell hardness should be 228 maximum.

Many of the same principles discussed in the hardening of high speed steel apply equally well in the hardening of this type. Tools should first be preheated at 1500°/1550°F., soaked until they are uniformly heated, and then transferred to a superheating furnace at 2150°/2200°F. An atmosphere of 6% to 12% carbon monoxide gives most freedom from scaling and protection from decarburization.   After heating uniformly they may be quenched in oil or cooled in air.

The hardened tools, after cooling to about room temperature, should be drawn for at least one hour.   The drawing temperature should be at least as high as the operating temperature.   It should be observed that tools can be left harder for any given service if the forger will take the time to warm the tools thoroughly before putting them to work.   Cold dies are likely to break on the first piece forged, but it is poor economy to require the hardener to draw the tools back tough enough to withstand these first blows and in so doing sacrifice hardness and wear resistance urgently needed when they have warmed up in use.

The hardness of a 9% tungsten hot work steel after treating and drawing at various temperatures is shown in Fig. 226.   Red-hardness at different temperatures determined by the mutual indentation method is shown in Fig. 227.

Heat Treatment of 5% Chrome Hot Work Steel.—For forging, this type should be heated to an initial temperature of 2000°/2075°F. preferably in a slightly oxidizing atmosphere.   Working should be stopped before the temperature drops to 1650°F., and the steel should be reheated as often as necessary.   Small simple forgings may be cooled slowly in lime, but the best practice for large forgings is to place them in a furnace heated to about 1550°F., soak uniformly at this temperature, then shut off the heat and cool slowly in the furnace.   This is **not** an anneal; when forgings are cool, they should be annealed.   Normalizing is not recommended.

The most effective annealing procedure is to pack in a suitable container with cast iron borings, heat uniformly to 1550/1600°F. and cool **very slowly** in the furnace.   Brinell hardness expected after such anneal is 223 maximum.

Tools may be hardened without danger of decarburization in controlled atmosphere furnaces, or in other furnaces if the atmosphere is adjusted for 1% to 3% excess oxygen.   Tools may be either cooled in air or quenched in oil.   When air treating, the empty furnace should be heated to 1850°/1875°F.   The cold tool should be placed in the hot furnace close to the thermocouple and allowed to heat "naturally" until it matches the color of the thermocouple.   It should then be soaked an additional five minutes and cooled in air.   An air blast is not necessary.

When oil treating, exactly the same heating procedure may be followed as in air treating, except that the hardening temperature should be dropped to 1825°/1850°F.

Hardened tools should be drawn for at least one hour. Since a secondary hardening range occurs at 950°/1000°F., there is no reason for drawing lower than this temperature. Tools should never be drawn at a temperature lower than their operating temperatures. The same remarks made on the 9% tungsten

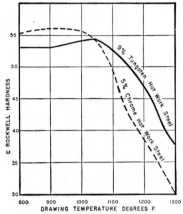 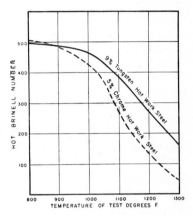

Fig. 226.—Room temperature hardness of 9% Tungsten and 5% Chrome Hot Work Steels drawn at various temperatures, 1 hour at heat.

9% Tungsten hardened in oil at 2175°F.—Rockwell as hardened C-53.

5% Chrome hardened in oil at 1850°F. or air at 1875°F.—Rockwell as hardened C-56.

Fig. 227.—Hot Brinell hardness of 9% Tungsten and 5% Chrome Hot Work Steels. 9% Tungsten oil treated 2175°F. and drawn 1 hour at 1000°F. to a hardness of C-54 Rockwell.

5% Chrome air hardened 1875°F. and drawn 1 hour at 1050°F. to a hardness of C-55/56 Rockwell.

type steel with reference to preheating of tools before placing in service apply equally to tools of the 5% chrome type.

Hardness after either air treating or oil treating, and then drawing at various temperatures is shown in Fig. 226. Red-hardness at different temperatures determined by the mutual indentation method is shown in Fig. 227. For purposes of easy comparison, both types are shown in each figure. Referring to Fig. 226, it will be seen that both steels have a secondary hardening range similar to that of high speed steel, but that the hardnesses are all lower on account of the lower carbon. Note that while both steels draw to about the same hardness up to 1050°F., above that temperature the 9% tungsten remains harder. Note in Fig. 227 that the red-hardness of 9% tungsten also is higher. Both these are the result of the higher stability imparted by the tungsten.

Uses.—Using as our text our earlier discussion on the various properties of these two steels and their relation to tools, we can now summarize by saying that 9% tungsten is adapted to tools requiring great red-hardness, and resistance to wear, and in which toughness is not so important; the 5% chrome type is adapted to tools requiring great toughness. When such tools encounter extremely high temperatures in service, they can be cooled with minimum danger of heat checking if made from 5% chrome. Characteristic uses of both steels are:

9% Tungsten	5% Chrome
Hot shear blades	Forging dies
Hot gripper dies	Heavy duty compression tools
Dummy blocks	Bulldozer dies
Hot extrusion dies	Hot forging dies with deep recesses or sharp corners
Die casting dies	Die casting dies
Forging dies	Aluminum extrusion dies
Bending dies	Bolt dies
Punch and die inserts	Hot piercing and forming punches
Hot compression tools not subject to sharp blows	Vanstoning dies
Hot punches for drawing or piercing	
Brass extrusion dies	

PART IV
THINGS WORTH KNOWING

The first three parts of this book comprise one continuous story. Taken together, they contain the *minimum* amount of information that a tool maker should have in order to capitalize the newest knowledge on tool steel.

From the volumes of other helpful information that could be added, there has been assembled into this Part IV a carefully selected group of "things worth knowing." They might be considered as a sort of *postgraduate* knowledge, the possession of which will be helpful in applying the methods described.

Each chapter in this part is devoted to an entirely different subject and they need not be read consecutively. The last chapter on "Trouble Shooting" will be extremely helpful to anyone engaged in the making, treating, using, or supervising of tools.

CHAPTER 14

THE RELATION OF DESIGN TO HEAT TREATMENT[1]

Design bears in many ways upon the serviceability of a tool or machine part, and unsatisfactory performance may frequently be traced directly to faulty design. This chapter is concerned only with design as it affects the heat treating operation—and through the heat treatment, the serviceability of the finished parts. It is the purpose of this discussion to bring about a better mutual understanding between the designer and the steel treater so that faulty design which may cause cracking, or distorting, during heat treating can be avoided.

The fundamental principles of good design from a heat treatment standpoint are quite simple. Heat treated steel has a certain strength depending upon the analysis of the steel, the quality of the metal, and the heat treatment which it has received.

When subjected to a combination of forces beyond its ultimate strength, the steel cracks or fails. There are two types of force combining to break the steel:

1. The internal strains set up during fabrication and heat treatment of the part.

2. The external forces of service.

Sometimes the internal strains alone exceed the strength of the metal and the part cracks in hardening. Again, the internal strains may equal 90% or more of the total strength, in which case failure will develop in service under relatively light loads. It therefore appears that the useful strength of a part decreases in proportion as the internal strains increase.

Internal strains arise from many causes, but the most serious by far are those developed during quenching, by reason of differential cooling. This differential cooling (or more accurately "temperature gradient"), is largely a function of the size and shape of the piece being quenched, in other words, the design. Here, then, is the relation of

[1] This chapter is quoted from the National Metals Handbook, 1939 Edition, published by the American Society for Metals, and is reprinted here by the permission of the Society. It was originally prepared by one of the authors for the A.S.M. sub-committee on Relation of Design to Heat Treatment, and has been augmented by valuable examples supplied by other members of the Committee.

design to heat treatment and the basic principle of successful design
is to plan shapes which will keep the temperature gradient throughout
a piece at a minimum during quenching.

Temperature gradient is the rate of variation in the temperature of
metal over a given unit distance.

Fig. 228 may be taken to represent a steel cube interrupted during
the process of quenching. Consider the points A and B separated by
a distance "d." If, at any given instant during the quench, A is 700°F.
and B is 300°F. and "d" equals 1 in., the temperature gradient between
these two points is 400°F. per in. If the points are only ½ in. apart,
the gradient is said to be twice as steep.

Some shapes are almost impossible to harden because of the abrupt-
ness in the change of section, but a certain latitude in design is recog-

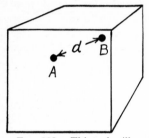

Fig. 228.—This cube illustrates what is meant by temperature gradient.

Fig. 229.—When quenched,
the point of this tapered pin
will cool faster than the
heavier section.

nized when using an oil-hardening or air-hardening steel. All things
being equal, the gradient between A and B, in Fig. 228, will be much less
in oil than in water, and will be less in air than in oil. Thus, a certain
design may be perfectly safe for one kind of steel, or one type of coolant,
and unsafe for another.

Errors in design reach farther than merely affecting the internal
strains during hardening. A sharp angle serves to greatly concentrate
the stresses of service, and the design of the part may be entirely
responsible for concentrating the service stresses at a point already
weakened by internal strains produced during hardening. Design
errors of this type are illustrated in Figs. 234, 241, 242, 250 and 251.
Concentration of service stresses frequently parallels concentration of
heat treating strains and is frequently caused and cured by the same
combination of circumstances.

Reducing all the above to a single statement a part is properly
designed, from a standpoint of heat treatment, when the entire piece
may be heated and cooled at approximately the same rate during the

heat treating operation. Perfection in this regard is unattainable because, even in a sphere, the surface cools more rapidly than the interior. The designer should, however, attempt to so shape his parts that they will heat and cool as uniformly as possible. The greater the temperature difference between any two points on a given part during quenching, and the closer these two points are together, the greater will be the internal strain and, therefore, the poorer the design.

There are really not many possibilities for subdividing this main thought. Almost every failure due to improper design can be attributed directly to a violation of the fundamental principle. Some general cases may, however, be considered.

Effect of Shape on Cooling Speed.—When a piece of steel is removed from the hardening furnace preparatory to quenching, it is presumably

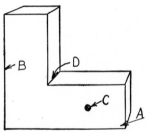

Fig. 230.—This illustrates the manner in which the different positions of a piece will cool when quenched.

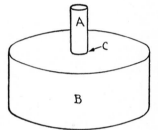

Fig. 231.—A light section adjoining a very heavy section.

at a uniform temperature. As soon as quenching begins, the temperature is different in almost every part of the section. This difference in temperature is due to two conditions. In the first place, the heat capacity or heat storage may be greater in one part of the section than in another, due simply to the fact that there is more metal in one part than in another. This is illustrated simply by a tapered pin, as shown in Fig. 229. Obviously, the point of this pin will cool faster than the heavy section, because there is less heat to be dissipated per square inch of cooling surface.

The rate of cooling is also affected by the shape of the surface. Fig. 230 illustrates a piece which is quite uniform in cross section, but which will not cool uniformly. The protruding corners, such as *A*, are cooled from three sides so that the extreme corner is giving off heat from approximately seven times as great an area as it is receiving heat. An edge, such as *B*, is cooled from two sides and is giving off heat through three times as great an area as it is receiving heat. A point on the flat side, such as C, receives heat from one side and delivers it from the other, and the cooling area and the heating area are approximately equal.

At a re-entrant angle, such as D, heat is being supplied to the surface through three times as great an area as it is being dispelled, and this point will naturally cool last. Sharp re-entrant angles are always objectionable from the standpoint of design. It is impossible to get uniform cooling during the quench in the immediate neighborhood of a sharp angle. Vapor pockets will frequently form in the corners and produce an actual soft spot. Even if no soft spot is formed, the rate of cooling at the point of the angle is bound to be slow, because the corner is so inaccessible to the coolant. Differential cooling thus sets up heavy internal strains at a point which is almost certain to receive concentrated stresses in service.

It will be seen from the above that it is possible for one part of a section as shown in Fig. 230 to cool many times faster than another part.

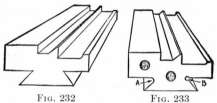

Fig. 232　　　　　Fig. 233

Figs. 232 and 233.—An under-cutting form-tool showing methods of dealing with heavy and light sections. Fig. 232 shows incorrect design and Fig. 233 shows correct design.

If we have a section as shown in Fig. 231, we have a combination of the conditions given in both previous illustrations. The heat capacity of the body "B" is much greater than the projection A, and we have a sharp re-entrant angle at point C. It would be practically impossible to harden such a shape in water without cracking at the sharp corner. Even oil quenching would be doubtful on a piece of these proportions, and only by cooling in air could we expect to keep the thermal gradients down to a safe point (where the design is such that there is danger of cracking, air quenching should be used). A few practical illustrations are given in Figs. 232 and 233 to illustrate the above principles.

Fig. 232 illustrates an under-cutting form-tool. It will be noticed that the cross section of this tool is made up of heavy and light sections joined together with sharp re-entrant angles. A tool of this shape would be extremely hazardous to harden either in a water-hardening tool steel or a high speed steel.

A corrected design for the above tool is illustrated in Fig. 233. Holes have been drilled through the two heaviest sections, and thus the weight of the metal has been fairly well balanced throughout the cross section of the tool. The sharp angles on the cutting edge cannot be eliminated because they are a part of the form of the tool. Two suggested treatments are shown for the angle at the base of the dovetail. The best treatment is shown at A, where a generous fillet is provided. An

FIG. 234.—Improper design for a double-ended side-mill or spot-facer. This shows an unbalanced condition and sharp corners at the base of the teeth.

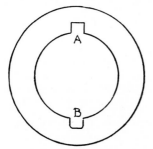

FIG. 235.—Correct and incorrect type of keyways. Sharp corners at "A" are incorrect design while the rounded corners at "B" are correct.

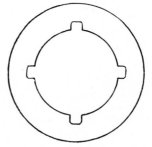

FIG. 236.—Method of balancing keyways to avoid warping.

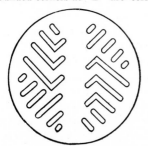

FIG. 237.—A blanking die with center rib heavier than the surrounding areas, which often causes warping when quenched.

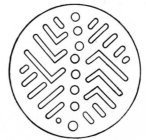

FIG. 238.—A similar die with holes drilled in the middle rib to equalize the amount of metal throughout the die, thus eliminating warpage difficulties.

alternative is shown at B, where the corner has been under-cut to provide a radius and still give the effect of a sharp corner. From a standpoint of quenching strains, the under-cut form at B has little to recommend it, but it does have the advantage that there is no absolutely sharp corner in which the stresses can accumulate.

Fig. 234 illustrates a case of improper design in a double ended side-mill or spot-facer. Each side of this tool has three teeth with the teeth placed opposite to each other. This is a badly balanced condition in the cross section of the piece and is made more serious by a sharp corner at the base of the teeth. Such a tool is almost certain to crack at the junction between the light and heavy section. This condition may be corrected by staggering the teeth on opposite sides of the tool and introducing a generous fillet at the base of each tooth.

Fig. 235 illustrates two principles of design. This is a ring shaped section containing two keyways on opposite diameters. The keyway A is shown with absolutely sharp corners. This is never good design, and while millions of keyways are being made and used with sharp corners, this does not alter the fact that it is poor design, and every effort should be bent toward making standard a round cornered keyway such as is shown at *B*.

The second interesting point about this ring is that when it is quenched it will not stay round. The section of the ring is weakened through the two keyways, and almost invariably the ring will become oval. This condition may be corrected by cutting in two more keyways at 90° to the first two, as is illustrated in Fig. 236. These keyways may be of no use but they certainly do no harm, and their presence will balance the section and keep it round.

Another example of a shape which will almost certainly warp during heat treatment is shown in Fig. 237. Let us assume that this is a blanking die. Even though this piece was made from an oil-hardening, non-changing, tool steel it would warp during quenching. The rib through the center would tend to prevent shrinkage in this direction, and the die would become oval. This figure is intended to illustrate a principle, and it is surprising how often it comes up in actual design. Certain portions of a die are held rigid by a web, while adjacent portions are unsupported, and warpage or distortion occurs during hardening which cannot be avoided without resorting to an air-hardening steel. Frequently it is possible to avoid the difficulty due to such a rib by drilling holes, as illustrated in Fig. 238. Holes drilled for such purposes should always be of such size and so located as to help balance the section, rather than to unbalance it. Success in preventing warpage, and other forms of internal strain, will be directly proportional to success in balancing the weight of the sections and producing uniform cooling conditions.

Large dies of intricate design are sometimes made up in sections which often simplifies the problem of heat treatment.

To further illustrate the principles covered above and to assist in avoiding faulty design, Figs. 239–251 are given. Each illustration depicts one or more errors of design which is explained in the caption together with the danger encountered.

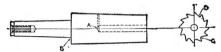

FIG. 239.—A large reamer. When quenched the stresses will concentrate at the junction of the two holes at "A." Blind holes are poor design. Such holes should be continued throughout the entire length. A good fillet should be used at "B" in order to eliminate cracking from the sharp corners during hardening. The roots of the cutters should have good fillets as shown at "C" instead of the dangerous sharp angle at "D."

FIG. 240.—A gear burnisher from which teeth were broken during hardening because practically no radius was provided at the roots of the teeth.

FIG. 241.—Twist drills of this design gave considerable trouble in service from breaking at "A." When a more generous fillet was allowed, the trouble encountered was eliminated.

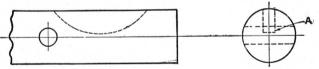

FIG. 242.—A stem pinion with a keyway about one-half the diameter of the stem. The base of the keyway is extremely sharp, as shown at "A." The piece is further weakened by a hole drilled through the center of the stem near the keyway.

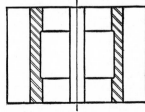

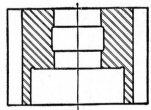

FIG. 243.—A gage with the hole out of proportion to the outside diameter. This will cause the piece to go out of round or into barrel shape when quenched.

FIG. 244.—A cutter with the counterbore too large for the design, which will cause the front end of the cutter to close in when treated.

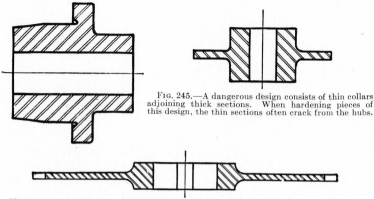

Fig. 245.—A dangerous design consists of thin collars adjoining thick sections. When hardening pieces of this design, the thin sections often crack from the hubs.

Fig. 246.—A cutting tool with a very narrow cutting edge with a thick hub. When quenched the cutting edge will often warp or buckle.

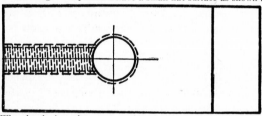

Fig. 247.—This shows the theoretical sharp points on cutting tools. These sharp points will burn off in hardening. They should have a small flat surface as shown at "A."

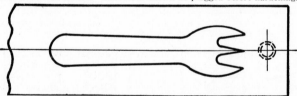

Fig. 248.—When hardening, the concentration of strains at the junction of the two holes in the center will cause failure. Such holes should be plugged before hardening.

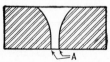

Fig. 249.—A blanking die poorly designed. Crack will occur from point of fork prong to set screw hole. The position of the set screw hole should be changed to eliminate cracking.

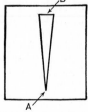

Fig. 250.—Longitudinal section of a cold drawing die. Stresses set up in heat treatment and in service concentrated at point "A" so a fillet should have been used to avoid chance of spalling at corners.

Fig. 251.—Blanking die (oil-hardening) from approximately a 3 × ½ in. section Stresses set up in heat treatment and in service concentrated at points "A" and "B." A slightly larger section such as 3½ × ¾ in. probably would have eliminated failure.

CHAPTER 15

THE HOT ACID ETCH TEST[1]

The tool room requires tool steel that is sound and free from injurious internal defects. This requirement was discussed in Chapter 5; the present chapter is added for the use of those who wish to make the actual inspection themselves.

The most convenient and effective method of inspection for internal defects known at the present time, is the so-called "hot acid etch," or "macro etch" test. Briefly, this consists in cutting a thin disc or slab crosswise from the bar, etching in an acid bath for a suitable length of time, and observing the character of the acid attack upon the cross section of the steel. While this test is an extremely valuable one, it is nevertheless beset by many variables which make it difficult to standardize, not only between different operators, but also between different tests by the same operator. Furthermore, the result of the test is not a numerical value, but depends upon the judgment of the operator. It is the purpose of this chapter not only to describe the most approved practice of deep etching, but also to discuss some of the variables encountered in the operation of acid etching, and to suggest means of standardizing both the actual operation of etching and the interpretation of results.

EQUIPMENT NECESSARY FOR ETCHING

The various pieces of equipment needed to carry out the deep etch test are listed below.

Saw or Cutting-off Machines.—The most satisfactory method of cutting discs is on a band saw or hack saw, since the saw cut surface may be etched without any further preparation. If a cutting-off tool is used, it is safer to either face off the disc on a lathe or to surface grind, since the parting tool tends to drag the

---

[1] The first part of this Chapter is taken almost entirely from "Technical Bulletin B" originally written by G. V. Luerssen and published by the Research Department of The Carpenter Steel Company.

metal and thus distort the structure. The most satisfactory surface for deep etching is a ground surface, but if saws are used for cutting discs, grinding equipment will not be necessary.

Hot Plate.—Either a gas or electric hot plate will be found satisfactory. Gas hot plates are usually quicker heating, and cheaper to operate and maintain. The hot plate should be installed under an efficient hood or in a fume closet, since acid fumes are very corrosive to equipment and irritating to the throat. In the absence of a better place, a small ventilated box can be built just outside of a window. Lowering the window sash will keep fumes out of the room.

Acid Dishes.—The etching solution may be heated in porcelain, glass or acid resisting metal dishes. Shallow rectangular dishes are best adapted to the work. Either Pyrex glass or Duriron[1] will be found satisfactory. Where a large number of discs are etched, Duriron is preferable since it is less fragile than either glass or porcelain.

Thermometer.—An inexpensive laboratory thermometer reading up to 250°F. will be found satisfactory.

Hydrochloric Acid.—Commercial hydrochloric acid or muriatic acid is entirely suitable, and is less expensive than the CP hydrochloric. Commercial acid is usually obtained in ten gallon carboys. The acid is most conveniently drawn from this carboy by raising it above floor level and fixing a glass syphon in the neck, by means of a vented stopper. The lower end of the syphon should contain a ground glass stop cock set below the level of the bottom of the carboy, so that once the syphon is filled the flow of acid is controlled entirely by the stop cock.

Running Water and Sink.—These are necessary for washing the discs clean after the etch. Hot water is not necessary although it is desirable.

Miscellaneous.—Tongs will be required for introducing the discs into, and removing them from the acid bath. A clock, a stiff scrubbing brush and a supply of paper towels complete the necessary equipment.

ETCHING PRACTICE

In the National Metals Handbook, published by the American Society for Metals, there appears a recommended practice for hot

[1] Cast Duriron dishes may be procured from The Duriron Company, Inc., Dayton, Ohio.

15 minutes.   30 minutes.   45 minutes.
This row of discs heated to 160°F. for the time noted.

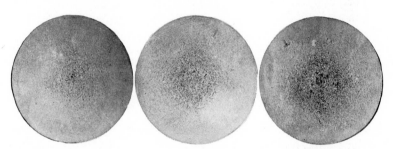

15 minutes.   30 minutes.   45 minutes.
This row of discs heated to 180°F. for the time noted.

15 minutes.   30 minutes.   45 minutes.
This row of discs heated to 200°F. for the time noted.

Fig. 252.—Effect of time and temperature on etching $3\frac{1}{4}''$ rd. carbon tool steel bar in 50:50 hydrochloric acid.

acid etching and a copy will be found at the end of this chapter. Since this recommended practice covers the operations of etching in a very comprehensive way, the reader is referred thereto for a description of the actual operations.

The four factors entering into the success of the test are surface finish, strength of acid, temperature of acid, and time of immersion. A ground, sawed or cleanly machined surface free from oil or grease will be satisfactory. If discs come in contact with oil, it is often desirable to clean them in caustic before placing in the etching bath. The etching solution should be made up of equal parts of water and acid. Both time and temperature have an important effect upon the depth of etching, and in order to obtain the most favorable depth for revealing defects, it is necessary to control these carefully. Time and temperature are factors which are governed by the type of steel being etched, and by the requirements of the particular operator. In this respect the recommendations laid down by the practice of the A.S.M. are quite satisfactory.

To illustrate the effect of time and temperature upon etching results, a series of nine discs of plain carbon tool steel etched for various times and at various temperatures is shown in Fig. 252. These nine discs were cut adjacent to one another from a bar having an objectionable amount of center segregation. It will be noted that 15, 30 and 45 minute etching at 160°F. and 15 minute etching at 180°F. all give approximately the same depth of pattern, and all reveal satisfactorily the defects present. It would appear therefore that for this type of steel a 20 minute etch at 160°/170°F. would be satisfactory. It should be further noted that etching for longer times and at higher temperatures, results simply in deeper pitting without revealing any further defects. In fact the deeper etch serves to confuse the test by masking the defects in a deeply etched background.

To demonstrate the effect of over etching, Fig. 253 shows a disc from a commercially perfect billet of steel, the disc having been etched for 45 minutes at 160°F. Figure 254 shows the same disc after being etched for 4 hours at 180°F. It will be observed that even though the steel is as nearly perfect as it is possible to make it, still prolonged etching has pitted the disc entirely through.

A variable that affects the depth of etch, and which really falls under the head of time, is the thickness of the disc. If discs are introduced into the acid cold, the thicker discs will require more time to come up to the temperature of the acid than will the thinner ones, and consequently they will not etch as deeply. It is for this reason that the A.S.M. committee recommends preheating discs to the temperature of the acid before immersion, when very accurate results are required.

Fig. 253.—Disc properly etched.

Fig. 254.—Same disc as Fig. 253 overetched.

For the information of those who may wish to acid inspect the twelve Carpenter Matched Tool Steels, all can be etched at a temperature of 160°/170°F. for 20 minutes.

INTERPRETATION OF ETCHED DISCS

The interpretation of etching patterns and general standardization of the test are less difficult when certain fundamental principles in connection with the macrostructure of tool steel are understood. Some of the more important of these are discussed in the following paragraphs.

Ingot Structure.—An ingot of tool steel can be considered as being made up of two parts, an outer shell of metal of considerable thickness which has frozen quickly, and an inner zone that has cooled more slowly. Due to the rapid freezing of the outer shell, the constituents in this portion of the ingot will be finely dispersed. Since the inner portion freezes more slowly however, certain constituents in this part of the ingot will be given time to agglomerate, with the result that these constituents will be of larger average size toward the center of the ingot than in the outer shell.   This is a condition that is inevitable, and arises from the natural process of freezing the ingot.   The constituents that behave in this manner are carbon, phosphorus, manganese, and sulphur—the latter two occurring as manganese sulfide.   As long as these constituents are evenly distributed, they are not harmful, even though agglomerated.   It is when they gather together in masses that they become undesirable.   Such a condition is known as **segregation.**

Deep etching will reveal these agglomerated or segregated constituents by reason of the fact that they are more readily soluble in hydrochloric acid than the surrounding metal.   Manganese sulfide is extremely soluble in the acid, and this is eaten out almost instantly.   Consequently in a correctly made ingot, the etched cross section would be expected to show a myriad of small pits increasing in size from surface to center.   Any segregations would be revealed as unusually large pits.   It would also be expected that the larger the ingot, the larger would be the average size of pits, and that consequently the larger sizes of bars will show heavier pitting than the smaller sizes.   This fact must be allowed for in interpreting results on larger discs.

Another natural process that affects the center of the ingot is shrinkage during freezing.   Since the center is last to freeze, the shrinkage is concentrated at this point, and must be corrected by feeding a continuous supply of molten metal into the axis of the ingot from the sink head, or "hot top."   Under these conditions it is obvious that the top of the ingot is the last to freeze, and consequently agglomeration of constituents is greatest at this point and would be revealed by uniformly larger pits after deep etching.

Still another natural process, and one that results from the fact that steel is crystalline, is the formation of so-called **dendrites,** or tree-like crystals.   All steel ingots are composed of these crystals.   Sometimes they are very small and cannot be seen except with the aid of the microscope.   In some cases they are large enough to be seen with the naked eye when the steel has been properly etched.   These dendrites are revealed in deep etching by reason of the fact that as each individual dendrite freezes, small quantities of impurities collect on its outer surface where it is in contact with other dendrites.   Since these impurities are partly composed of very minute particles of manganese sulfide, each dendrite is thus clearly outlined by the acid etch.

In addition to the conditions already described as resulting from natural freezing conditions (and therefore inevitable) the ingot may contain certain accidental characteristics which should and can be avoided. Entrapped **slag** or **dirt** may occur as small inclusions, usually distributed throughout the ingot, although occasionally segregating to the center. If the steel has not been melted properly, large quantities of gas may be given off during the freezing of the ingot which will result in **blow holes.** In the ingot these are round or oval shaped holes with smooth surfaces. If proper provision has not been made for feeding the center of the ingot during freezing, the axis may contain an axial cavity or **pipe.** This will be an irregular cavity with rough walls, often containing perfectly formed crystals.

Effect of Hot Work on Ingot Macrostructure.[1]—Reheating the ingot for hot working, and subsequent cooling of the resulting billet entirely recrystallize the metal. However, many of the agglomerated constituents and imperfections in the ingot have no part in this recrystallization, and these are consequently drawn out into strings during the hot working operation. Only part of the carbon segregation is diffused, and this therefore will reappear as bands in the billet. Phosphorus, while completely in solution in the iron does not diffuse and thus reappears as bands. Manganese sulphide is totally insoluble, and therefore simply draws out into strings. Inclusions of slag will draw out in a manner similar to manganese sulphide. A deep etched cross-section of the billet will therefore not show much change in the constituents, excepting that they are grouped more closely together. Dendrites will be completely recrystallized in reheating but since they were outlined in the ingot as already described, their outline will still be visible after etching, although distorted to a degree depending upon the amount of hot work. Blow holes will elongate and tend to close up under sufficient work, although

[1] In these terms *macro* etch and *macro* structure, the prefix *macro* means "visible to the naked eye"—as contrasted with *micro* which means "visible under a microscope." *Macro* structure is therefore the crystalline structure as made visible to the naked eye by means of the acid etch. (See Chapter 1, page 38.)

they do not weld up completely; pipe will behave likewise. Deep etching will consequently reveal these as partially welded porous spots.

While the constituents and impurities making up the ingot are drawn into strings during hot working, it is possible by this same operation to introduce new conditions and defects that will later be revealed in the etch test. **Center bursts** may occur due to overstressing the axis of the ingot during hot working, or they may result from "clinking" (internal cracking) the ingot in heating. **Internal cracks** may occur as a result of unfavorable cooling conditions after hot working; and **laps** or **seams** may be produced on the surface. These conditions can readily be distinguished from those arising in the ingot if it will be kept in mind that the latter are always drawn out to a degree proportionate to the amount of hot work.

Magnification of Defects by Etching.—Deep etching always greatly magnifies the various conditions observed. While this fact is the very thing that makes the test so valuable, at the same time it must be taken carefully into account when interpreting the results. Manganese sulphide inclusions, for example, have been observed that were magnified 200 times their actual diameter by deep etching. Segregations in the center of a bar can readily be made to look like porosity by an average etch. Deep etching will reveal dendrites clearly, even though it is usually impossible to distinguish the constituents composing dendrites under the microscope, and it is equally impossible to distinguish the various parts of the dendrite by chemical analysis.

It is therefore extremely important to keep in mind the magnifying effect of the acid attack, and in interpreting results to make certain allowances where conditions are greatly exaggerated by the etch.

EXAMPLES OF VARIOUS CONDITIONS REVEALED BY DEEP ETCHING

Some of the conditions that may be revealed by the deep etch test are illustrated by the following photographs. All of the pieces shown have been etched for fifteen minutes at a temperature of 180°F.

Surface Seams.—Fig. 255 shows a disc cut from a 4″ round bar containing deep surface seams resulting from inadequate preparation of the billet. The interior of this bar would be considered satisfactory. The lines across the face of this disc and some of the subsequent discs are marks left from the saw cut.

Flakes.—Fig. 256 shows a disc cut from a 6″ square billet containing internal cracks or "flakes."

FIG. 255.—Surface seams.

FIG. 256.—Internal cracks or flakes.

FIG. 257.—A "piped" billet.

FIG. 258.—Porous center.

Pipe.—Fig. 257 shows a disc cut from a 4″ square billet containing pipe. This disc was cut close to the top, or pipe end, of the billet and indicates that insufficient crop or discard was taken from the top of the ingot. Otherwise the steel is satisfactory.

Porousness.—In Fig. 258 is shown a 3″ round bar having a porous center. The dark areas close to the center indicate spongy metal resulting from insufficient feeding during solidification of the ingot.

FIG. 259.—Center segregation.

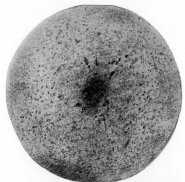

FIG. 260.—Blow holes.

FIG. 261.—Slag.

FIG. 262.—Half of disc showing dendritic structure.

Segregation.—Fig. 259 shows a disc from a $3\frac{1}{2}''$ round bar containing axial segregation. The etching acid has attacked the segregates in the center revealing them as black pits.

Blow Holes.—Fig. 260 represents a disc showing numerous blow holes that have closed up in the rolling operation, but which are readily revealed in etching. The dark spot in the center of the disc is a spongy area.

Slag.—Fig. 261 shows a disc cut from a bar containing slag stringers. These are revealed as black pits occurring in an irregular manner over the section of the disc.

Dendrites.—Fig. 262 is a disc in which the dendritic structure has been clearly revealed. This disc would not ordinarily be considered objectionable.

CORRELATION OF MACROSTRUCTURE WITH SERVICE RESULTS

The ultimate purpose of the deep etch inspection is to determine which steel is suitable for making into tools, and which is not. Some aggravated defects such as pipe, visible slag inclusions and blow holes are of course quite obvious, and their effect upon tools cannot be debated. However, when the defects present are small, or when dendritic patterns and segregations are revealed, interpretation is not so easy, since the suitability of the steel depends upon the degree to which these conditions occur. Judgment alone will not suffice to determine which is good and which is bad. Judgment must be backed by actual experience with tools made from steel having known characteristics as determined by deep etch test. Snap judgment may result not only in needless rejection of good steel, but in the acceptance of steel that will later give trouble if made into tools. Too much stress cannot be put upon the necessity of basing inspection standards upon actual tool performance.

Another phase of this question is the importance of close cooperation between the maker and user of the steel in developing between them a reasonable interpretation of results, and a mutual standard of inspection. Many of the troubles encountered in using this test are due to misunderstandings which can readily be overcome when the maker understands the requirements of his customer and the customer on the other hand understands something of the origin of defects and their effect upon tool service.

MACRO ETCHING OF IRON AND STEEL[1]

RECOMMENDED PRACTICE FOR A STANDARD MACRO ETCH
TEST FOR ROUTINE INSPECTION OF IRON AND STEEL

General.—The macro etch test reveals readily and quickly many of the characteristics of steel, but in some instances, further examination by standard testing methods is required to evaluate them properly. The knowledge that a piece of steel is dendritic or contains metallic and nonmetallic segregates is not sufficient evidence in itself on which to base definite conclusions of the properties of the steel. There is real value in the macro etch test when used to separate materials which are obviously defective from those which are not. It is easily made, but requires experience and judgment to interpret the results.

Preparation of Sample.—When it is desired to reveal the surface defects, such as seams, laps, and grinding checks, preparation of the sample is frequently unnecessary. If oil or grease is on the surface, it should be removed for best results. Scale on the surface of the material will be removed by the acid, so that the surface defects will become visible, but in order to reveal the internal structure or defects, a section must be prepared by cutting through the metal at a point where inspection is desired. For best results, the samples to be etched should be in a soft annealed condition, and the method of preparing the sample would be such that no metal is smeared or flowed over the surface.

The surface finish of the specimen depends on the etching solution used. A machined surface is recommended as the standard surface finish in this practice. A smooth ground and polished surface is not necessary and in many instances a fairly smooth sawed cut is satisfactory. This latter statement is true for the higher carbon steels and for tool steels in general. On the very soft steels, a machined surface not too coarsely cut or a sawed surface, rough ground to remove all traces of flowed metal is desirable.

Etching Solution.—A solution of one part commercial hydrochloric acid and one part water is recommended. This solution has the advantage that it can be heated with little or no change in concentration. The fumes of this mixture are corrosive so that the work is best done under a hood. (A solution consisting of

[1] Reprinted by permission of the American Society for Metals, from the National Metals Handbook—1947 Ed.

38% hydrochloric acid, 12% sulphuric acid, and 50% water is sometimes used in the same manner as the recommended hydrochloric acid solution. This solution has been used extensively by a number of forging manufacturers, and was originally suggested by the Watertown Arsenal. The apparent advantages appear to be a more sharply defined etched pattern and less susceptibility to rusting.)

It is not necessary to throw away the acid after each test, but for the best results a fresh solution should be used for each test. Irregular etching effects are obtained if the etchant solution is dirty or contaminated.

For containers pyrex glass, porcelain dishes, or corrosion resisting metals can be used. Satisfactory results have been obtained with hydrochloric acid and particularly with sulphuric acid using a lead lined iron pan or wooden tank provided care is exercised in the application of heat. It is felt, however, that a wooden tank is the least satisfactory type of container and its use should be avoided if at all possible. For heating the solution the method which gives the best temperature control should be preferred.

Temperature of Acid.—A temperature of 160°F. is recommended. This temperature gives a vigorous reaction and does not evaporate the solution too readily. If the temperature rises much above 175°F., the etching solution tends to lose its selectivity and a reaction with the entire surface occurs rather than at just the localized points of attack as it is desired. On the other hand a solution temperature below 160°F. will usually unnecessarily prolong the etching operation with little gain resulting. The temperature should be determined with a good thermometer.

The ordinary procedure is to put the cold specimens into hot acid at the temperature 160°F. and then carefully adjust the process so that a temperature of about 160°F. is maintained at all times. Methods of maintaining this temperature will vary with different users, and will depend upon the number of specimens being etched in the pan at one time, the volume of etching solution used, and the heat conductivity of the container. For extreme constancy of results, it is recommended to first clean the specimens and then heat them in hot water to the same temperature as the acid. The specimens are then transferred to the acid bath, which has first been heated to the proper temperature. By so doing it is much easier to control the time element than if the specimens were put into cold acid and brought up to temperature with the solution, or cold specimens put into hot acid with its resulting fluctuation of acid temperature.

Time of Etching.—The time of etching will depend upon the type of steel to be etched, the condition of the surface, and the

TABLE XXVIII.—RECOMMENDED ETCHING TIME IN MINUTES FOR VARIOUS STEELS[1]

(Half-Strength Commercial Hydrochloric Acid)

Tool Steels

Steels	Etching Time
Carbon and Carbon-Vanadium	20 min.
Manganese Oil-Hardening	20 min.
Tungsten Hot Die Steel	20 min.
Chromium Hot Working Die Steel	20 min.
High-Carbon High-Chromium	20 min.
High Speed	20 min.

Stainless Iron and Steel

Chromium Type	30 min.
Cr-Ni Type	1 hr. or more depending on how low carbon (C < .10)

Free-Machining Stainless

Chromium Type	20 min.
Cr-Ni Type	20 min.

S.A.E. Steels

1010	60 min. (S < .020)
1050 to 1095	20 min. (S < .020)
3115	45 min.
3150	20/30 min.
3215	60 min.
3250	20/30 min.
3312	45 min.
3340	30 min.
3450	20/30 min.
71360	20 min.
7260	30 min.
9255 and 9260	20/30 min.
2015, 2115 and 2315	60 min. (S < .015)
2350	30/45 min. (S < .015)
2515	60 min. (S < .015)
4100, 4300 and 4600 Series	20/30 min.
5100 Series	30 min.
52100	20 min.
6115	30 min.
6140	20/30 min.
6150	20 min.

[1] For convenience, this table has been rearranged and condensed by the authors. The acid temperature in all cases is 160°F.

physical condition of the steel, such as annealed or hardened. For best reproduction of results, it is extremely important that the time be accurately determined, and maintained from batch to batch. If the steel is not etched long enough, the sample will not give all of the information desired; if it is etched too long, some of the more delicate details will be masked by the general destruction of the surface.

When the specimens are in a soft annealed condition, the etching periods given in Table XXVIII have been found to give good average results. It is to be emphasized that this table has only a limited value, and should serve only as a guide in the length of time that may be required to produce the proper etched surface. Marked variation in the susceptibility of steels to acid attack will be found between heats of steel, different methods of heat treatment, position of the specimen in the ingot as influenced by degree of segregation, and particularly with regard to the machined finish of the specimen. A little practice with the macro etch test will enable the operator to develop a macro etch surface which will be sufficiently deeply etched to fully bring out the structure, but not over-etched to develop excessive pitting which masks the structure and frequently deceives the examiner.

Washing and Preserving Specimens.—After the sample is etched, it should be removed from the hot acid and washed under running water, and the "smut" deposit on the specimen should be removed by scrubbing with a stiff brush. Live steam is also an excellent method of washing etched work. The piece is first thoroughly rinsed and placed under the live steam nozzle. This results in rapid and complete drying with freedom from rust. For drying the specimens after washing, they can be blotted with a paper or cloth towel or dried with a blower.

As a simple means of avoiding rusting temporarily, the specimen may be rinsed in water to remove the acid, dipped in ammonia and washed in hot water. For longer preservation, after the specimen has been dried, it should be covered with a thin coat of transparent lacquer, or a film of oil which may be applied with the palm of the hand. Rusting may be delayed temporarily and mild rusting may be removed by the application to a dried sample of a solution of 50-50 syrup of phosphoric acid to which a little sugar has been added. The excess solution may be blotted up with a cloth or paper towels. Caution is recommended in the use of this solution as it will roughen the hands and disintegrate cloth, if allowed to remain in contact an extended time.

Interpretation of Results.—The results obtained on properly etched samples are of great value if correctly interpreted. Surface seams, internal cracks, and pipe are easily recognized. It is the improper interpretation of the evidences of segregation and dendritic structures as revealed by deep etching that furnishes the greatest possibility of expensive errors and the needless rejection of material. **It is not true, moreover, that every pit developed indicates the occurrence of an inclusion, since pitting may also occur as a result of acid attack around carbide particles.** Irregular etching effects are obtained if the surface under examination has contained any oil or grease, if it was prepared by improper machining method resulting in a smearing or rubbing action of the metal, if the piece has been in contact with other specimens in the etching bath, or if the etching solution was dirty or contaminated.

Cracks from Etching.—Hardened or otherwise highly stressed steels should be sufficiently tempered before etching to prevent cracking, since otherwise sound steel may crack in the etching solution and thus lead to false conclusions.

Grinding Cracks.—Grinding cracks can be easily distinguished by the standard macro etch test and are usually, but not always, identified by a pattern of some symmetry. Again it is emphasized that hardened pieces should be softened prior to hot etching.

Surface Cracks.—Surface cracks as revealed by deep etching usually follow an irregular path and may result from improper handling during heating, forging, rolling, or during cooling from the finishing temperature. With heat treated material, surface cracks may be caused by improper treatment, by improper grinding after hardening, or by surface stresses.

Seams.—Seams in rolled material are of varying depth and usually extend in a straight path parallel to the direction of rolling. With forged material, seams generally follow the contour of the forging and the flow of the metal. The most detrimental result of the presence of seams is their tendency to start fatigue failures, or to open up into deep hardening cracks if the metal is heat treated. This detrimental effect is avoided if, in the manufacturing operations, the surface is machined to a sufficient depth to remove the seams.

Surface Appearance.—Steels may etch with a comparatively smooth surface or with a highly rough or pitted surface, depending upon variables in manufacture, and composition. Therefore, a highly roughened surface is not necessarily detrimental. It has been found that smoother surfaces can be obtained by adding several drops of organic inhibitor, namely, triamylamine, to the hot etching solution. Inclusions are then attacked in preference to the metal, thereby eliminating the general roughness and consequently producing better patterns.

Irregularity in pitting may usually be attributed to one or more of the defects given below. Certain manganese, oil-hardening types are more readily attacked by the acid and are often decidedly roughened without in any way being defective.

Center Porosity.—Porosity may be the result of an actual discontinuity within the metal, in which case it is probably more proper to classify the defect as a pipe. Usually, however, the porosity is of such a nature that it is not visible until the specimen has been subjected to the etch. This condition can be found in widely varying degrees and the question of whether the steel should or should not be used is one of experienced judgment. Porosity is generally restricted to describing segregations which are partially torn open on hot rolling, or forging.

Pipes and Bursts.—Pipes are internal cavities formed during ingot solidification and carried through the various manufacturing processes to the finished product. Pipe is invariably associated with segregated impurities which are deeply attacked by the etching reagent. Cavities in the center not associated with deeply attacked impurities are often mistaken for pipe but such cavities can usually be traced to bursts caused from improper handling of the steel during forging or rolling. Either of these defects should be visible after deep etching, and can generally be distinguished from each other by the degree of sponginess surrounding the defect. Piped material usually shows considerably more sponginess than burst material.

Unsound Steel.—Numerous blow holes and nonmetallic inclusions visible as the result of the deep etch are usually indicative of both gases and oxides being distributed throughout the steel at the time of casting.

Nonmetallic Inclusions and Metallic Segregates.—Nonmetallic inclusions usually appear as pits and must not be confused with pits occurring from the etching out of metallic segregates. When nonmetallic inclusions are suspected in highly alloyed steels which may contain metallic segregates, a comparison should be made of an annealed specimen and a hardened specimen etched alike. If the etching pits are the result of nonmetallic inclusions, they will appear similarly in both the annealed and hardened conditions. If they are the result of a metallic segregate, they will differ. The macro etch test is not recommended for a cleanliness test, since unambiguous results are only obtained in the case of large slag inclusions.

Segregations are revealed by the severity of the acid attack on the affected areas. The segregations may occur at the center and be so deeply attacked after etching that they may appear as a pipe, or the segregation may be grouped in some fairly regular form about the center, depending on the shape of the ingot and the mechanical work that has been done upon it.

Ingot corner segregation is of frequent occurrence in macro etched discs obtained from large forgings. It should be emphasized that evidences of ingot corner segregation sometimes appear as cracks, whereas actually they may represent a segregate which has been eaten out during the acid test.

Segregation as revealed by macro etching is not always an indication of defective material. The segregation revealed by macro etching can be identified by examining a polished specimen under the microscope to determine if it is metallic segregation, crystalline arrangement, or a concentration of impurities. The microscopic identification of segregation may also be supplemented by chemical means; such as analysis of center drillings for carbon, phosphorus and sulphur, or by analysis of inclusions after chemical extraction of same.

Internal Cracks.—Internal cracks, sometimes called flakes, cooling cracks, or thermal cracks, can be detected by the macro etch test and their identity can be verified by a fracture test of a hardened specimen on which they are revealed as brightly crystalline spots. These cracks are an actual discontinuity in the metal and, depending on their nature and distribution, may make the steel unfit for use unless they are removed by further hot reduction.

Dendritic Pattern.—Etching often reveals a dendritic structure which is the result of the crystalline characteristics of the ingot. Dendritic patterns are detected even in steel that has been subjected to repeated mechanical reduction. It has not been proved that dendritic patterns are associated with service failures, provided the material has been subjected to sufficient mechanical working and provided the segregation accompanying the dendritic formation is not in the form of nonmetallic inclusions which are incapable of dispersion.

In the formation of dendrite crystals, the intercrystalline material contains minute metallic segregations which are largely diffused into the crystals. However, when nonmetallic inclusions are thus segregated, they are incapable of diffusion. The use of the microscope is suggested in such cases to supplement the macro examination.

Pattern Effect.—Pattern effect is almost wholly the result of the crystallization of the ingot and naturally results from that part of the bar which was the columnar structure of the ingot etching differently from that part which was the granular structure of the ingot. Should the steel contain considerable sulphide and silicate inclusions, then the area of contact between the columnar structure and the granular structure may be particularly noticeable. In the absence of large amounts of sulphides and silicates, the pattern effect probably is of no serious consequence.

Grain Size.—While the deep etch test is of no definite value in determining grain size, nevertheless the manner in which many specimens etch may indicate something of the grain size. Generally the larger the grain, the coarser will be the appearance of the etched surface.

Decarburization and Carburization.—Generally the areas which have been either decarburized or carburized will etch differently from the remainder of the specimen, the chief difference being one of color. Decarburized parts will appear lighter in color and carburized parts darker.

If the section to be examined is small enough, it can be given a polished final finish and then cold etched, say from 5 to 30 seconds, in nital (3% HNO_3—97% ethyl alcohol). This will generally result in excellent contrast and if the polish is good enough, the same sample can be examined microscopically as well as visually.[1]

---

[1] This recommended practice continues to discuss macro etching for other specific purposes. See National Metals Handbook, 1947 Edition.

CHAPTER 16

TIMBRE AND HARDENABILITY TESTS

In Chapter 4 we discussed hardenability and timbre, and defined these as follows:

Hardenability is the tendency of steel to harden, and means the same thing as "hardness penetration" or "hardening penetration."

Timbre is that property of steel which controls the grain size and toughness resulting from heat treatment.

It was explained that the effect of timbre is most evident in the plain carbon tool steels. In the alloy steels the effects of timbre, while present, are not so evident, and hardenability is governed primarily by analysis.

It was stated in that chapter also that the hardenability of a tool steel may be expressed in four ways:

(1) As the depth to which a standard sized specimen will harden in a certain quenching medium,
(2) As the largest sized section which will just harden through,
(3) As the depth to which a standard round specimen will harden in from the end when quenched only on that end,
(4) As the critical quenching rate in degrees per second, from which figure any of the other values can be estimated.

All hardenability tests presently in use give an answer in one or more of these four terms, and consequently fall under several types.

THE P-F TEST

In Chapter 4 a simple timbre test for plain carbon steel was described, which consisted in examining the fracture of a $\frac{3}{4}''$ round sample that had been hardened in brine from 1550°F. For average tool making purposes, this simple test will answer every requirement but it is possible to more thoroughly explore the timbre characteristics of a steel, and this is sometimes desirable

416

as the basis for a rigid specification for carbon tool steel. B. F. Shepherd has devised a refinement of this test that permits a numerical evaluation of both timbre and hardening penetration.[1] This falls under our first general type of test, namely that giving the depth of penetration on a standard section. It is known as the "*P-F* Test" (*P* = penetration; *F* = fracture grain size).

Fig. 263.—(*Shepherd*) Set of martensitic fracture grain standards showing protective covers removed from specimens 2 to 10.

In order to conduct the *P-F* test, it is necessary to acquire a box of fracture grain size standards. These standards are illustrated in Fig. 263, and are procurable from the Thermist Company, Phillipsburg, N. J. The set consists of ten $\frac{3}{4}''$ round fractures ranging from #1—which is extremely coarse grained, to #10—which is so fine as to appear silky. These are compared to the "unknown" fracture that is being tested and the "unknown" is given a rating. An experienced observer can assign fractional ratings—that is, a fracture half way between #7 and #8 would be rated $7\frac{1}{2}$, and one between this and #8 would be rated $7\frac{3}{4}$. The actual conduct of the test can best be quoted from Mr. Shepherd's article:

[1] This test is described in the Transactions of the A.S.M. Volume XXII, page 979, and the detailed instructions for making the test are reprinted here by permission.

The classification of fractures requires a great deal of personal skill. Even though a set of fracture standards is available, proper technique must be used in interpreting values. The following suggestions are made as an aid to such interpretations:

1. Any fracture determinations should be an agreement of two qualified observers. Disagreement by more than $\frac{1}{2}$ fracture number shall result in arbitration by a third observer and the apparent true fracture number recorded.

2. To assist in eliminating personal error, classifications are made to $\frac{1}{4}$ number.

3. Observers are to be qualified by passing the following tests on a set of approximately twenty samples of various fracture classifications.

(a) Ability to check their own classifications on different days to within $\frac{1}{4}$ fracture number on 90% of the samples.

(b) Apparent true values should be established on approximately twenty samples by two or more observers passing Test No. 1. To qualify, at least 80% of these samples must be classified within $\frac{1}{4}$ fracture number.

A representative qualification test is shown in Table XXIX.

TABLE XXIX.—(*Shepherd*) QUALIFICATION TEST FOR FRACTURE OBSERVER

Sample No.	Apparent true fracture No.	Observer variations from apparent true No.			
		A	B	C	D
1	8	$+\frac{1}{4}$	0	$-\frac{1}{4}$	-1
2	$4\frac{1}{2}$	0	0	0	-1
3	$7\frac{1}{2}$	0	$-\frac{1}{4}$	0	-1
4	$8\frac{1}{4}$	0	-1	0	$-2\frac{1}{4}$
5	$3\frac{1}{2}$	$+\frac{1}{4}$	$+\frac{1}{4}$	$-\frac{1}{4}$	$-\frac{1}{4}$
6	$8\frac{1}{2}$	0	$+\frac{1}{4}$	0	$-\frac{1}{2}$
7	5	0	0	$+\frac{1}{4}$	0
8	$8\frac{1}{4}$	0	0	$+\frac{1}{2}$	0
9	3	0	$+\frac{1}{4}$	0	0
10	$8\frac{3}{4}$	$-\frac{1}{4}$	$-\frac{1}{4}$	$+\frac{1}{4}$	0
11	$8\frac{3}{4}$	$+\frac{1}{4}$	$-\frac{1}{4}$	0	$-\frac{1}{4}$
12	$7\frac{1}{2}$	0	0	$+\frac{1}{4}$	-2
13	$4\frac{1}{4}$	0	0	$+\frac{1}{2}$	$+\frac{1}{4}$
14	$8\frac{3}{4}$	0	$-\frac{1}{4}$	$+\frac{1}{4}$	$-\frac{1}{2}$
15	$3\frac{3}{4}$	$+\frac{1}{4}$	0	$-\frac{1}{4}$	0
16	$8\frac{1}{4}$	0	$-\frac{3}{4}$	$-\frac{1}{4}$	$-\frac{3}{4}$
17	$3\frac{1}{4}$	0	0	$-\frac{1}{4}$	$+\frac{1}{2}$
18	$8\frac{3}{4}$	$-\frac{1}{4}$	0	$-\frac{1}{4}$	$-\frac{1}{4}$
19	8	0	$+\frac{1}{2}$	0	$+\frac{1}{2}$
20	3	0	0	$-\frac{1}{4}$	0
Grade		100	85	90	50

PENETRATION (P)—FRACTURE (F) TEST METHOD

1. *Preparation of Test Pieces.*
   (a) It is most important to obtain metal that is representative of the heat of material to be tested. Therefore, stock whose diameter is greater than $1\frac{1}{4}''$ is reduced in size to $1''$ round (approximately) by suitable forging. Approximately $14''$ of material is required in lengths not less than $3''$. When possible, the original marking is allowed to remain untouched in the forging operation, thus avoiding mixed samples.
   (b) The sample material may be annealed before machining (1325°F. air or 1450°F. furnace cool, as convenient).
   (c) Four specimens are machined $\frac{3}{4}''$ round, plus or minus $0.001''$ and $3''$ long. Each piece is stamped with a suitable code or number for identification. The pieces are also stamped on both ends, 1450, 1500, 1550 and 1600 respectively, one number to each piece.

2. *Normalizing.*—All samples are given an oil quench from 1600°F. after holding the pieces at temperature a minimum of 40 minutes after heating through.

3. *Hardening.*
   (a) Heating.—An electric furnace should be used for heating. The heating rate should be similar to or the equivalent of that obtained in an 11 KW top and bottom element electric furnace with a hearth size of $12'' \times 30''$ and not more than four samples shall be heated at one time. The samples shall be placed erect in the furnace, and so located that all samples are heated at the same rate. Temperatures of 1450°, 1500°, 1550° and 1600°F. respectively, shall be used, the samples having been so identified previously. The samples are in the furnace for 30 minutes for each temperature.

   Accurate control of the time-cycle and temperature must be maintained. This is extremely important because penetration of hardness and fracture grain size tend to increase with time and temperature on all except very stable heats.
   (b) Quenching.—The samples shall be quenched in a standard vertical jig (2″ pipe overflow, Fig. 264), flushed with 10% brine at room temperature.

   Fig. 264 shows a specimen in the tongs being placed in the spray. The tongs have a shoulder which enables the specimen to be placed easily in the center of the spray.

4. *Fracture Grain-Size.*

   (*a*) Breaking.—The samples are notched halfway between ends with a thin ($\frac{1}{16}$ to $\frac{3}{32}''$) friction wheel, to a depth not over $\frac{1}{16}''$. The fracture is obtained preferably by transverse impact because transverse static loading to rupture tends to pull or otherwise distort the grain.

Fig. 264.—(*Shepherd*) Showing method of quenching specimens in a standard vertical jig.

   (*b*) The grain size is determined by comparing and matching the case or hardened zone of one of the broken halves with the fracture grain size standards, and shall be expressed as the number or quarter number nearest the corresponding standard sample. Determination of the grain size number is made according to the standard method.

5. *Penetration.*—The penetration tests are made on the second half of the hardened and fractured sample. A smooth cross section surface is prepared not less than $1''$ from the original end of the hardened sample. Final finish on the cross section surface is on an "O" or finer abrasive. The polished surface is etched for three minutes in a 50–50 hydrochloric acid and water at 180°F.

The hardness penetration is measured, macroscopically, to the nearest half of $\frac{1}{64}''$ and shall be expressed as the numerator of such a fraction. A convenient scale is shown in Fig. 265.

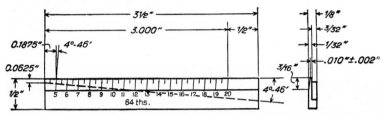

Fig. 265.—(*Shepherd*) Gage for measuring P-value.

6. *Designation.*—The P-F characteristic is recorded as 8 numbers. The first four numbers represent the penetration in $\frac{1}{64}$ths of an inch, and the last four numbers the fracture grain size. The first number of each group represents the P-F result for a temperature of 1450°F., the second number of each group represents the P-F for a temperature of 1500°F. and so on.

The characteristic then appears in the following form:

5. 6. 8. 12. / 9. 8. 6. 4.

When all the results do not concur with the whole numbers, the characteristic may appear as follows:

$5\frac{1}{2}$. 6. $8\frac{1}{2}$. 13. / $8\frac{3}{4}$. $8\frac{1}{4}$. $7\frac{1}{2}$. 5.

This is the end of the quotation from Mr. Shepherd's article, the comments below are the authors'.

The above method makes available a timbre and hardenability test of extreme exactness. If it were written into a specification, few steel mills today would be able to comply with its complete requirements. At the present stage of the art, it is more practical to consider only *two* quenching temperatures—namely, 1450° and 1550°F. This reduces by half the time and expense of the test, and it prescribes steel as accurately as it can be commercially supplied—even by steel mills which have specialized on timbre control. The great contribution of this P-F test is the fact that it proposes actual numbers by which the timbre characteristics can be recorded. Its one limitation, and an important one, is that on account of the small diameter of the specimen used, it can be adapted only to the shallower hardening plain carbon steels. The deeper hardening carbon steels will so nearly harden through in the $\frac{3}{4}''$ round section that an accurate measure of penetration is not possible. When quenched at elevated temperatures, they will usually harden entirely through. Consequently for any but the shallow hardening carbon steels, some other type of test should be used, and any specification for tool steel involving the P-F test should be carefully worked out between the supplier and the consumer.

Consumers who do not forge, normalize or oil treat their carbon tool steel after purchase—but simply machine the tools and then harden them—should not introduce any normalizing (or oil treatment) in the timbre test. Such users simply want to know whether the new shipment of steel will behave normally in hardening and they should therefore make the timbre test on the material as received. Here a caution is in order however, for a preliminary oil treatment before the final hardening will affect the depth of penetration, the exact effect depending upon the carbon content. On steels under about .95% carbon a preliminary oil treatment will deepen the penetration, while on steels above .95% carbon it will cause the penetration to be shallower. If tests are made on material as received therefore, proper allowance has to be made if they are to be compared with tests made by the standard method.

It is important to emphasize that not one tool maker in a hundred has any interest in asking the steel manufacturer to supply a "special" timbre; but *every* tool maker should be sufficiently concerned with this property of his steel to object to receiving all sorts of different timbres mixed together. Protection against such gross mixtures is amply assured by the simple test described in Chapter 5. This single test at 1550° is just as effective as the complete P-F test for distinguishing tough timbre from brittle timbre, and it gives a reasonable indication of the hardness penetration.

THE SHEPHERD DISC TEST

A convenient hardenability test for carbon tool steel first described by B. F. Shepherd[1] consists in cutting discs of various thicknesses in steps of $\frac{1}{32}''$, from the bar to be tested, for example $10\frac{1}{32}''$, $11\frac{1}{32}''$, $12\frac{1}{32}''$, etc. It is important that the discs be machined or ground accurately to size. A series of these discs is

[1] B. F. Shepherd. "Hardenability of Tool Steels." A.S.M. Vol. 17, 1930, page 90.

quenched in a brine or water flush from the desired temperature, then cut in half crosswise with a thin abrasive wheel, and the sections etched in 1:1 hydrochloric or muriatic acid for about 5 minutes at a temperature of 160°F., to bring out the depth of hardening. Such a series of etched sections is shown in Fig. 266.

The hardenability is rated as the smallest thickness of disc in thirty-seconds of an inch which shows a definite unhardened core. In Fig. 266 since the $11/_{32}''$ disc does not show a definite core, while the $12/_{32}''$ disc does, this steel would be rated as "12 hardenability." Note that this test falls under our second group, those based upon the size of section which just hardens through.

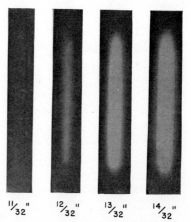

$11/_{32}''$ $12/_{32}''$ $13/_{32}''$ $14/_{32}''$

Fig. 266.—Shepherd Disc Test. Sections of discs of various thicknesses of 1.05% carbon steel quenched in brine at 1450°F., sectioned and etched.

THE CARPENTER CONE TEST

Recognizing the limitations of the P-F test on the deeper hardening carbon steels, there was developed in 1940 in the Carpenter laboratory[1] a test adapted to cover a wide range of hardenabilities, and to permit at the same time expressing the result if desired, in terms of critical quenching speed. This is known as the Carpenter Cone Test.

The specimen consists of a cone having a blunted tip, machined from the steel to be tested, and having the dimensions shown in Fig. 267.

This specimen is quenched in brine from the desired temperature, then split exactly through the lengthwise axis with a thin abrasive wheel. Fig. 268 shows a series of such sections etched in 1:1 hydrochloric acid taken from five steels of different hardenabilities, after quenching in brine at 1450°F. The blackened

[1] See a paper entitled "Hardenability of Shallow Hardening Steels," by C. B. Post, O. V. Greene and W. H. Fenstermacher (The Carpenter Steel Co.). Trans. of A.S.M. 1942, Vol. 30, page 1202.

outside portion represents the hardened layer. For comparison, the Shepherd hardenability numbers obtained by the disc test are also given under the different cones. Note the various advantages of this test. First, it shows on one specimen the

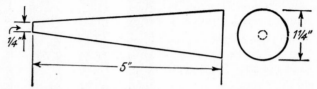

FIG. 267.—Dimensions of Cone Test Specimen.

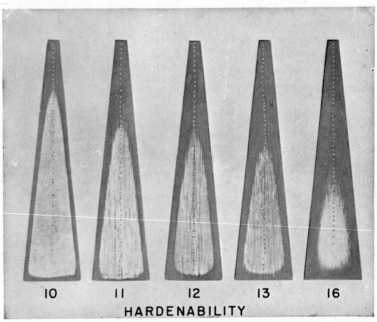

HARDENABILITY

FIG. 268.—Cone test pieces from five steels of different hardenability, quenched in brine at 1450°F., split lengthwise and etched.

penetration to be expected in various diameters. Second, it shows the diameter which will just harden through. This is sometimes called the "critical diameter." The third advantage, however, is probably the most important. Fig. 269 shows what might be called a contour map of the section of a cone quenched at 1450°F. in brine, in which speed of cooling at each depth has been determined experimentally. Each dotted line represents a certain cooling rate and all points on any one of these lines has the same rate. For example, all the points on the first line forming a nose at the left have a cooling rate at 350°F. per second, all points on the second line have a cooling rate of 300°F. per second, etc. By cooling rate we refer to the speed of cooling through about 1100° to 1300°F., which it will be noted from Chapter 4 is the so-called "gate temperature." It is obvious now that if we superimpose these lines representing cooling speed, over an actual quenched and split specimen, such as shown in Fig. 268, the line which fits the depth of penetration of that specimen will show the speed at which the steel was just able to harden—or in other words it will show the critical quenching speed of the steel.

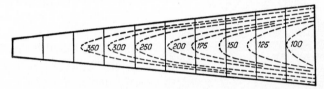

Fig. 269.—Equal cooling rate lines, degrees F per second for Taper cone specimen. Brine quenched at 1450°F.

A more accurate way of making this comparison is to take Rockwell hardness readings down the axis of the cone, and finding the point at which the hardness has dropped to C-55 Rockwell, this being the hardness of tool steel quenched just at its critical cooling speed. By marking off this distance on Fig. 269, the critical quenching rate of the steel can be read quite accurately.

The advantage of expressing the hardenability of steel in terms of critical quenching rate has already been indicated briefly in Chapter 4. It frees us of the necessity for describing the hardenability of a steel in terms of the size of section, the quenching medium, etc. Knowing the critical quenching speed of the steel for any one hardening temperature, and the section of the tool to be hardened, it is possible to predict how deep the steel will harden, or if it will harden at all, in any one quenching medium. Up to the present time it has been made use of principally by the steel maker, who finds it convenient as a means of control and as a "common denominator" of the many hardenability and hardness penetration tests appearing in specifications. It will undoubtedly find wider application in the future, when we may speak of "specific hardenability" much the same as we do "specific gravity"—a figure everyone can understand and interpret.

THE "P-V" TEST

Recently there has been developed a test for shallow hardening steels, known as the "P-V test,"[1] which combines the advantage of obtaining specific hardenability values with that of easy specimen preparation. This test employs a wedge-shaped specimen whose two faces form an angle of 90 ± 1 degree. The specimen is heated to the desired hardening temperature, and the two faces of the wedge are water flushed in a special fixture. By means of a thin grinding wheel, a longitudinal slice is then cut normal to these two faces producing a section which, after light etching, is illustrated in Figure 270.

FIG. 270.—Etched slab from P-V Test showing hardened shell, and series of Rockwell impressions.

A series of Rockwell hardness readings is taken inward from the apex. The distance from the apex to any specified hardness level affords a measure of hardenability. A high degree of accuracy in making this test can be obtained through the use of a specially designed micrometer stage which spaces the impressions at the desired intervals. Rockwell "C" or "A" readings are commonly employed in making the test, although when extremely close spacing is desired the Superficial Rockwell machine (30N scale) is necessary to prevent overlapping of the impressions.

The depth at which the specimen shows the specified hardness can be taken as a measure of hardenability, or, since the rate of cooling of various parts of the wedge in water quenching is known, the results can be converted into specific hardenability expressed as critical quenching speed in degrees per second.

---

[1] B. F. Shepherd, "Hardenability of Shallow Hardening Steels Determined by the P-V Test." Paper presented before the A.S.M. November, 1946.

THE END QUENCH (JOMINY) TEST

The so-called "End Quench" hardenability test first described by W. E. Jominy,[1] while primarily used on construction alloy steels, has found some application to tool steel. The test bar used is a cylinder 1″ in diameter by 4″ long with flat machined ends. This specimen is heated to the quenching temperature, then suspended vertically over a water jet which flushes the specimen only on one end without touching the sides. In this test the effect of the size and shape of the specimen is eliminated, and a true indication of penetration or hardenability is obtained. The test as now standardized is conducted as follows:

A vertical pipe with an orifice ½″ in diameter is fitted with a valve to control the flow of water so that the free height of the jet is 2½″ above the orifice. The pipe is also fitted with a quick acting valve above the pressure control valve. Clear water at a temperature of 75°F. is used. The specimen is heated to the proper quenching temperature, removed from the furnace and placed vertically over the orifice so that the end to be flushed is ½″ above the orifice. The jet is then turned on by opening the quick acting valve, and the end flushed for not less than 10 minutes, after which the entire specimen is quenched if not entirely cold. Two flats .015″ deep are ground lengthwise on opposite round faces, so that Rockwell hardness determinations may be made the entire length of the specimen. Since only the end is quenched the hardnesses from the flushed surface backward are much the same as they would be if a very large block had been quenched only on one face, and sectioned inward. The hardness readings are then plotted in a curve such as that illustrated in Fig. 271, which shows the Rockwell hardness at various depths under the surface.

The curve may be interpreted and used in several different ways. The point *A*, where the curve changes direction, is usually picked as measuring the depth of penetration. In high carbon steels this occurs at about C-55 Rockwell. By simply determining previously the rate of cooling of the test piece at various distances from the end, as in the cone test, it is possible to assign to this point a cooling speed, which is of course the critical

[1] W. E. Jominy, "A Hardenability Test for Carburizing Steels," **Trans.** of A.S.M. 1938, Vol. 26, page 574.

cooling speed of the steel. In specifying hardenability of alloy construction steels on the basis of the end quench test, it is often the practice to specify minimum Rockwell hardnesses at the surface, and at some definite depth under the surface.

It should be noted that all end quench tests are water quenched regardless of whether the steel being tested is the water-hardening

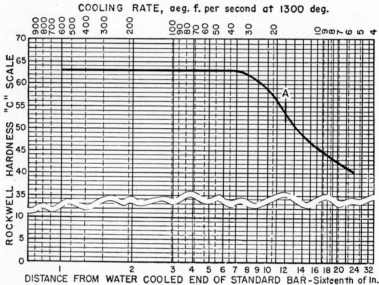

FIG. 271.—End quench hardenability curve. Oil-hardening tool steel, flushed at 1450°F.

or oil-hardening type. It should be remembered, therefore, that the end quench test on an oil-hardening steel gives only an approximate indication of how the steel will perform when oil quenched, and does not show actually either the penetration or the hardness expected by oil quenching. In testing oil-hardening steels it is of advantage therefore to express the result of the test in terms of critical quenching rate, which as we have already said is a distinct property of the steel independent of size, quenching medium, etc. The curve illustrated in Fig. 271 is of *manganese oil-hardening* tool steel, and shows how hardenability is determined routinely in the Carpenter laboratory on oil-hardening steels, which are too deep hardening for the cone test. The results are always expressed in critical quenching rate in degrees per second.

HARDENABILITY TESTS FOR AIR-HARDENING STEELS

It is obvious that none of the tests so far described could be applied to air-hardening steels, since all these tests involve cooling rates far above that of air cooling. Hardenability tests on these steels are difficult and costly to make, but fortunately they are seldom necessary on account of the fact that the hardenability of the air-hardening steels can be predicted from the analysis of the steel, other factors having little or no influence. A successful test for air-hardening steels has been developed, however,[1] and if the reader wishes to pursue this subject further we would refer him to the paper mentioned in the footnote below.

In concluding this section on timbre and hardenability testing it might be remarked that very few users of tool steel would wish to make these tests themselves, since many of them are costly and time consuming. It is believed, however, that many consumers of tool steel are interested in knowing whether or not the tool steel they purchase has been so tested by the manufacturer, and having at least a speaking acquaintance with the methods available to the steel maker for testing and controlling his tool steels to insure their uniformity. It is with this thought in mind that a brief description of these various tests has been included in this book.

[1] "Air Hardenability of Steels" by C. B. Post, M. C. Fetzer and W. H. Fenstermacher (The Carpenter Steel Co.). A.S.M. 1945, Vol. 35, page 85.

CHAPTER 17

SPARK TESTING

Sometimes a tool maker gets hold of a piece of tool steel that has lost its markings—and wants to find out as quickly as possible what kind of steel it is. If he does not have the slightest idea what kind of steel it is, or where it came from, the only safe way is to get a complete chemical analysis. However, if he is using only a limited group of tool steels, and he knows that the piece in question is one of these steels—but does not know which one— then there is a pretty good way to tell, and tell quickly. This is done by means of the "spark test."

Here again—as in Chapters 7 and 12—it is necessary to depart from the theoretical Matched Diagram names OIL-WEAR, OIL-HARD, etc., and discuss real tool steels, since only in this way can the use of the spark test be illustrated. It so happens that the sparks from the twelve Carpenter Matched Tool Steels described in Chapter 7 differ enough so that, with a little practice, they can be distinguished from each other and an unknown member of the group identified.

INSTRUCTIONS FOR SPARK TESTING

The Grinder Used.—The spark test is best conducted by holding the steel stationary and touching it with a high speed portable grinder as illustrated in Fig. 272. The data in this chapter were secured by using an electric grinder rated at 16,000 r.p.m. with a 2″ diameter, 40 grain wheel (about 8,000 surface feet per minute).

In the absence of a portable grinder, an ordinary grinding stand can be used (Fig. 273) but care should be exercised to hold the work against the wheel lightly and without bumping. An 8″ wheel mounted on a 3,600 r.p.m. spindle will give a surface speed of 7,500 feet per minute.

The Effect of Wheel Speed.—The faster the wheel, the larger and longer the spark stream—and the less pressure is needed.

A wheel turning at only 3,500 surface feet per minute requires a lot of pressure or else will give very little spark stream.

The Effect of Wheel Grain Size.—Grain size of the abrasive in the wheel does not appear to be very important. A 30 grain wheel will give somewhat less spark—with shorter flight—than a 60 grain wheel (when speed, pressure, etc. are the same).

Dressing the Wheel.—It is *very important* that the wheel be dressed clean before spark testing. A wheel is often "loaded" with steel particles that will give off their own sparks and mix

Fig. 272.—Spark testing with portable electric grinder.   Fig. 273.—Spark testing with stationary grinding stand.

with those from the sample being tested. These mixed sparks can seriously confuse the test.

Preparing the Sample.—Many tool steel bars or forgings have a skin or "bark" that is decarburized. This low carbon skin has a different spark from the steel itself, and in order to be sure of an accurate result the spark test should not be made on this bar surface, but preferably on the sawed or fractured cross section of the bar, making sure the wheel does not touch the decarburized rim.

Hardened vs. Annealed Tool Steels.—Of the tool steels containing relatively small amounts of alloys any one particular steel will show practically the same spark whether in the hardened or annealed condition. As the alloy content increases, the hardened steel will throw a longer and fuller spark stream than the annealed steel.

In steels containing appreciable amounts of tungsten, particularly high speed steels and those of relative high chromium content, this difference in spark between the hardened and annealed steel is particularly noticeable, and should be taken into consideration before reaching any conclusions about the spark test.

How Hard to Press.—Use only enough pressure to maintain a steady contact between the steel and the wheel. Slightly more pressure may be needed on a slow wheel—or a very coarse wheel—or on an annealed steel when comparing it with a hard steel of the same brand.

Where to Make the Test.—Do not make a spark test in bright sunlight—or in the dark. Diffused daylight is the best. *Be sure there is no object in the way to interfere with seeing the full length of the spark stream.*

How Long Does It Take to Learn?—As in all other things—practice makes perfect. A beginner should not trust his own judgment the first time he tries, but should practice a little every day on pieces that he knows, until he is able to recognize their sparks just as he could recognize the voice of a friend when he hears it in the dark.

Pictures of Sparks.—The schematic spark diagrams shown in this chapter provide the most detailed characteristics for each of the Carpenter Matched Tool Steels. While some spark streams have been photographed with considerable success—these diagrammatic sketches will more nearly duplicate the spark stream as it would appear to the eye while actually making the test.

EFFECTS OF VARIOUS ELEMENTS ON SPARKS

Carbon.—Causes bursts—the higher the carbon, the more plentiful and complicated the bursts, (see *No. 11 Special*) except in steels containing appreciable amounts of alloys, (see *Star-Zenith* and *T-K*).

Manganese.—In steels where the amount of other alloys present is small, manganese tends to brighten the spark and increase the "spray" around the periphery of the wheel (see *Stentor*). In steels containing moderate or large amounts of other alloys, the effects of manganese are not visible on the spark stream.

Silicon.—Suppresses the carbon bursts. When the silicon content is about 1% or more it causes a pattern of relatively coarse "fuzz" (consisting of short curved lines) close to the wheel (see *Solar*), except in steels containing appreciable amounts of other alloys (see *No. 883*).

Chromium.—Suppresses the stream and the bursts—imparts an orange color (see *Hampden, No. 610* and *No. 484*).

Nickel.—Causes forked tongues (see *R. D. S.*). Nickel also suppresses the stream and bursts slightly, but not as much as chromium.

Tungsten.—Very easy to detect its presence because it tends to suppress the effects of all other elements upon the spark stream. When tungsten content is between about 1% and 15% it causes single bright-orange tongues at the ends of the carrier lines; the higher the tungsten content, the smaller the tongues. In high tungsten steels (see *Star-Zenith* and *T-K*) the carbon bursts are suppressed altogether. Tungsten also imparts a reddish-orange color to the carrier lines.

Vanadium.—In steels where vanadium is present, spark testing is limited to its detection only and an estimate of the percentage present is not practicable. Vanadium tends to brighten the spark stream as a whole.

Molybdenum.—On steels in which other elements are not high, molybdenum causes a characteristic "spear point" at the end of the carrier lines. (See *Solar* and *Vega*.) Where relative high percentages of other elements are present these sometimes have the effect of masking the spear points. (See *No. 484, No. 610* and *Speed Star*.)

WARNING

The spark test does not *analyze* the steel. It is useful only to distinguish between steels whose spark characteristics are already familiar. The statements made in this chapter are based on spark testing the Carpenter Matched Tool Steels. They will serve further as a guide for setting up a spark testing procedure to meet individual tool room requirements.

COMMENTS ON SPARK STREAMS

It will be helpful to discuss each of the steels in the four Matched Sets, directing special attention to the *difference* in their sparks.

The Air-Hardening Matched Set.—See pages 436 and 437.

No. 610 (AIR-WEAR).—There is not much difference in the spark between *No. 610* and *Hampden*. After all, the analyses of these two steels are similar except for the lower carbon content and the presence of molybdenum in *No. 610*. The lower carbon content of *No. 610* produces less carbon bursts than *Hampden* while the molybdenum spear points are completely suppressed by the high chromium. Its color is characteristic of high chromium —being intermediate between the light colored spark of *No. 11 Special* and the reddish-orange spark of the tungsten steels. When seen together with *Hampden*, the *No. 610* spark appears a shade darker in color than the *Hampden*. The length of the *No. 610* spark stream is appreciably shorter than any of the other steels in the Matched Set except *Hampden* and *Star-Zenith*. Note: To make certain distinction between *No. 610* and *Hampden*, a hardening test should be used. Cut a slug or disc, *at least 1″ thick*—heat it to 1750° to 1800°F. and cool to room temperature in lime. If it has a hardness of Rockwell C-60 or higher, it is *No. 610*. *Hampden* will not show more than about Rockwell C-40 when so treated.

No. 484 (AIR-HARD).—This stream is somewhat longer than *No. 610* but not as long as *R. D. S.* The characteristic effects of the chromium have suppressed the stream more than in *R. D. S.* but not as much as in *Hampden* and *No. 610*. The molybdenum spear points are also somewhat suppressed by the chromium. The stream is fuller (more carrier lines) and the appearance as a whole is somewhat brighter in color than *No. 610* and *Hampden*.

Vega (AIR-TOUGH).—The spark of *Vega* should not be confused with any of the other steels in the Matched Diagram with the possible exception of *R. D. S.* and *Solar*. The outstanding difference between *Vega* and *R. D. S.* is found at the outer edge of the stream, where *R. D. S.* shows forked tongues and *Vega* shows the characteristic molybdenum spear points. However, the spark of *Vega* is quite similar to that of *Solar*, the difference being as follows:

1. The carbon bursts of *Vega* are slightly more numerous than in *Solar* and are not as much suppressed.

2. When seen together with *Solar*, the *Vega* spark as a whole tends to be a shade darker in color than *Solar*.

To make certain distinction between *Vega* and *Solar*, a hardening test should be used. Cut a slug or disc, *at least 1″ thick*—heat it to 1550°F., and cool to room temperature in air. If it has a minimum hardness of about Rockwell C-60, it is *Vega*. *Solar* will not show more than about Rockwell C-30 when so treated.

The Oil-Hardening Matched Set.—See pages 438 and 439.

Hampden (OIL-WEAR).—The suppressed appearance of the *Hampden* spark stream can only be confused with *No. 610*. However, when seen together, the *Hampden* spark as a whole tends to be slightly brighter in color than *No. 610*. See comments above under *No. 610*.

Stentor (OIL-HARD).—There is really not much difference between *Stentor* and *No. 11 Special*. After all, the analyses of these two steels are practically identical except for the higher manganese of *Stentor*. However, when seen together, the *Stentor* spark tends to be brighter in color and has a greater tendency to follow the periphery of the grinding wheel (see the spark diagrams).

To make certain distinction between *Stentor* and *No. 11 Special*, a hardening test should be used. Cut a slug or disc *more than* ½″ *thick*—heat it to 1440°F. and quench in oil. If it becomes harder than C-60 Rockwell, it is *Stentor*. *No. 11 Special* will show only about C-45 when so treated. Very small pieces of *No. 11 Special* will become file hard in oil and that is why the piece should be more than ½″ thick.

R. D. S. (OIL-TOUGH).—This spark should not be confused with any of the other steels in the Matched Set with the possible exception of *Solar* and *Vega*. The carbon bursts in *R. D. S.* and *Vega* are somewhat alike while the carbon bursts in *Solar* are more suppressed. *Solar* also shows a "fuzz" of short curved lines close to the wheel which *R. D. S.* and *Vega* do not have. The outstanding difference is found at the outer fringe of the stream. *Solar* and *Vega* show the characteristic spear points of molybdenum, while *R. D. S.* shows forked tongues.

The Water-Hardening Matched Set.—See pages 440 and 441.

K-W (WATER-WEAR).—This steel throws a characteristic reddish-orange tungsten spark. It cannot possibly be confused with *Star-Zenith* or *T-K* because these steels have no carbon bursts while *K-W* has. *K-W* differs conspicuously from *Speed Star* in the fact that its spark stream consists in absolutely nothing but disjointed, reddish-orange carrier lines, clear out to the carbon bursts which appear on the tongues, whereas the volume of the *Speed Star* stream is greater and consists of both disjointed and continuous lines with bright orange tongues and an occasional suppressed burst together with some few sprigs throughout.

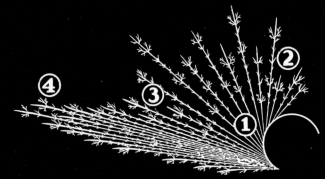

FIG. 274 No. 610 (AIR-WEAR)

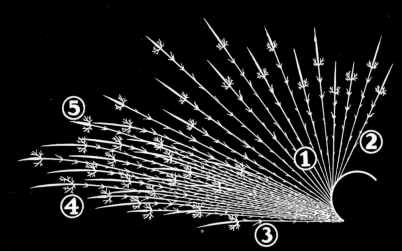

FIG. 275 No. 484 (AIR-HARD)

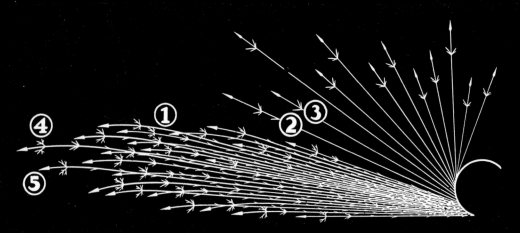

FIG. 276 VEGA (AIR-TOUGH)

NO. 610 (AIR-WEAR)

The spark stream of *No. 610* is *short* and *scant,* having the appearance of being suppressed. The carrier lines are continuous and have an *orange* tint. The stream is composed of sprigs preliminary bursts and typical high carbon main bursts all

of which are suppressed ... *No. 610* shows a moderate tendency for the spark to be carried around the periphery of the grinding wheel ... NOTE: See note under *No. 610* in paragraph, "Comments on Spark Streams." Also, see paragraph "Hardened vs. Annealed Tool Steels."

NO. 484 (AIR-HARD)

The spark stream of *No. 484* is composed of continuous carrier lines having an *orange* tint, numerous sprigs preliminary bursts and main bursts all of which are suppressed. Some of the main carrier lines are tipped with partially formed spear points, a shade *darker* than the lines proper.

No. 484 shows a moderate tendency for the spark to be carried around the periphery of the grinding wheel ... NOTE: See paragraph, "Hardened vs. Annealed Tool Steels."

VEGA (AIR-TOUGH)

The carrier lines of *Vega* are continuous and have a *slight* orange tint. The stream is composed of sprigs preliminary bursts and main bursts all of which are suppressed. The carrier lines are tipped with spear points a shade darker

than the lines proper. *Vega* shows a moderate tendency for the spark to be carried around the periphery of the grinding wheel ... NOTE: See comments under *Vega* in paragraph, "Comments on Spark Streams."

NOTE: All the nomenclature used is in agreement with U. S. Bureau of Standards practice.

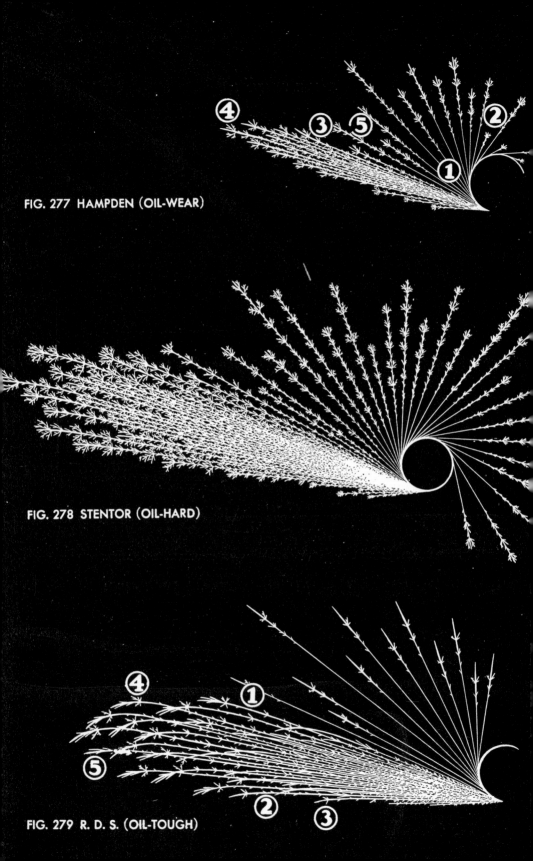

FIG. 277 HAMPDEN (OIL-WEAR)

FIG. 278 STENTOR (OIL-HARD)

FIG. 279 R. D. S. (OIL-TOUGH)

HAMPDEN (OIL-WEAR)

The spark stream is *short* and fairly *scant,* having the appearance of being suppressed. Carrier lines are continuous **1** and have an *orange* tint. Stream is composed of sprigs **2** preliminary bursts **3** and typical high carbon main bursts **4** all of which are suppressed. *Hampden* shows a moderate tendency for the spark to be carried around the periphery of the grinding wheel...NOTE: See note under *No. 610* in paragraph, "Comments on Spark Streams," also see paragraph "Hardened vs. Annealed Tool Steels."

STENTOR (OIL-HARD)

The spark stream of *Stentor* is basically the same as *No. 11 Special,* plus two additions.

1. The sparks show a greater tendency to follow the periphery of the grinding wheel—like a spray.

2. The stream as a whole is even brighter in color than *No. 11 Special.*

R. D. S. (OIL-TOUGH)

The carrier lines of *R.D.S.* **1** are continuous and have a *slight orange* tint. Stream is composed of sprigs **2** preliminary bursts **3** and some main bursts **4** all of which are suppressed. Many of the carrier lines end in forked tongues **5** instead of the usual single tongue. *R.D.S.* shows a moderate tendency for the spark to be carried around the periphery of the grinding wheel.

NOTE: All the nomenclature used is in agreement with U. S. Bureau of Standards practice.

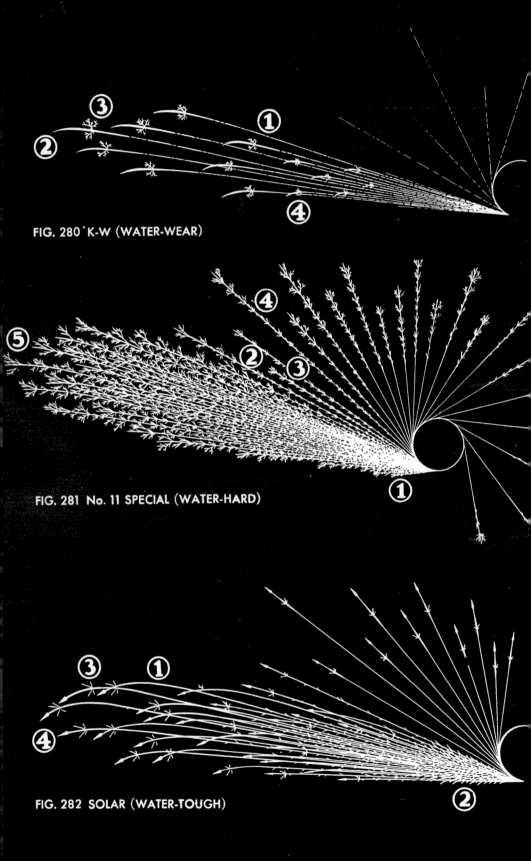

FIG. 280 °K-W (WATER-WEAR)

FIG. 281 No. 11 SPECIAL (WATER-HARD)

FIG. 282 SOLAR (WATER-TOUGH)

K-W (WATER-WEAR)

K-W is characterized by *reddish-orange*, almost continuous carrier lines
1 Main carriers are tipped with rather heavy *bright orange*
tongues **2** having a downward curvature. Some main carbon
bursts **3** and suppressed carbon bursts **4** are present on
the tongues. Occasional ghost-like carrier lines tend to be carried around the periphery of the grinding wheel...NOTE: See paragraph, "Hardened vs. Annealed Tool Steels."

No. 11 SPECIAL (WATER-HARD)

This spark is one of the most spectacular to observe. The stream is full and
brilliant. It is characterized by a dense stream **1** adjacent to
the wheel. Carrier lines **2** are relatively long, continuous,
brilliant, *almost white*. Stream is composed of sprigs **3** preliminary
bursts **4** and main bursts **5** none of which are sup-
pressed. There is a marked tendency for the spark to be carried around the periphery of the grinding wheel...NOTE: See comments under *No. 11 Special* and *Stentor* in paragraph, "Comments on Spark Streams."

SOLAR (WATER-TOUGH)

The carrier lines **1** of *Solar* are continuous and *more yellow* than
No. 11 Special. Adjacent to the wheel is a dense, relatively coarse fuzz,
2 composed of very short lines having definite upward and downward curvatures. Bursts are somewhat suppressed **3** Carrier
lines are tipped with spear points **4** a shade *darker* than the
lines proper. *Solar* shows a moderate tendency for the spark to be carried around the periphery of the grinding wheel...NOTE: See comments under *Vega* in paragraph, "Comments on Spark Streams."

NOTE: All the nomenclature used is in agreement with U. S. Bureau of Standards practice.

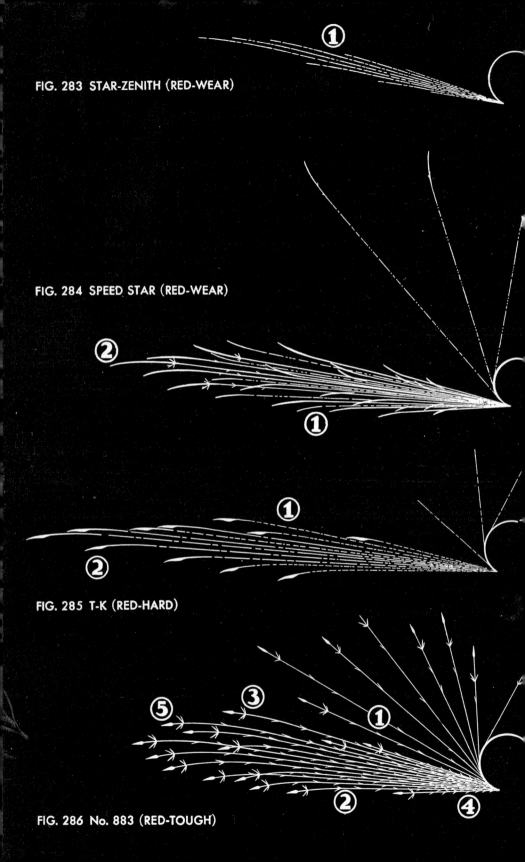

FIG. 283 STAR-ZENITH (RED-WEAR)

FIG. 284 SPEED STAR (RED-WEAR)

FIG. 285 T-K (RED-HARD)

FIG. 286 No. 883 (RED-TOUGH)

——————— STAR-ZENITH (RED-WEAR) ———————

This is a typical 18-4-1 "high speed steel" spark. Stream is very scant, carrier lines are disjointed ═══✎══ relatively short, and *reddish-orange* in color. Occasional ghost-like secondary carrier lines are present. Carbon bursts are absent...NOTE: See paragraph, "Hardened vs. Annealed Tool Steels."

——————— SPEED STAR (RED-WEAR) ———————

The spark stream of *Speed Star* is composed of *reddish-orange* carrier lines, varying in length and thickness. The thicker ones are continuous while the thinner ones are disjointed. ═══✎══ The thicker lines gradually swell into *bright orange tongues*, having slight upward or downward curvatures. ══✎══ A few sprigs and an occasional suppressed burst are visible.

The molybdenum spear points are completely suppressed by the tungsten content. There is a tendency for some occasional ghost-like lines to be carried around the periphery of the grinding wheel...NOTE: See paragraph, "Hardened vs. Annealed Tool Steels."

——————— T-K (RED-HARD) ———————

The spark stream of *T-K* is composed of disjointed and some almost continuous carrier lines ═══✎══ which are *reddish orange* in color. The carrier lines are tipped with relative short, *bright orange tongues* ═✎══ having a slight downward curvature. Carbon bursts are absent. An occasional ghost-like carrier line tends to be carried around the periphery of the grinding wheel. The stream is somewhat longer and fuller (more and thicker carrier lines) and is somewhat lighter in color than *Star-Zenith*...NOTE: See paragraph, "Hardened vs. Annealed Tool Steels."

——————— No. 883 (RED-TOUGH) ———————

The carrier lines of *No. 883* are continuous ═══✎══ and have an *orange* tint. The stream is composed of sprigs ═✎══ and some few bursts ═✎══ which are suppressed. There are only traces of the pattern of coarse fuzz (characteristic of silicon) ═✎══ close to the wheel, this pattern being suppressed by the chromium. The carrier lines are tipped with spear points ═✎══ a shade darker than the lines proper. Occasional carrier lines are carried around the periphery of the grinding wheel... NOTE: See paragraph, "Hardened vs. Annealed Tool Steels."

NOTE: All the nomenclature used is in agreement with U. S. Bureau of Standards practice.

No. 11 Special (WATER-HARD).—The brilliant spark display of this steel can only be confused with *Stentor*. See also comments under *Stentor*.

Solar (WATER-TOUGH).—The only steels in the Matched Set which could possibly be confused with the *Solar* spark are *Vega* and *R. D. S.* See also comments under *Vega* and *R. D. S.*

The Red-Hard Matched Set.—See pages 442 and 443. These steels can be compared as follows:

Color.—*Star-Zenith, T-K* and *Speed Star* have the characteristic reddish-orange tungsten spark; *Star-Zenith* is the darkest, *T-K* is next and *Speed Star* is the lightest. *No. 883* has the characteristic orange chromium spark.

Volume.—*Star-Zenith* throws the least sparks; *T-K* next, *Speed Star* next and *No. 883* the most.

Length.—The *Star-Zenith* stream is relatively short; *T-K* and *Speed Star* are of almost equal length and somewhat longer than *Star-Zenith* while *No. 883* is even longer.

Bursts.—There are no carbon bursts in *Star-Zenith* or *T-K* and only a few occasional suppressed bursts in *Speed Star* while more suppressed bursts will always be seen in *No. 883*.

Star-Zenith (RED-WEAR).—This steel can be confused only with *T-K* because these are the only two that show no bursts. The *Star-Zenith* stream is darker in color, shorter, scarcer, and lacks the small bright orange tongues seen on *T-K* at the ends of the carrier lines.

Speed Star (RED-WEAR).—*Speed Star* can become confused only with *K-W* since these are the only two steels with a reddish-orange tungsten spark that have any carbon bursts. See comments under *K-W*.

T-K (RED-HARD).—This can only be confused with *Star-Zenith*. See comments under *Star-Zenith*.

No. 883 (RED-TOUGH).—This stream has an orange tint being a shade darker than *R. D. S.* The volume is somewhat greater than *T-K* but less than *Solar*. The stream is approximately the same length as that of *No. 484*. The bursts are somewhat suppressed. The spear points at the ends of the carrier lines are not quite as sharp as those seen in *Solar* and *Vega*.

A FINAL INSTRUCTION

Learn to look *closely* at spark streams. Do not try to see them as a whole. Pick out the details, one by one. Look at the *carrier-lines*—watch them until you can see clearly their *size* and *color*—whether they are continuous like *Solar* or *R. D. S.* or whether they are disjointed like *T-K* or *Star-Zenith*.

One of the most important features of the spark is what happens at the end of the carrier line as it vanishes. Does it end with a spear point (*Solar, Vega, No. 883*), a single tongue (*K-W*), or a forked tongue (*R. D. S.*)? It is necessary to look long and earnestly before seeing these details, but once the eye is trained to it, each characteristic may be clearly seen.

There is a fascination about spark testing. Take *Star-Zenith* (18.50% tungsten) showing nothing but dark reddish-orange carrier lines—and very few of those. The high tungsten content completely suppresses the spark effects of all other elements present. Then look at *T-K* (9.00% tungsten). Here, with 9% less tungsten, the spark has started to come to life. It struggles to burst—travelling many feet as though it hated to die. But it always does—it seems never to realize its ambition to explode. Now compare *K-W* (3.50% tungsten)—see the characteristic reddish-orange carrier lines—they travel quite a distance and nothing happens, then suddenly they burst into a scintillating flowery spark and from this emerges a bright flaming tongue. The carbon has overcome the tungsten and the spark seems to live for an instant before it vanishes.

While spark testing cannot separate all of the hundreds of different tool steel brands that might find their way into a shop, it is nevertheless a convenient, rapid, and effective way of unscrambling mixed stocks where only two or three known steels might be involved. It deals entirely with *analysis types* and, of course, tells nothing about the timbre of the steel. The sparks from brittle timbre and tough timbre carbon tool steel would be identical. Neither is it possible to separate two steels belonging to the same analysis family with only minor differences in the amount of the various alloys present.

In making the spark test it is extremely helpful to keep on hand some "standard" specimens representing the various types of tool steel that are regularly used. By comparing "unknown" samples with these known standards, quite accurate deductions may be drawn.

CHAPTER 18

FURNACE ATMOSPHERE

Furnace atomsphere and its effect on the surface of tools was for years the subject of much study and discussion which yielded very little in the way of practical information for the heat treater. The many conflicting statements formerly made concerning atmospheres were probably due partly to preconceived notions on the subject, and partly to lack of full understanding of the many factors involved. In order to get down to the core of the problem, it was necessary to discard many old *beliefs* about the heating of steel, and start fresh to find the *facts*. Out of the former chaos has now come a semblance of order, and we are able to give clear cut recommendations for atmosphere on all of the Matched Set steels, with definite suggestions on how to obtain them in various types of furnaces. It should be good news to the hardener that most of these recommendations are quite easy to put into practice, and in some instances, once they are understood, probably involve less time and less trouble than practices he is now using.

The subject of furnace atmosphere has been touched upon elsewhere in this book. Introductory to this present chapter, and for the convenience of the reader, we shall briefly review what has been said in other chapters so that reference to these can be made if desired.

In Chapter 10, page 218, the three general types of atmosphere, oxidizing, reducing and neutral, were mentioned. It was stated that the composition of the steel, temperature to which it is heated, and degree of circulation of the atmosphere all influence the way these various atmospheres act on the surface of the steel being heated. The chemical composition of furnace atmospheres was then quite simply discussed, and a description was given of the Orsat apparatus for gas analysis, for the benefit of those who wish to make actual analyses. In discussing hardening furnaces, page 237, we stated that there are two general methods of con-

446

trolling atmospheres; first, in a fuel-fired furnace by regulation of the air-fuel ratio; and second, in either fuel-fired or electric furnaces, by introducing a synthetic or prepared atmosphere into the furnace, independent of the gases resulting from the fuel. The various methods in use for obtaining these specialized atmospheres were touched upon.

In Chapter 12, recommended atmospheres are given for the twelve Matched Set steels. In Chapter 19, page 487, the effect of character of atmosphere on the speed of heating is discussed. In Chapter 13, page **354**, will be found a rather complete discussion of the effects of atmosphere in the heating of high speed steel and hot work steels.

In the present chapter we shall avoid as much as possible, repetition of what has been said elsewhere. The three recognized **types of atmosphere,** oxidizing, reducing and neutral, will be defined. The **effects of atmosphere** on the steel will then be discussed. Practical methods of **determining atmospheres** will be described, and **recommended atmospheres** for the Matched Set steels will be discussed, and it will be shown why such atmospheres are recommended.

TYPES OF ATMOSPHERES

An oxidizing atmosphere is created when the valves of a fuel fired furnace are adjusted so that there is more air in the mixture than is needed to burn the fuel. Fig. 287 shows a gas furnace running with an oxidizing atmosphere. Note that there is no flame playing out through the ports in the roof. All of the fuel is being consumed at the burners, and there is none left to burn on the outside of the furnace. The hot burned gases in the furnace contain excess oxygen.

A reducing atmosphere is secured by cutting down the supply of air until there is not enough to burn all of the fuel. The excess fuel that is unburned inside the furnace will ignite and burn at the ports where it makes contact with oxygen of the outside air. Fig. 288 shows the gas furnace running with a reducing atmosphere.

If a block of wood is thrown into an oxidizing atmosphere, and the door of the furnace is closed, it will burst into flame and burn vigorously. This is illustrated in Fig. 289 which is an actual photograph made of this experiment. The wood is burned by the excess oxygen in the furnace.   If the supply of air is decreased (or the fuel supply increased) until a flame appears at the ports, the piece of wood will cease to burn—because all of the available

FIG. 287.—Gas furnace with oxidizing atmosphere.

FIG. 288.—Gas furnace with reducing atmosphere.

oxygen has now been consumed by the fuel at the burners.   This is illustrated in Fig. 290 where the charred block is clearly seen near the pyrometer tube.   The flame has been extinguished by the reducing atmosphere.

It was first believed that "an atmosphere that cannot burn wood cannot burn steel," and it is certainly a reasonable assumption that such an atmosphere would neither scale the steel, nor burn out the carbon from the surface. The assumption about scale is correct, but the one about surface decarburization frequently is not. It is now known that, under certain conditions, carbon can be removed more rapidly from the surface of a piece of steel under a reducing atmosphere than under an oxidizing atmosphere. It was stated in Chapter 10 that the decarburizing tendency of a reducing atmosphere is most active at hardening

FIG. 289.—Wood block burning in oxidizing atmosphere.

FIG. 290.—Wood block extinguished by reducing atmosphere.

temperatures up to 1600°F. At hardening temperatures above 1700°F., the decarburizing tendency is not so active and the reducing atmosphere serves to protect the steel from excessive scaling.

A neutral furnace atmosphere is a balanced condition midway between oxidizing and reducing. Theoretically, such an atmosphere is impossible to maintain—but practically, the word is used to describe that "twilight zone" which is neither definitely oxidizing nor definitely reducing. With a neutral atmosphere there is no flame burning outside the furnace ports, but upon looking through the peep hole, ghost-like flames can be seen floating through the heating chamber. There is supposed to be just enough air (or oxygen) to consume all of the fuel and no more.

THE EFFECTS OF ATMOSPHERE

The effects of furnace atmosphere on tool steels are primarily confined to the surface, and may be most simply stated as scaling, decarburization, and carburization.

While some **scaling** always occurs in oxidizing atmospheres, its extent depends upon such factors as time at temperature, amount of water vapor present in the atmosphere, etc. It can therefore be controlled and its objectionable features minimized by proper observance of heating time and care in operation of the furnace. Generally speaking, oxidizing atmospheres will scale tool steel to an objectionable degree only at very high temperatures, *i.e.*, over about 1700°F.; but since such atmospheres at this elevated temperature usually decarburize the steel, in general they should be avoided, and all tools heated above 1700°F. should be heated in a pack or in a controlled

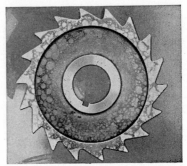

Fig. 291.—High speed cutter hardened in reducing atmosphere.   Fig. 292.—High speed cutter hardened in oxidizing atmosphere.

reducing atmosphere. The only exception to this statement among the Matched Set steels is Red-Tough of the 5% chromium type, which, on account of its relatively low carbon content and other features of its composition, can be hardened in an oxidizing atmosphere successfully, even though the heating range is 1850° to 1875°F. It is a fortunate circumstance that at the relatively low hardening temperature where a slightly oxidizing atmosphere is desirable in preventing decarburization, such atmosphere will not scale heavily, while at the high temperatures where scaling must be prevented by the use of the reducing atmospheres, such atmospheres will not decarburize.

The problem of scaling thus becomes one of intelligent handling of the furnace. Figs. 291 and 292 illustrate the scaling of high speed tools hardened at 2350°F. A strongly oxidizing atmosphere at this temperature not only produces a lot of scale, but it tends to melt the scale after it is formed, giving it a greasy, glistening appearance which the hardener refers to as "sweating." Under severe conditions, this is accompanied by a boiling action and the scale accumulates in rounded blisters. After the tool has been quenched it will appear as shown in Fig. 292. These blisters are not caused by too much heat; they result from too much air at the burners.

Decarburization is much more difficult to control than scaling for the reason that its effects are not so obvious. Most hardeners have had the experience of taking out of the quenching bath a beautiful tool to all outside appearances only to find that it has a soft skin. If the tool is one on which the entire working surface can be ground, no harm comes from it, (except the cost of grinding). If however the tool happens to be a blanking die having an irregular profile such as illustrated in Fig. 293, it is impossible to get into the holes to grind them. Since the walls of the holes form one side of the cutting edge, no matter how much is ground off the flat top, the cutting edge will always be low in carbon, and will cause a burr on the stamping after a short time in service. When the surface metal of a tool is *completely* decarburized and becomes dead soft like pure iron, the user can immediately detect it, and take steps to prevent the condition.

Fig. 293.—Blanking die, illustrating tool which cannot be ground to remove partial surface decarburization.

But a 1.00% carbon steel for example will frequently only partially decarburize on the surface to perhaps .60% or .70% carbon. Since a .60% carbon steel will become quite hard when quenched, it might appear file hard and pass unnoticed. The operator is thus deceived into thinking he has a good tool until early failure in service proves it otherwise. It is important, therefore, in order to get full value from a tool to have the full carbon content out to the surface.

Now, as a matter of actual experience and test, many tools do not meet this requirement, and consequently the operator is not getting the full value for the price he paid for the steel, to say nothing of the labor expended in making the tool. This is due not so much to mishandling in hardening, as to lack of knowledge of the principles involved.   With our present knowledge all the steels in the Matched Set can be hardened free from decarburization if these principles are understood and translated into practice, and in fact some will show a slight skin of **carburization,** which will add to wear resistance without detracting noticeably from toughness.   Hardening tools free from decarburization can be accomplished in any well designed and constructed furnace. The first step in this direction is to understand something of the actual composition of the atmospheres which we call "oxidizing" and "reducing," and how they may be determined in the average hardening room.

METHODS OF DETERMINING ATMOSPHERE

In Chapter 10, we described the Orsat apparatus for making actual chemical analysis of furnace atmosphere, and this is a very convenient and valuable instrument.   However, we realize few hardeners have access to such equipment, and the Carpenter Laboratory therefore has worked out methods for "analyzing" furnace atmosphere "by eye."   In describing these methods it is necessary to borrow from the chemist some of his language— particularly the so-called chemical "symbols."   When the chemist wishes to write "oxygen" he uses the symbol "O"; when he wishes to write "hydrogen" he uses the symbol "H." These are simply abbreviations, just as "Mr." is an abbreviation for the word "Mister."   Some of the symbols we will need in our discussion follow:

O_2 = oxygen (the air we breathe is 21% oxygen.   The little figure 2 means that the oxygen atoms occur in pairs).

N_2 = nitrogen (the remaining 79% of the air is largely nitrogen).

H_2 = hydrogen (the very buoyant gas used in balloons. It is an important constituent in most city gas).

C = carbon (as in coal, soot, or graphite).

H_2O = water (ordinary water—or steam—or ice.   They all have the same analysis).

CO = carbon monoxide (the partially burned poisonous gas from an automobile exhaust—and also an important component of city gas).

CO_2 = carbon dioxide (this is the completely burned gas from the coal fire in your cellar furnace—or from your gas stove).

C_xH_y = hydrocarbon gas (the numbers x and y can indicate several things—methane, propane, butane, natural gas, etc., are all hydrocarbon gases—so is volatilized fuel oil. There is also a lot of hydrocarbon in most city gas mains).

When you bank your coal fire in the cellar at night, if the stack damper is closed the house will fill up with poisonous carbon monoxide (CO). This is produced by the *partial* (or smothered) burning of coal. In fact, that is how the gas company *makes* CO for your city gas mains. When you ignite it at a gas burner, you complete the burning and produce CO_2(carbon dioxide). We know that partially burned gasoline also gives off CO—and the same thing is true of partially burned fuel oil or natural gas. Hence, whenever we find CO gas present in the final products of combustion, we know that the combustion was *not* complete— and the more CO we find, the less complete was the combustion. For this reason (and also for simplicity) we will use CO as the *measure* of reducing atmospheres. If there is *no* CO present, we know that combustion was complete and the furnace atmosphere is not reducing at all. If there is a little CO, the atmosphere is slightly reducing, and if there is a lot, it is very reducing.

The hardener increases the percent of CO in his furnace atmosphere by reducing the supply of air and increasing the supply of fuel. The practical limit to this is when the furnace starts to smoke. Any effort to increase the CO beyond this point will cause soot to deposit.

Now let's look at the oxidizing side. As we shut down the fuel and increase the air, the percent of CO becomes less and less until it just disappears. Here we have complete combustion and a **neutral** atmosphere. If we add still more air beyond this point, we begin to get an excess of oxygen (O_2) in the furnace atmosphere and it becomes **oxidizing.** The amount of excess air can be increased more and more, until a point is reached where the burners blow out and the temperature of the furnace can no longer be maintained. The most oxidizing atmosphere possible is that found in an electric furnace through which pure room atmosphere is blown. This contains 21% oxygen (the rest is nitrogen).

Oxidizing Atmospheres.—Since oxidizing atmospheres are by far the most important for hardening the Matched Tool Steels, we will discuss the "analysis" for O_2 first.

Here is the equipment required.

(1) A number of little blocks of wood about $\frac{3}{4}''$ in size. Any kind of wood will do—the tests shown here were made with ordinary southern pine box lumber.

(2) A few small lumps of soft coal.

(3) A long portable gas torch made up of a length of $\frac{1}{4}''$ pipe, a piece of rubber hose, and connected into the gas line through a needle valve.

How to Use a Wood Block to Estimate Oxygen between 0% **and 6%.**—Have the furnace up to heat—say 1450°F. Put the wood block on the hearth and close the door. Observe the block through the peep hole.

Note these things: When first put in, does the block smoke?

Does it burn with a flame?

Is the flame intermittent or continuous?

Is the flame blue, partly luminous, or entirely luminous?

Confine your attention entirely to what is happening within 6″ of the block. Do not pay any attention to smoke or flame at the ports of the furnace—or anywhere else. Just watch the block and its immediate vicinity. After several minutes, all the volatile matter will have burned out of the wood, and you will see a red hot piece of charcoal free from flame. Observe these things in the charcoal.

It may not glow hotter than the furnace at all.

It may show a flickering glow on the corners and edges of the block.

It may glow all over.

When you have made these observations, the test is over. The pictures on pages 456 and 457 will tell you what percent of oxygen is present. This test is accurate, within plus or minus 1% oxygen; that is, if you estimate the oxygen to be 3%, it will be between 2% and 4%—which is plenty close enough for our purpose.

How to Use Soft Coal to Estimate 8% to 10% Oxygen.—Use a piece of soft coal about equivalent to a $\frac{1}{2}''$ cube. It is convenient to place the coal on a *flat* piece of scale-resisting sheet metal—like stainless steel. The furnace gases must be able to circulate freely past the lump of coal. Make these observations:

Does the coal start to smoke, and how much?

Is there a flame—intermittent or steady—and how *soon* does it appear.

Does the coal burst into flame immediately with no preliminary smoking?

After the volatile matter is gone, does the coke glow; and if so, how much?

Pages 456 and 457 provide the key to this test.

**How to Use a Gas Torch to Estimate Oxygen between 6%
and 10%.**—The torch can be bent as in Fig. 294 so that it will
project through one of the roof
ports and will not reach the
bottom of the furnace. Before
placing the torch in the furnace, light it and adjust the
valve to produce a flame about

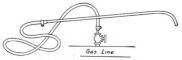

Fig. 294.—A gas torch.

3″ long. Then, with the flame burning, insert it in the furnace and watch through the peep hole in the door. The following may be observed.

There may be a very faint blue flame. This is hard to see, and it will help if you pinch the rubber tube with your fingers so the flame will be intermittent.

The flame may have a blue base and luminous tip.

The flame may be practically *all* luminous.

In any event, the flame in the furnace will usually be much bigger than it was in the air.

If the furnace is small, use a smaller tube, or pinch the end down to form a small flame. Obviously this gas flame eats up some of the oxygen in the furnace and therefore the flame should not be a large one. You will get your *best* observations with the torch immediately after you put it in the furnace and before the torch has a chance to use up much oxygen. If you "miss it," pull the torch out, wait a few minutes, and then put it in the furnace again.

The key to the torch observations is given on pages 456 and 457.

Since the tendency for a steel to decarburize depends primarily upon its analysis, it is obvious that the oxygen content recom-

These instructions apply to oil-fired furnaces, gas-fired furnaces and gas curtain electric furnaces.

This column describes:
1450°F. with 0 to 2 % O₂
1550°F. with 0 to 1½ % O₂
1650°F. with 0 to 1 % O₂

This column describes:
1450°F. with 2 to 2½ % O₂
1550°F. with 1½ to 2 % O₂
1650°F. with 1 to 1½ % O₂

This column describes:
1450°F. with 3 to 3½ % O₂
1550°F. with 2½ to 3 % O₂
1650°F. with 2 to 2½ % O₂

This column describes:
1450°F. with 4 to 4½ % O₂
1550°F. with 3½ to 4 % O₂
1650°F. with 3 to 3½ % O₂
1850°F. with 2 to 2½ % O₂

FIG. 295.—Wood block smokes and chars—no visible flame. The remaining charcoal does not glow.

FIG. 296.—Wood block smokes—then intermittent flashes of pale blue flame. The charcoal does not glow.

FIG. 297.—Wood block smokes slightly—then burns with an intermittent blue flame with luminous tip. Charcoal does not glow.

FIG. 298.—Only a trace of smoke—wood block burns with steady lazy flame—mostly luminous. Flickering glow on edges of the charcoal.

◀─────────────── Below about 6 % O₂, the gas torch gives no visible flame. ───────

◀─────────────── Soft coal will merely smoke, and not burn at all under about 4 % O₂. As the O₂ is progressively increased above 4 %, flame will appear mixed with smoke. ───────

↑

Use this Atmosphere for Hardening

Solar
(WATER-TOUGH)

↑

Use this Atmosphere for Hardening

No. 11 Special
(WATER-HARD)

Stentor
(OIL-HARD)

K-W
(WATER-WEAR)

Vega
(AIR-TOUGH)

↑

Use this Atmosphere for Hardening

No. 883
(RED-TOUGH)

Photographs show hearth of a gas-fired, semi-muffle furnace, and thermocouple protective tube.

This column describes:	This column describes:	This column describes:	This column describes:
1450°F. with 5 to $5\frac{1}{2}$ % O₂	1450°F. with 6 to $6\frac{1}{2}$ % O₂	1450°F. with 7 to $7\frac{1}{2}$ % O₂	1450°F. with 8 to 10 % O₂
1550°F. with $4\frac{1}{2}$ to 5 % O₂	1550°F. with $5\frac{1}{2}$ to 6 % O₂	1550°F. with $6\frac{1}{2}$ to 7 % O₂	1550°F. with $7\frac{1}{2}$ to $9\frac{1}{2}$ % O₂
1650°F. with 4 to $4\frac{1}{2}$ O₂	1650°F. with 5 to $5\frac{1}{2}$ % O₂	1650°F. with 6 to $6\frac{1}{2}$ % O₂	1650°F. with 7 to 9 % O₂

Fig. 299.—Wood block burns with a steady, active, luminous flame. The charcoal definitely glows.

← Above $5\frac{1}{2}$ % O₂, there is no significant change in the flame from a wood block. →

→

Fig. 300.—Gas torch burns with a pale blue flame—better seen when made intermittent by pinching the rubber tube.

Fig. 301.—The gas flame is partly luminous. Note that all gas flames are much larger in the furnace than outside.

Fig. 302.—In this oxygen range, gas torch will show full luminosity characteristic of the particular type of gas used in the torch.

← The amount of smoke from soft coal will gradually decrease and practically vanish at 10 % O₂. Above 10 % O₂, there is no change. →

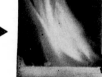

Fig. 303.—A lump of soft coal ignites with only a trace of smoke, and burns with a clear luminous flame. The remaining coke definitely glows.

Note: The other Matched Tool Steels—*No. 610* (AIR-WEAR), *No. 484* (AIR-HARD), *Hampden* (OIL-WEAR), *T-K* (RED-HARD), *Star-Zenith* (RED-WEAR) and *Speed Star* require strongly **reducing atmospheres** for hardening.

ESTIMATE OF OXIDIZING
FURNACE ATMOSPHERE

Use this Atmosphere
for Hardening

R. D. S.
(OIL-TOUGH)

mended for it, and consequently the method of determining the oxygen content, must depend also upon its analysis. So in discussing the application of these various tests it is necessary for us now to talk about specific steels, and while we shall use the descriptive Matched Set names, we shall in addition use brand names to illustrate the exact type of steel under discussion.

After studying the photographs and descriptions on pages 456 and 457, it will be seen that here are simple and practical methods by which the hardener can estimate the percent of free oxygen in a furnace that is running with an oxidizing atmosphere. To test the accuracy of the method, ten operators were given these instructions and asked to estimate various oxidizing atmospheres. After they had made their guess "by eye," an actual chemical analysis of the atmosphere was made. None of them missed it by over 1%, and many of the estimates were within $\frac{1}{2}\%$.

The question might well be asked, "How does furnace temperature affect these estimates of furnace atmosphere?" As a matter of actual experience, it has little effect. Let us consider a case in which the operator using the wood block test saw a blue flame with a slightly luminous tip, and the residual charcoal did not glow. If the furnace temperature were 1450°F., he would estimate the atmosphere to be about $3\frac{1}{2}\%$ O_2. If the temperature were 1550°F., he would estimate it at 3% O_2, and at 1650°F., $2\frac{1}{2}\%$ O_2. In making our estimate, therefore, each 100°F. increase in temperature may be assumed to be the equivalent of about $\frac{1}{2}\%$ oxygen within the temperature range discussed.

ATMOSPHERE IN VARIOUS TYPES OF FURNACES

Most tool hardeners are using one or more of the following types of furnaces:

(A) An Electric Muffle Furnace with Nothing but Room Atmosphere.—Obviously there is no use in analyzing the atmosphere in such a furnace. We know what it is—about 21% oxygen, 79% nitrogen. However, if the furnace is reasonably tight and free from leaks, this "room" atmosphere will *not* remain constant when a charge of tool steel is put in. The air in the furnace will react with the surface of the steel and will gradually acquire a **decarburizing** nature. We do *not* recommend throwing in charcoal or sawdust to try to create an artificial atmosphere because such atmospheres are of unknown quality—and many of them are harmful.

On this type of furnace two things can be done that will help. One is to put a small hole in the bottom and another in the top of the furnace, so that a slow draft of air will flow through the furnace. This will keep the O_2 at about 20%, and will *not* decarburize any of the seven Matched Tool Steels that require an oxidizing atmosphere. The biggest objection will be scale but this will all fly off in the quench, leaving a clean tool with a fully hard surface. Scale can be minimized by having the furnace up to heat before the work is put in, and letting the tools heat as fast as they naturally can. Soak only long enough to be absolutely sure they are up to heat and then quench. This will do a good job.

The second thing that can be done is to insert a small Bunsen gas burner in the bottom of the furnace—put a vent in roof—and then control the atmosphere as recommended on pages 456 and 457. This also does a good job—it holds scaling to a minimum, and the tools come from the quench nice and clean.

(B) An Electric Muffle Furnace of the Gas Curtain Type.— You can easily run such furnaces oxidizing and determine the atmosphere by the wood block (or soft coal) method. Having once calibrated the manometers on such a furnace, the proper atmosphere can be duplicated time after time by returning to the same manometer settings. This is just the kind of work these furnaces were made for.

(C) A Gas-fired Semi-muffle Furnace.—These are excellent furnaces for controlled atmosphere hardening—especially on the oxidizing side. If you do not already have one, get an **inspirator** installed. This is a rather inexpensive device sold by furnace builders to mix the gas and air in a definite proportion before it enters the furnace. Fig. 304 shows an inspirator (*I*) installed on a gas furnace. At the back of the drum there is an adjusting screw. By turning this screw, the mixture can be controlled to any degree of reducing or oxidizing atmosphere. On the furnace illustrated, an extension pointer (*P*) has been attached to this adjusting screw, and a scale (*S*) has been attached to the side of the furnace. This scale is marked off into graduations numbered from 1 to 30, and the scale is calibrated as follows.

The pointer is set at each graduation in turn and the furnace is operated long enough to arrive at a constant atmosphere for that setting. A gas analysis is then made of the furnace atmosphere. This is done for each graduation, and the hardener can then return to any given atmosphere by simply moving his pointer to the proper spot.   In the absence of an **Orsat** apparatus, he can calibrate the **oxidizing** side of the scale with the wood blocks, etc.

When an inspirator is used, only one valve (V) is needed to control the furnace temperature, and the operator need not "lose" his atmosphere every time he adjusts the furnace.   It is difficult to maintain a certain atmosphere with *two* valves— because every time one of them is changed to adjust the temperature, the atmosphere changes also.

FIG. 304.—Inspirator installed on a gas-fired hardening furnace.

(D) An Oil-fired Semi-muffle Furnace.—The wood block (or soft coal) method will work just as well, and just as accurately, in an oil-fired furnace as in the previously described types.   We have been taught to believe that when a flame appears at the ports, we have a reducing atmosphere.   This is *not necessarily true* of an oil-fired furnace.   Many of them will show a definite flame when the oxygen content in the heating chamber is 4% or more.   Frequently such furnaces will start to smoke at 3% oxygen, so that reducing atmospheres become quite impossible. The moral is, don't depend on the flame at the ports, but use wood blocks to estimate your atmosphere.   This observation refers to an oil-fired furnace running at about 1450°F.   As the temperature is raised, the oil burns more completely and it is quite possible to produce a reducing atmosphere in this type of furnace when operated at high speed hardening temperatures.

Controlling *both* temperature and atmosphere by means of *two* separate valves (oil and air) is again quite a job in an oil-fired furnace. Recently the burner manufacturers have put on the market oil burners that automatically maintain a constant oil/air ratio, and allow the temperature to be controlled by means of a single lever.

The seven Matched Tool Steels that require an **oxidizing** atmosphere can be very satisfactorily hardened in an oil-fired furnace.

NOTE: You cannot preserve a uniform atmosphere in *any* fuel-fired furnace that is equipped with an "on-and-off" temperature regulator. However, the seven Matched Tool Steels that require an **oxidizing** atmosphere can be hardened quite well—even with such a regulator. The atmosphere in the "on" position should be properly set for the steel being hardened—and in the "off" position, they will be getting largely room atmosphere, which is not necessarily harmful to these seven steels. However, a steady, controlled atmosphere is much more desirable.

(E) Electric Furnace with an Oil Gas Atmosphere.—Atmosphere controlled electric furnaces that use a cracked special oil for the atmosphere are found in many tool hardening rooms. The atmosphere so produced is *much more reducing* than any atmosphere that can be produced in any of the furnaces thus far described. Such atmospheres are the equivalent of CO in excess of 25% or 30%, and the furnace can readily be operated to have a strong **carburizing** action on the surface of the tools.

The control and application of these furnaces has received much study by their manufacturers, and complete instructions for their use may be had from this source. These very high CO atmospheres are beyond the scope of our present discussion.

(F) Carbon Muffle Furnaces.—Pure carbon muffles are available for tool hardening. They can be inserted in any conventional type of furnace, or furnaces may be secured that are specially designed for their use. These generate their own atmosphere from the partial oxidation of the muffle.

We have done a small amount of work with these carbon muffles and find that the atmosphere in them tends to approach about 34% CO. It is probably a reasonably pure mixture of CO and N_2. These muffles are normally used for hardening temperatures between 2100°F. and 2400°F., although they can be used at temperatures as low as 1700°F. when properly baffled. With good manipulation they will produce work free from either decarburization or scale within this temperature range.

REDUCING ATMOSPHERES

No simple method has yet been devised to estimate the **reducing** characteristics of various furnace gases. The determination of oxidizing atmosphere is quite simple as we have seen, because when all the combustible gases are completely burned, the excess constituent left over is oxygen; and since all oxygen is alike, all that is needed is to find out how much oxygen there is left. In studying reducing atmospheres, however, we are dealing with conditions *before* all the combustibles are consumed, and at this stage the unconsumed gases may be of a great many varieties and combinations depending upon:

(a) What kind of raw gases you start with.

(b) The extent to which they have burned.

(c) How hot the furnace is run.

At any given temperature, with one particular furnace, and a definite kind of fuel, the reducing nature of the atmosphere can be *approximated* by simple tests. One "tell-tale" is the color and size of the flame issuing from the ports. For example, in one of our laboratory gas-fired furnaces, burning by-product coke oven gas from the city mains, the following observations are typical for a temperature of 1550°F.:

Per Cent of CO in Furnace Atmosphere	Description of Flame at Furnace Ports
0% to 1%	No flame at all
1% to 3%	Small flame down *inside* the port
3% to 4%	Blue flame about 3″ long
4% to 7.5%	Blue flame 3″ to 6″ long

7.5% CO is the maximum that can be had with this particular set-up, but higher percentages of CO would give a flame with yellow in it. These observations might not apply to your furnace at all—and even in our own furnace, they change for every temperature.

In a gas curtain electric furnace, using bottled propane gas, we observed the following at 1550°F.:

Per Cent of CO in Furnace Atmosphere	Description of Flame at Shutter in Door
0% to 3%	No flame
3% to 13%	Increasing blue flame
13% to 14.6%	Half blue, half luminous flame

This set-up starts to deposit soot at about 14% CO.

In general, reducing atmospheres are best obtained and regulated by the various methods of specialized atmosphere control briefly discussed in Chapter 10. When such equipment is not available, however, users of the Matched Set steels can get excellent results fortunately without the necessity of estimating reducing atmospheres. The members of the Matched Set that require reducing atmospheres are *No. 610* (AIR-WEAR), *No. 484* (AIR-HARD), *Hampden* (OIL-WEAR), *T-K* (RED-HARD), *Star-Zenith* and *Speed Star* (RED-WEAR). *No. 610, No. 484* and *Hampden* are recommended to be pack hardened preferably in cast iron borings, so that the atmosphere problem is solved for them. *Star-Zenith* and *T-K* will both respond successfully to the most reducing *clean* atmosphere obtainable in a fuel-fired furnace. Hence, in the heating of these Matched Set steels, gas analysis is not absolutely necessary.

RECOMMENDED ATMOSPHERES FOR THE MATCHED SET STEELS

Before going into this subject in detail it is desirable now to collect together a number of facts learned in the preceding pages, so that these are firmly in mind. We indicated that in order to understand the difference between reducing and oxidizing atmospheres it was necessary to look at the actual chemistry of these two types of atmosphere. We find that a reducing atmosphere consists of a mixture of *unburned* gases such as hydrocarbons (C_xH_y), hydrogen (H_2), and carbon monoxide (CO), together with water vapor (H_2O). We find on the other hand that in an oxidizing atmosphere these gases are completely burned to water vapor (H_2O), and carbon dioxide (CO_2), and that on top of this there is present an excess of free oxygen (O_2). We said that in a reducing atmosphere the content of CO *indicates* how strongly reducing the atmosphere is; and that in an oxidizing atmosphere the content of free oxygen (O_2) *indicates* how oxidizing the atmosphere is. Now we are going to make a statement which is of extreme importance in understanding the reasons for recommending certain atmospheres for the various steels. It is this:

In a reducing atmosphere the other unburned gases beside the CO, such as the hydrocarbons and hydrogen, plus the water vapor have a profound effect on whether or not the steel will decarburize. If much of these gases are present we have a

so-called "wet" CO atmosphere which will most surely decarburize tool steel.

In an oxidizing atmosphere, these gases are consumed, and the resulting products in the presence of free oxygen have no decarburizing effect.

The reason for the so-called specialized atmosphere furnaces and equipment discussed in Chapter 10 now becomes clear. With proper control, in specialized equipment, reducing atmospheres can be obtained which will not decarburize. But in the average hardening room where such special equipment is not available, a reducing atmosphere might give good results one day and extreme decarburization on another day, depending upon such things as weather conditions. The obvious thing is to use oxidizing atmospheres wherever possible, since we know these are reliable under all conditions; and where they are not possible, as on the steels requiring high hardening temperatures, pack harden—(the exception is high speed steel, as we have already indicated.) With this preface we are now ready to discuss atmosphere recommendations for the Matched Set steels.

We can best determine the effect of various atmospheres by taking cleanly machined and centered blanks about 1″ diameter by 6″ long and hardening these from the various atmospheres to be studied. If surface Rockwell hardness tests, or even file tests are made on such pieces, they might seem satisfactorily hard, even though partially decarburized. So we must resort to a chemical test in order to definitely determine if the surface carbon has changed. The slugs, after hardening, are therefore drawn in a lead pot at 1000°/1200°F. which softens them sufficiently for machining. The surface is then cleaned, and after again centering in the lathe a light cut .0025″ deep is taken, and the chips analyzed for carbon. This result can be taken as the surface carbon, and can be compared with the original known carbon content of the steel to determine if decarburization or carburization has occurred in heating.

Fig. 305 shows graphs of the various Matched Set steels (except for the hot work steels, which are discussed in Chapter 13) indicating the behavior of surface carbon when hardened from various atmospheres. The horizontal line marked "O" indicates no change in the original carbon. Points above this line indicate the number of "points" of carbon added to the

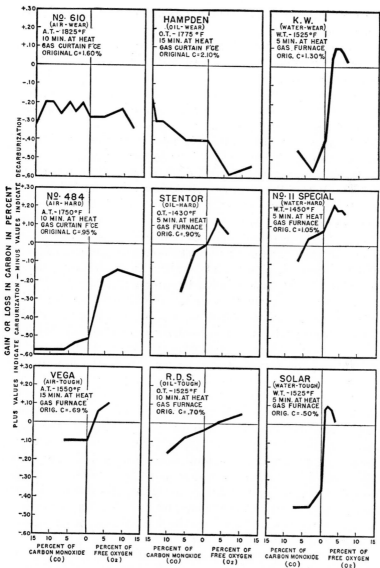

FIG. 305.—Graphs showing change in surface carbon from the original on various Matched Set Steels. Determination made from turnings to depth of .0025″.

surface, and those below the line represent the number of points lost as decarburization. The vertical line marked "0" indicates a neutral atmosphere, to the right oxidizing, with the percentage of free oxygen, and to the left reducing with the percentage of carbon monoxide. These tests were made in a gas-fired furnace in all cases where it was not necessary to go over about 7% CO. On the steels which it was desirable to study up to 16% CO, a gas curtain furnace was used.

It is important to note that if another operator would repeat this work in another furnace, using another gas, and possibly on another day, he might not get exactly the same result on the reducing side of the diagram. But since all the tests here were made under *average* conditions, it is reasonable to expect that the average results of other operators would be close to the curves shown. Note also that only the CO content is shown on the reducing side. As we have said before, this is used to *indicate* how strongly reducing the atmosphere is. Other unconsumed gases are present, but their exact quantity is not known.

A study of the graphs in Fig. 305 brings forth the rather astonishing observation that all the steels having hardening temperatures up to 1550°F. actually *gain carbon when heated in an oxidizing atmosphere.* These are *K-W* (WATER-WEAR), *No. 11 Special* (WATER-HARD), *Solar* (WATER-TOUGH), *Stentor* (OIL-HARD), *R. D. S.* (OIL-TOUGH) and *Vega* (AIR-TOUGH). When this fact was first brought forth it was considered very "unorthodox," and was the subject of much checking and cross checking. Subsequent experience, however, both in the laboratory and in the practical hardening room, has fully confirmed this carburizing effect, and it is now recognized as a very powerful and reliable weapon in the hands of the tool hardener. In his everlasting battle against **burrs, die scratches, loading, stoning,** and kindred enemies, it gives him tools that cannot possibly have a soft skin; it means tools where the first "tenth" on the surface is just as hard and just as wear resisting as any of the metal underneath; it means that he doesn't have to grind or stone the surface in order to get down to "good metal"; it means tools that come from the hardening room with a slippery hard skin to resist loading or scratching; and lastly, it involves a method which is easy to apply and control.

The microstructures of carburized surfaces obtained in oxidizing atmospheres are quite interesting. Figs. 306 and 307 show cross sections of the surface metal of *K-W* (WATER-WEAR) hardened in both oxidizing and reducing atmospheres. The larger white particles are the high tungsten carbides that act like wearing studs, and give *K-W* (WATER-WEAR) its "slippery hard" surface. It will be noted that while these continue out to the very surface in Fig. 306, they are absent to a depth of

FIG. 306.—*K-W* (WATER-WEAR)— hardened in 3% O₂ atmosphere. White particles are high tungsten carbides. Magnified ×100. Rockwell hardness at surface—C-67/68.

FIG. 307.—*K-W* (WATER-WEAR)— hardened in 3% CO atmosphere. Partially decarburized. Magnified ×100. Rockwell hardness at surface —C-64/65.

about .005″ in Fig. 307. The Rockwell hardness figures do not show a significant difference—but if a tool having this partially decarburized surface got into service, it would certainly score and pick up long before the one hardened in the oxidizing atmosphere.

Fig. 308 is a similar microsection of *No. 11 Special* (WATER-HARD) hardened in a 4% oxygen atmosphere. The gray background is the hardened matrix of the steel, while the white particles are the excess carbides which do not go into solution during hardening. Note how these hard carbides are concentrated at the extreme surface.

A rather graphic demonstration of the effectiveness of this hard surface is given in Fig. 309. This shows a block of *Stentor*

(OIL-HARD) steel which was hardened from a 3% oxygen atmosphere in oil. The edge, just as it came from the quenching bath, is capable of easily scratching a block of glass, showing that even the extreme corner is up to the full carbon content.

The depth of surface carburization occurring in oxidizing atmospheres never exceeds .002″ to .004″. While this is sufficient to insure the absence of decarburization, it is not sufficient to affect the toughness of the surface. Length of time at temperature usually has little effect, except to increase the

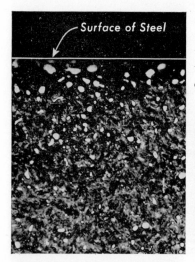

Surface of Steel

Fig. 308.—*No. 11 Special* (WATER-HARD)—hardened in 4% O₂ atmosphere. Showing enrichment of carbide particles at the surface. ×500.

Fig. 309.—*Stentor* (OIL-HARD) as quenched—and before drawing. This glass scratching test indicates absence of soft skin.

amount of scale. Consequently it is recommended that tools be held just a sufficient length of time to heat uniformly. This subject is covered in Chapter 19.

While there is no general agreement on the reason for carbon increase in an oxidizing atmosphere, the most probable explanation is that at the hardening temperature the metallic portion of the surface tends to oxidize in preference to the carbides. As the scale is formed, the carbon tends to move back into the steel and enlarge the particles already there. The action therefore is not carburization, but rather a migration of carbon from the scaled surface.

Let us now look briefly at the reducing side of the six steels in this group. Tests in various types of fuel-fired furnaces show that the *depth* of decarburization may vary from .005″ to .016″.

The decarburizing effect in reducing atmospheres is thus much more pronounced than the *carburizing* effect in oxidizing atmospheres—and it is quite unreliable, as we have already indicated. They are therefore to be avoided, and definite recommendations of atmosphere for the six steels are as follows:

K-W (WATER-WEAR)..........................	2 to 4% O_2
No. 11 Special (WATER-HARD)................	2 to 4% O_2
Solar (WATER-TOUGH)........................	1.5 to 4% O_2
Stentor (OIL-HARD)..........................	2 to 4% O_2
R. D. S. (OIL-TOUGH)........................	8 to 10% O_2
Vega (AIR-TOUGH)...........................	2 to 3% O_2

There is one precaution which must be observed in applying any of the foregoing information: *the oxidizing atmosphere must circulate past the tool, even though very slowly.* If stagnant spots develop, it is obvious that the atmosphere at these places might readily change in composition and become less oxidizing. This is exactly what happens where there are blind holes, or where tools are in contact with one another, or with the bottom of the furnace. Fig. 310 shows four such possibilities, the light areas indicating the points subject to decarburization. The depth of this surface effect has been greatly exaggerated in these sketches to make the illustrations easily understandable.

Turning now to the graphs in Fig. 305 of the three steels requiring hardening temperatures above 1700°F., namely *Hampden* (OIL-WEAR), *No. 610* (AIR-WEAR) and *No. 484* (AIR-HARD), it will be seen that neither oxidizing nor reducing atmospheres offer insurance against partial surface decarburization —although as we have already said, this statement does not necessarily apply where carefully controlled specialized atmosphere furnaces are available. It will be seen from the graphs that an atmosphere containing 15% CO will do quite a good job of hardening on both *Hampden* (OIL-WEAR) and *No. 610* (AIR-WEAR), and the surfaces will be just as clean and smooth as though the tool had been pack hardened. While there is no "wood block test" to apply to this highly reducing atmosphere, it so happens that at 15% CO the furnace starts to smoke and deposit soot—and this fact can be used as a measuring stick. If *Hampden* (OIL-WEAR) or *No. 610* (AIR-WEAR) must be hardened (without packing) in an oil-fired or gas-fired furnace, the best procedure is to run as far on the reducing side as possible. In the case of *No. 484* (AIR-HARD), if pack hardening is out of the question, and special atmosphere furnaces are not available, obviously an oxidizing atmosphere is to be preferred.

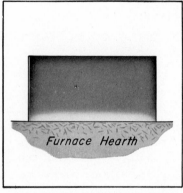

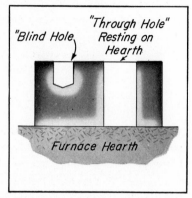

Tool surfaces exposed to circulation of oxidizing atmosphere will *not* decarburize. The surface in contact with the hearth *will* decarburize. If *two* tools lie close together, they will decarburize on the contacting faces.

Since the atmosphere cannot circulate through blind holes, or through holes that rest directly on the furnace hearth, these inside surfaces will tend to decarburize.

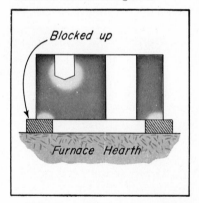

With the tool blocked up off the hearth, atmosphere can now circulate in the through hole, and the only decarburization will be in the blind holes and the spots where the tool rests on the blocks (look out for sagging).

Tool resting on edge will decarburize only in the blind hole and the edge that rests on the hearth. There is always *some* surface on a tool where a little soft skin won't matter.

FIG. 310.—Illustrating the effect of stagnant areas in an oxidizing atmosphere, and the remedy.

In the average hardening room, however, if entire absence of partial decarburization is required, pack hardening of these

steels is always recommended. Cast iron borings are preferred
to charcoal for packing because they do not carburize as actively
at the high temperatures, and because they conduct heat faster.
A comparison of the behavior of these two materials when used
for packing *Hampden* (OIL-WEAR) is given in Table XXX.

TABLE XXX.—EFFECT OF PACKING MATERIAL ON *Hampden* (OIL-WEAR)
1″ rd. sample packed in 6″ dia. pack—1775°F.—oil quenched
Carbon before hardening = 2.10%

Type of packing material	Surface carbon	Time to reach temperature
New charcoal—pea size down to dust..........	2.53%	3 hrs., 40 mins.
Spent[1] charcoal—pea size down to dust........	2.37%	3 hrs., 40 mins.
New cast iron borings......................	2.22%	2 hrs., 30 mins.

[1] Charcoal previously used at the same temperature.

It will be seen that cast iron borings yield a slight carbon pick-up
comparable to that secured on *No. 11 Special* (WATER-HARD)
or *Stentor* (OIL-HARD) when these steels are hardened in an
oxidizing atmosphere. If trouble is encountered in having
borings adhere to the tool, this can be prevented by wrapping
each tool in ordinary brown paper. Upon opening the pack the
charred paper will fall away and not interfere with the quench.

CHAPTER 19

THE TIME REQUIRED TO HEAT TOOL STEEL

Probably 95% of all the literature printed on the subject of heating tool steel is devoted to the question "How hot?." There are very little data available on "How fast?" or "How long?." Many of the instructions devoted to the **time** of heating say no more than—"Heat *slowly* and *uniformly* to a temperature of . . . ." About the only actual figure in general circulation is "one hour per inch of thickness." It is therefore highly desirable for the guidance of the hardener that someone publish specific data on how tool steel heats. This is the purpose of the present chapter.

Obviously one must know the actual *facts* about how steel heats before he can make any decisions on the subject. For example, it is generally believed that the surface of a tool reaches the furnace temperature before the inside is fully up to heat. Now this is either a fact—or it isn't. If it is true, then the hardener must know how *long* it takes for the center to catch up in all different sizes, and at all different temperatures, so he may decide how long to soak the tool after it looks right on the surface. If the belief about cold centers is *not* true (and, as a matter of fact, it isn't) then he wants to know it, so that he may not needlessly soak the piece for a long time—to its possible detriment.

In the course of his work the hardener is confronted with many specific questions to which he should be given specific answers. This chapter is constructed around a number of such definite questions, answers to which have been determined by actual test. In the discussion of many of these questions, definite recommendations are made concerning the time of heating, based on the facts presented. These recommendations will be found extremely simple and easy to apply. Some of them will sound so revolutionary as to be almost unbelievable. Frankly, it was hard at first to believe them ourselves—but for many months they have been tested and retested on the **various**

Matched Tool Steels—and they work. They make heat treat-ment very much easier, and turn out better tools. Whether they will work on *all* tool steel is a serious question. We know from long experience that no one would have dared use them on *brittle timbre* tool steel. We have reached the point where it has become necessary to turn our backs on the "old fashioned" heat treating recommendations and apply new methods to new prod-ucts. It is not that the old fashioned recommendations won't work on the new steels—be-cause they will—but the new methods give better results and are much easier to use.

How does a piece of tool steel heat?

It will be easier to answer this question if we pick out a defi-nite example. Suppose we are heating a piece of WATER-HARD 3″ round by 6″ long in an elec-tric muffle furnace to 1450°F. In Fig. 311, T_1 is the furnace thermocouple, T_2 is a thermo-couple embedded in the *surface* of the steel and peened in place, and T_3 is a thermocouple buried in the *center* of the steel.

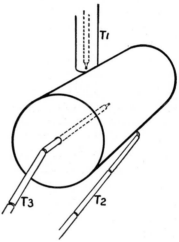

Fig. 311.—Illustrating shape of specimen, and placement of thermo-couples for measuring rate of heating.

The outside surface continuously absorbs heat from the furnace gases until it finally reaches the same temperature as these gases—then it stops. The center of the piece can get heat in only one way, by conduction from the surface. As long as the center is colder than the surface, it will continue to draw heat from the surface, thus cooling the surface and heating the interior.

Now think about that surface for a minute. The surface is the thing you see when you look at the piece. It has no thick-ness—or it wouldn't be a surface—it has no weight, and no mass, hence it has no capacity to "store" heat. It is just what it appears to be—the outside surface of the steel. It absorbs heat from the furnace gases on the one side, and gives it up to the interior metal on the other. It would be impossible for the surface to be as hot as the furnace (in which case it would absorb no heat) and still have a cold interior (to be cooling the surface by conduction). The only way for the surface to ever reach the furnace temperature is for the center to stop cooling it from below, and this happens only when the entire piece is uniformly heated. That is why the center and surface must arrive at the furnace temperature together.

In the early stages of heating, we have a different picture. Suppose the furnace is at 1450°F., and the surface is only 1000°F. —what then? The center of the piece *must* be colder than 1000°F., and here's why. Look at that surface again, remembering that it has no thickness, no mass, and no heat capacity. If something were not keeping it cool, it would rush up instantly and be the same temperature as the furnace. What is it that holds it back? It is the "drag" of the metal in the interior conducting heat away from its under side. But if the center and surface were the same temperature, no heat could pass inward and the surface wouldn't be losing any heat. Hence, the center must be colder than the surface at all times until the entire mass reaches the temperature of the furnace. Actually, within the limits of reading commercial pyrometers, the center and surface appear to arrive at the same temperature 25°F. or even 50°F. below furnace heat—after which they appear to travel together.

Let's put that piece of 3″ round WATER-HARD into a furnace. We will hold the temperature of the furnace constant at 1450°F. and will connect the surface thermocouple T_2 and the center thermocouple T_3 to a two point recorder and watch them heat. The chart will look like Fig. 312.

NOTE: In this—and all other experiments—when we say that the furnace is "maintained at a constant temperature," we mean that the furnace is up to that heat when the piece is put in, and the controls are set to keep it at that temperature. There is always more or less cooling of the furnace when the steel is introduced, but the aim is to get it back to heat as soon as possible and then hold it there.

Observe from the chart that the steel heats rapidly at first when the temperature "pull" is greatest, but very slowly as it approaches the furnace temperature. The flat spots at about 1350°F. mark the critical point of the steel. It takes about as much heat to force WATER-HARD through its critical as would be needed to heat it 150°F. Hence, when this point is reached, the steel stops heating until it has soaked up enough heat to complete the critical transformation.

In Fig. 312, the solid curve follows the heating of the *surface*, and the dotted curve follows the *center* of the piece. At first glance they seem very close together, but on more careful examination, it will be seen that the actual *difference* in temperature

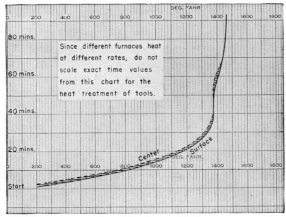

FIG. 312.—Heating curve for WATER-HARD—3″ round × 6″ long. Electric muffle furnace maintained at 1450°F.

between center and surface is represented by the length of the horizontal lines that connect the two curves. Even so, the difference in temperature is only about 100°F. during the early stages of heating, and much less as the steel approaches the critical point. It is very important to note that the curves run together during the last 25°F. or 30°F. of heating. This is true of all sizes tested and holds good at all temperatures—thus proving that *when the surface is up to heat, center is also up.*

We might do well to pause a moment and think over the significance of these statements in terms of heating actual tools. They mean that many of the older precautions to heat "slowly" are not necessary. The only possible reason for slow heating is to prevent a large difference in temperature between the center and the outside, which might result in destructive strains. But we have shown that in normal heating, with the furnace at temperature before introducing the steel, this difference is probably never over about 100°F., which is not sufficient to harm a modern tough timbre tool steel. This means then that **tools made from the newer steels can be put right in the hot furnace, and allowed to come to temperatures as fast as the steel will absorb the heat.**

As we have already seen, the surface and center come to temperature at the same time. Hence in order to make sure the entire tool is at temperature it is necessary only to make sure that the surface is up to heat—but it is extremely important that all portions of the tool *are* up to heat, and of uniform temperature. The only way you can tell when the outside of the tool is up to heat, is to compare its color with that of the thermocouple in the furnace. Experience in our laboratory shows that the normal eye will say they are alike when the thermocouple attached to the surface is about 5°F. colder than the furnace. In other words, you can't see those last few degrees. By accurately timing various sizes, we find for a temperature of 1450°F. that it takes about 5 minutes per inch of thickness for the steel to cover those last few degrees. At lower temperatures it would take longer—and at higher temperatures it would take less than 5 minutes per inch of thickness.

Here it is necessary to throw out a word of caution. Never use the exact time values taken from these curves for heating actual tools. There are many other things that influence the speed of heating beside the size of the piece, as we shall see later in this chapter. One of these is the character of the furnace itself, and its speed of heating. Our only reason for showing these heating curves is to illustrate some rule or prove some point that would be true in *any* furnace. For example, the curve in Fig. 312 is published here to show:

1. That the center and surface of a piece of tool steel reach the furnace temperature together.
2. That heating is delayed at the critical point.
3. The general shape of the curve—rapid heating at first, and very slow heating at the end.

Therefore *do not scale these curves.* After we have developed the rules and laws of heating, we will have a much *easier* method of finding the correct heating time than scaling it off curves. Let us now answer a very practical question based on the principles we have just discussed.

How can one tell when the center of a tool is up to temperature in any oven type furnace?

To answer this question we will take a specific steel—WATER-HARD. Neither the size of the piece nor the design of the furnace affect the method to be described. The procedure is as follows:

1. Place the furnace thermocouple behind the *heaviest section* being heated so the tool and the thermocouple can be seen in one "eyeful." (As in Fig. 311.)

2. As the steel approaches temperature, raise the door occasionally and compare the color of the steel and the thermocouple. Looking through the peep hole may fool you—the steel often looks *colder* when viewed through the peep hole. (If, in raising the door a little, you get a cold draft of air—partly cover the furnace ports with a brick and eliminate the "chimney effect.")

3. When the heaviest part of the tool looks "almost exactly" the same color as the thermocouple tube—and the dividing line between them disappears, start counting time.

4. For a temperature of 1450°F., allow 5 minutes additional time for each inch of thickness in the heaviest section of the tool —and then the piece will be up to temperature—clear through.

NOTE: If loose scale bulges from the sides of the piece, this will get hotter than where the scale is tight. Either scrape the loose scale off with your poker or don't look at it—look only at the tight scale in comparing colors. Loose scale will not appear if a proper furnace atmosphere is maintained (for WATER-HARD, use an oxidizing furnace atmosphere having 2% to 4% excess oxygen.)

How does the initial furnace temperature affect the total time required to heat tool steel to that temperature?

For example—if it takes 30 minutes to heat a block of WATER-HARD to 1450°F. in a certain furnace, how long will it take to heat the same piece to 1600°F., or 1375°F., or 1000°F., or 400°F.?

Let us assume that our piece of WATER-HARD is 1 $\frac{1}{2}''$ round by 3'' long and that we have a thermocouple embedded in the very center of the piece. (We do not need to bother with the *surface* temperature, because we know that the surface will be "up" when the center is "up.") The term *Tmax* will be used to indicate "the maximum temperature" employed in any particular heating cycle. The furnace will be heated to Tmax before the steel is put in, and will be held at this temperature as nearly as possible during the entire period of heating.

Imagine that we are using a curve-drawing recording pyrometer, that we set the furnace at 300°F. and put our piece on the
hearth.   As soon as the steel reaches 300°F., we mark the end of
the curve with an "X" and remove the piece of steel.   Now we
will raise *Tmax* to 500°F., we will turn the recorder chart back to
"scratch," put in another piece of steel, and draw the 500°F.
curve right alongside the 300°F. curve.   We will raise *Tmax* for
each new piece until we have finally reached a temperature of

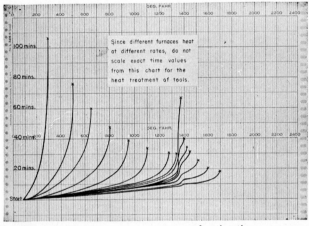

Since different furnaces heat
at different rates, do not
scale exact time values
from this chart for the
heat treatment of tools.

FIG. 313.—Effect of initial furnace temperature on heating time.   WATER-HARD—
1½" round, 3" long—thermocouple at center of piece.

1700°F.   When we have finished these curves, our very much
over-worked recorder chart will look like Fig. 313.
     The vertical distance from the starting line to the "X"
measures the total heating time for each temperature.   These
are listed in Table XXXI.
     Referring again to Fig. 313, we can draw a line through the
row of "X's" to form a new curve.   This new curve is reproduced
in Fig. 314, and it shows the manner in which furnace temperature affects total heating time.   The vertical distance from the
starting line to the curve indicates the total time needed to heat
the piece to that temperature.   This is another of those "do not
scale" charts, because the exact time will vary with the type of
furnace used—but it teaches some valuable fundamental truths.
Looking only at that part of Fig. 314 which lies below the critical
point (below 1350°F.), it is evident that in this range **the hotter**

TABLE XXXI.—EFFECT OF FURNACE TEMPERATURE ON HEATING TIME[1]
WATER-HARD—$1\frac{1}{2}''$ rd. $\times$ $3''$ lg.—heated in electric furnace—thermocouple
at center of piece

Furnace Temperature	Heating Time
300°F.	107 mins.
500°	77
650°	60
800°	48
950°	39
1100°	34
1275°	31
1340°	30
1375°	67
1400°	40
1425°	34
1450°	32
1525°	25
1600°	21
1700°	17

[1] Since different furnaces heat at different rates, do not use these exact values for the heat treatment of tools.

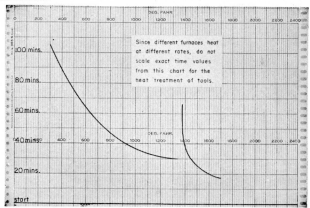

FIG. 314.—Tmax Curve. Effect of initial furnace temperature on heating time. Curve derived from Fig. 313. Total time to reach temperature is measured by the distance from the starting line to the curve.

the furnace, the shorter the total heating time.[1] Or, if we look at that portion of the curve that lies *above* the critical zone

[1] The shape of the curve below the critical is in accordance with the Stefan-Boltzman law:

$$Q = KFt \left(\frac{T}{100}\right)^4 \text{ where}$$

Q = quantity of heat in B.T.U.
F = area of surface in square feet
t = time in hours
T = absolute temperature, deg. F.
K = constant

(say above 1400°F.), we again find the time *decreasing* as *Tmax increases*.

It is important to understand the significance of that break in the curve which occurs at the critical. Of course, it is quite obvious that "150 degrees" of heat must be supplied to complete the critical changes. However, the *time* that will be required to soak up this much heat will depend entirely on the rate at which the heat is being supplied.

Let us imagine we have two furnaces exactly alike, and we set one for a Tmax of 1365°F., and the other for a Tmax of 1450°F. In each furnace we place one of our pieces of 1½″ round WATER-HARD. Both pieces of steel will reach 1355°F. fairly promptly—the one in the 1365°F. furnace will take about 15 minutes and the one in the 1450°F. furnace will take about 8 minutes. But now comes the big difference. Both pieces need "150 degrees of heat" for the critical changes but the one in the hotter furnace has a "pull" on it of 95°F., while the other has "pull" of only 10°F. If we apply the Stefan-Boltzman formula to these two problems, we find that it would require about *ten times as long* for the critical changes to become complete in the 1365° furnace as it would in the 1450°F. furnace. This is one of the reasons why it is not commercially practical to harden any tool steel from a temperature *in* the critical, or *just above* the critical. The time required would be a matter of hours which of course would be neither practicable nor advisable. Every tool steel, regardless of analysis, shows one of these "blind spots" somewhere in its *Tmax* heating curve—and to the tool hardener it means **DANGER—DON'T QUENCH FROM THIS TEMPERATURE.**

What effect has the surface or finish of the steel on the time required to heat?

This question must be answered by dividing it into two parts:

(*a*) Effect of surface when heating to a relatively low temperature—in the tempering (or drawing) range.
(*b*) Effect of surface when heating to a high temperature—especially when heating over the critical point.

In low temperature heating, if heat is applied by means of an oil bath, a salt bath, or a hot air furnace with *forced* circulation, the condition of the surface does not make much difference. However, if a *still* hot air furnace is used, where most of the heat is transmitted to the piece by radiation, then the surface can make quite a big difference. Everyone knows that radiant energy is *reflected* by a bright surface and is absorbed by a dark surface—and this is just what happens in a still air tempering furnace. Let us take two of our pieces of WATER-HARD, 1½″

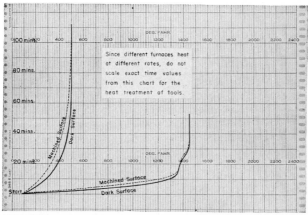

Fig. 315.—Effect of surface brightness on heating time. WATER-HARD—1½″ round, 3″ long—thermocouple at center. Heated in electric muffle furnace—still atmosphere below the critical—controlled atmosphere above the critical.

round by 3″ long, one of the pieces having a dark scaled surface, and the other having a bright, smooth machined finish. We will heat them both to 500°F. in an electric tempering oven without forced circulation of air. Heating curves for the *center* of the pieces will appear as those at the left in Fig. 315. Note that the scaled piece reached temperature in about 70 minutes, while the machined piece required about 100 minutes. If we were to *polish* the machined piece to an even finer finish, it would take over 2 hours to reach temperature. In other words, it takes about twice as long for a highly polished surface to heat under these conditions as for a piece with a dark or scaled surface.

In high temperature heating for hardening, the steel scales during heating—so regardless of whether it starts out bright or dark, it will be *dark* when it reaches the "slow" part of the heating cycle. Hence it makes very little difference in total time what the original finish of the piece was. Such a test run on WATER-HARD is shown in the curves at the right of Fig. 315. It will be seen that the bright machined piece was a little slower getting started, but after it acquired a tarnish it quickly caught up. By repeating this test at various temperatures both high

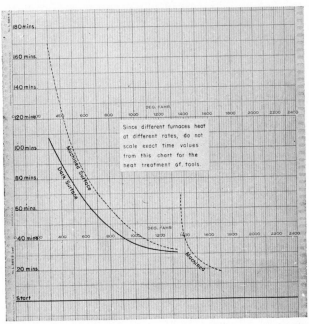

FIG. 316.—Tmax Curve. Effect of surface brightness on heating time. WATER-HARD—1½″ round, 3″ long—thermocouple at center. Heated in electric muffle furnace—still atmosphere below the critical—controlled atmosphere above the critical.

and low, we can add a new line to the Tmax curve previously shown in Fig. 313. That curve represented the total time required to heat a *dark* or *scaled* surface to various furnace temperatures. Fig. 316 reproduces this "dark surface" curve as a solid line, and adds a dotted line to represent the additional time needed when the piece has a bright machined surface. Still another, and higher, line could be added to show the time for a *polished* surface. Above the critical the effect of surface is so small (see Table XXXII) that only one line has been drawn. For purpose of record, however, this line above the critical is for a *machined* surface—that being the condition of practically all tools preparatory to hardening.

Not only polished, machined, and scaled surfaces were investigated, but many other possible (or likely) conditions were tested. Some of the more important figures are given in Table XXXII.

TABLE XXXII.—EFFECT OF SURFACE FINISH ON HEATING TIME
WATER-HARD—1½″ rd. × 3″ lg.—heated in electric furnace—thermocouple at center of piece

Type of surface	Total time to heat to 800°F. (still atmosphere)	Total time to heat to 1450°F. (controlled atmosphere)
Highly polished.............	80 mins.	38 mins.
Ground, No. 36 emery.......	60	36
Finish machined...........	60	36
Rough machined...........	65	36
Threaded.................	65	36
Sandblasted..............	55	36
Pickled in 1:1 muriatic acid..	45	34
Temper tarnished at 800°F...	45	36
Scaled at 1400°F...........	50	34

These time values are useful to compare with one another, but they cannot be transferred bodily to your own hardening room, because you may have different furnace conditions than ours. However, these same *ratios* would be expected to hold in another furnace.

Here, briefly, are the conclusions from the above data:

1. Surface condition makes no difference in the heating rate unless you are using some form of radiant heat.
2. Even with radiant heat, the surface condition can be ignored in hardening because at these temperatures the differences are very small.
3. In the low temperature drawing range (but only when using radiant heat) the surface finish *does* influence heating time; the brighter the surface, the longer it takes to heat.
4. Since 99% of all low temperature drawing is done on tools that are discolored from hardening, the tools will absorb radiant heat at the fast rate.

5. About the only time this subject would ever be important would be when a tool that had been finish ground came back to the hardening room for redrawing. In such cases (if using a still hot air oven) allow about twice the usual time for the tool to reach temperature and you will be perfectly safe. Don't forget to add the "soaking" time on top of this.

How does the size of a piece of steel influence the time required to heat it?

Obviously it takes longer to heat a big piece than a little piece; the question is, "How *much* longer?" Suppose we have a furnace, plenty big for the purpose, heated to 1450°F., and we lay on the hearth the following pieces:

$\frac{3}{4}''$ round $\times$ 2'' long   3'' round $\times$ 6'' long
$1\frac{1}{2}''$ round $\times$ 3'' long   6'' round $\times$ 12'' long

Suppose further, that there is a thermocouple buried in the center of each piece, and that these are all connected to a 4-point recording pyrometer. The chart we would get is illustrated in Fig. 317. Each of the four curves is marked at the point where that particular piece of steel arrived at the furnace temperature. It will be seen that the $1\frac{1}{2}''$ round took twice as long as the $\frac{3}{4}''$ round; the 3'' piece took twice as long as the $1\frac{1}{2}''$ piece; and the 6'' round again doubled the time. This shows that **the time required to heat a solid cylinder is directly proportional to its diameter.** If we were to repeat this test at many different furnace temperatures, we would find that for every temperature the same rule applies. This is *not* the same thing as saying, "Allow 'so long' per inch of *thickness*"—because a 1'' sphere, a 1'' cylinder, and a 1'' plate will heat at entirely different rates, as we shall now see.

How does the shape of the piece influence the time required for heating?

There are an infinite variety of detailed shapes that can turn up in a finished tool. However, most of them are "like a cylinder" or "like a cube" or "like a rectangle," etc. In any event, it is possible here to give the effect of only a few simple shapes; and since all the data presented so far have been for cylinders, this shape will be used as a basis for comparison.

Let us consider flat bars—all measuring $1\frac{1}{2}''$ thick, but

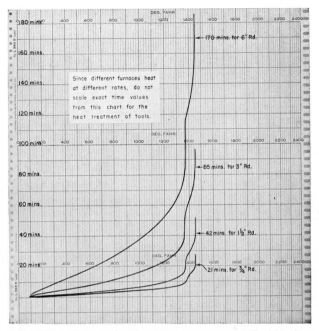

FIG. 317.—Effect of size on heating time. WATER-HARD Tool Steel
¾″ round, 2″ long   3″ round, 6″ long
1½″ round, 3″ long   6″ round, 12″ long.
Heated to 1450° F. in electric furnace—atmosphere controlled.

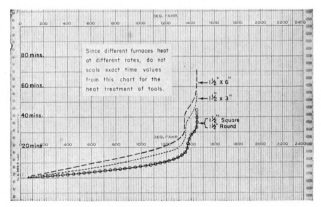

FIG. 318.—Time required to heat flat bars. WATER-HARD Tool Steel
1½″ round, 3″ long   1½″ × 3″ flat, 6″ long
1½″ square, 3″ long   1½″ × 6″ flat, 12″ long.
Heated to 1450°F. in electric furnace—atmosphere controlled.

having different widths—like $1\frac{1}{2}'' \times 1\frac{1}{2}''$, $1\frac{1}{2}'' \times 3''$, $1\frac{1}{2}'' \times 6''$, etc. With a thermocouple buried at the center of each, it is an easy matter to record their heating curves and compare them with a bar of $1\frac{1}{2}''$ round. This is done in Fig. 318. It will be seen that the $1\frac{1}{2}''$ square follows the same curve as the $1\frac{1}{2}''$ round; they heat at exactly the same rate. The wider flats, however, take longer, as shown in Table XXXIII.

TABLE XXXIII.—TIME REQUIRED TO HEAT FLAT BARS
(Atmosphere controlled electric furnace maintained at 1450°F.)

Size and Shape	Heating Time
$1\frac{1}{2}''$ round	36 minutes
$1\frac{1}{2}''$ square	36 "
$1\frac{1}{2}'' \times 3''$	51 "
$1\frac{1}{2}'' \times 6''$	62 "

The $1\frac{1}{2}'' \times 3''$ heats $\frac{36}{51}$ or 70% as fast as the $1\frac{1}{2}''$ round. The $1\frac{1}{2}'' \times 6''$ heats $\frac{36}{62}$ or 58% as fast as the $1\frac{1}{2}''$ round. By rather complicated mathematical calculations, it is possible to work out a theoretical ratio like this for all simple shapes. The calculated values check quite closely with values determined by actual test. The figures are summarized in Table XXXIV.

TABLE XXXIV.—RELATIVE HEATING SPEED OF VARIOUS SHAPES COMPARED TO A LONG CYLINDER[1]

	Shape	Speed Factor
	Long cylinder (dia. = D)	1
	Long square (D × D)	1
	Long rectangle (D × 2D)	.7
	Long rectangle (D × 3D)	.6
	Infinite plate (very wide, thickness = D)	.5
	Sphere (dia. = D)	1.5
	Cube (D × D × D)	1.5

[1] These calculated factors were furnished by Mr. Howard Scott, and permission to use them here is gratefully acknowledged.

To use this table, it is necessary to know how long it would take a *cylinder* to heat under the particular conditions at hand. Then to determine the time for the other shapes, *divide* the time of the cylinder by the "speed factor" for the new shape. For example, if a long cylinder 1″ round takes 30 minutes to heat, then a long flat measuring 1″ × 3″ would take 30 minutes ÷ .6, or 50 minutes to heat, and a 1″ cube would require 30 minutes ÷ 1.5 or 20 minutes to heat.

Does the internal structure of a piece of tool steel affect its heating rate?

Within the limits of our tests, the answer is "No." It has been pretty generally believed that a piece of tool steel, after oil treating (or even normalizing in air) heats quite a little faster than when in the soft annealed condition. Here is apparently what happens.

If you take two similar machined specimens of soft annealed WATER-HARD tool steel, and first oil treat one piece from say 1550°F., then put both pieces together into a furnace heated to 1450°F., there is no question but that the oil treated piece heats faster than the annealed piece. It is easy to tell the difference simply by eye, the oil treated piece becoming red hot while the other piece is still "black." This, however, is *not* due to the difference in structure. The fast heating of the oil treated piece is due to its *black* surface, and the slowness of the machined piece is due to its *bright* surface. If the reader will refer back to Fig. 315, it will be seen that a dark surface will reach about 1200°F. while a bright surface is only up to about 1000°F.—and this is a big difference when observed in a hardening furnace. To *prove* that this observed "faster heating" of an oil quenched piece is not due to structure, you need only *polish* both pieces before comparing their heating speeds. With the same surface on both pieces, they will heat alike—in spite of their difference in structure.

Does the type of atmosphere in the hardening furnace influence the heating rate?

Apparently it does not. Furnaces fired with gas or oil can be operated all the way from "definitely oxidizing," through "neutral" to "definitely reducing." The same thing can be done in modern atmosphere controlled hardening furnaces.

Tests were run in a gas-fired semi-muffle furnace, and also in a gas-curtain atmosphere-controlled electric furnace. The specimens of tool steel included water-hardening high carbon steel, high speed steel, and high-carbon high-chromium steel. The results are summarized in Table XXXV.

TABLE XXXV.—EFFECT OF FURNACE ATMOSPHERE ON HEATING TIME
All pieces 1½″ round, 3″ long—thermocouple at center of piece

Type of furnace	Atmosphere			Description	WATER-HARD 1.10% carbon tool steel heated to 1450°F.	RED-WEAR 18-4-1 high speed steel heated to 1600°F.	OIL-WEAR high-carbon high-chrome tool steel heated to 1600°F.
	CO_2	O_2	CO				
Gas-fired semi-muffle	7.8%	3.7%	0.0%	Oxidizing	30 mins.		
	10.0	0.0	0.5	Neutral	31 mins.		
	7.5	0.0	4.3	Slightly reducing	30 mins.		
	4.8	0.0	8.1	Reducing	29 mins.		
Electric muffle, controlled atmosphere	0.0	20.0	0.0	Room atmosphere	50 mins.		
	7.3	9.5	0.0	Oxidizing	39 mins.	28 mins.	24 mins
	13.5	0.0	0.0	Neutral	37 mins.		
	10.3	0.0	5.2	Slightly reducing	38 mins.		
	7.5	0.0	9.9	Reducing	38 mins.		
	5.5	0.0	12.3	Very reducing	....	27 mins.	24 mins.

At first glance, there appears to be quite a little difference among the various figures, but on closer inspection, these differences cannot be laid to variations in the furnace atmosphere. First note the four figures obtained on WATER-HARD in the gas-fired furnace. These are close enough to be regarded as good checks. Now examine the figures in the electric furnace. The low values for RED-WEAR and OIL-WEAR are explained by the high *Tmax* (see Fig. 322). Therefore in the present test, each of these two high alloy steels can be compared only with itself, and the results clearly show that it makes no difference in the heating time of either of them, whether the furnace be run oxidizing or reducing.

There is still one more apparent discrepancy in the figures. Observe that all of the WATER-HARD values in the electric furnace are quite close excepting the *first* one—the one heated without the use of any artificial atmosphere. This is not due to the chemical composition of the atmosphere, but to the *absence of circulation* in the furnace, and that subject will be discussed in the next section. Hence, we arrive at this conclusion:

The composition of the furnace atmosphere appears to have no effect on the heating rate of tool steel within the temperature range investigated.

What effect has the speed of circulation of the furnace gases?
Circulation of furnace gases can have a very important effect on the total time required for a tool to come up to heat. In a **high temperature** furnace such as is used for hardening, we normally get three different degrees of circulation.

(1) The muffle type furnace with stagnant atmosphere—practically no circulation.
(2) The muffle type furnace with controlled atmosphere—lazy circulation.
(3) The fuel-fired semi-muffle type furnace—more or less active circulation.

Figures taken from Table XXXV for 1½″ round WATER-HARD at 1450°F. under these three conditions show the following total heating times:

No circulation	50 minutes
Lazy circulation	38 minutes
Active circulation	30 minutes

These figures are just about as would be expected. The more rapidly the furnace gases circulate, the faster the steel heats.

In the **low temperature** range, hot air ovens such as are used for tempering (or drawing) offer two degrees of circulation.

(1) Ovens with stagnant atmospheres—practically no circulation.
(2) Ovens with mechanical fans—extremely active circulation, depending upon the speed of the fan.

Figure 319 shows the Tmax heating curves for 1½″ round WATER-HARD under four different furnace conditions. It is interesting to note that the two ovens with circulating fans heat the steel in about the same time—*regardless of temperature.*

Since most tool steel is tempered below 500°F., it would appear that the time-saving value of tempering ovens with circulating fans would strongly recommend them for production work. Their advantages would be even more apparent if the furnaces were well loaded with work.

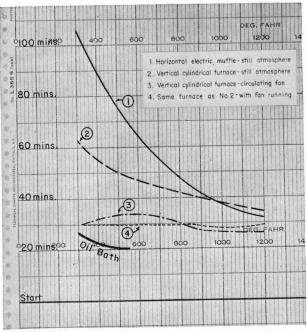

FIG. 319.—Tmax Curve for different types of electric tempering ovens and oil tempering bath. Heating 1½″ round WATER-HARD with dark surface. Time required to reach temperature is measured by vertical distance from "start" line to the curve.

How fast does a lead pot heat?

When a cold piece of tool steel is hung in a lead pot, it quickly chills the lead in its immediate vicinity, and if the piece is large, or the pot is small, it will chill the whole pot. It takes an appreciable time to heat the lead back to *Tmax*, and this disturbs to a great extent any effort to measure the exact time required to heat the steel. That is, the steel may reach the temperature of the lead before the lead is back to *Tmax* and you find yourself measuring how fast the furnace works, instead of how fast the steel is heating. For this reason, and also because tools hardened in a lead pot are usually of small cross-section, we will discuss this particular question through the use of a ¾″ round specimen. The tests were run on WATER-HARD, ¾″ round by 6″ long, with a ¹⁹⁄₆₄″ thermocouple hole drilled 4½″ deep. This permitted the thermocouple to reach within 1½″ of the bottom of the piece, and still enabled the top end to be held in the tongs without affecting the readings.

Fig. 320 shows a Tmax curve for heating in both a lead pot and in an atmosphere-controlled electric furnace. It will be

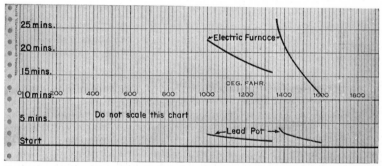

FIG. 320.—Tmax Curves—relative heating time in lead pot and furnace. Heating WATER-HARD ¾″ round bright surface, thermocouple at center of piece.

seen that the steel heats about 6 to 10 times as fast in the lead as it does in the furnace.

How fast does an oil tempering bath heat?

An oil tempering bath heats somewhat faster than a hot air oven with a circulating fan. Fig. 319 shows the Tmax curve for an oil bath compared to the several types of electric ovens. Fast as the oil bath is, it is doubtful whether it could maintain all this advantage over a fan-driven hot air oven when tempering a basket full of small parts.

The data presented here for tempering furnaces seem at first glance to be a little discouraging. Neither the furnace nor the tools are incandescent—you can't *see* the temperature—and it is necessary to adopt some arbitrary "minutes per inch of thickness" to allow the tool to reach the tempering heat before you can start counting the "soaking" time. Yet different furnaces heat at such different rates that it seems hopeless to arrive at a useful figure.

The picture will not look quite so black if you will refer back to Fig. 313. Note the *shape* of the heating curve at 300°F. It took 107 minutes for the piece to reach heat in this slow furnace, and yet after 60 minutes, it was within 20° of the temperature desired. If the hardener had started to count "soaking time" after 60 minutes, and had soaked the tool one hour, it would have had a full hour between 280° and 300°F., and the last 40 minutes would have been above 290°F. This would constitute quite a good tempering job.

TABLE XXXVI.—APPROXIMATE HEATING TIME FOR TEMPERING
Per inch of diameter of thickness, with furnace maintained steadily at Tmax.
Steel having dark or scaled surface[1]

Tempering temperature	Time required (per inch) to reach furnace temperature					
	In a hot air oven, without circulation			In a circulating air oven, or an oil bath[2]		
	Cubes or spheres[3]	Squares or cylinders[3]	Average flats[3]	Cubes or spheres[3]	Squares or cylinders[3]	Average flats[3]
250°F.	30 mins.	55 mins.	80 mins.	15 mins.	20 mins.	30 mins.
300°	30	50	75	15	20	30
350°	30	50	70	15	20	30
400°	25	45	65	15	20	30
500°	25	40	60	15	20	30
600°	25	40	55	15	20	30
700°	20	35	50	15	20	30
800°	20	30	45	15	20	30
900°	20	30	40	15	20	30

Temperatures above 900°F. are visible—watch the color.

[1] The figures apply to a dark or scaled surface on the tool. If the tool surface is finish ground, or otherwise brightened, allow *double* time in a still hot air oven. No extra allowance need be made for bright surfaces in a circulating oven, or in an oil bath.

[2] An oil bath can be used only at the lower temperatures.

[3] See Fig. 318 and Table XXXIV.

Taking all things into consideration, Table XXXVI will be found useful and fairly accurate—much more so than "guessing."

After the tool reaches the proper tempering temperature it should be *soaked at heat* to allow the internal changes to take place. The Carpenter Torsion Impact Curves are all based on soaking *one hour* at heat. Large or intricate tools should be soaked longer than one hour. As a general rule, the drawing temperature should be reduced 20° to 25°F. every time you double the soaking time over one hour—for example:

TABLE XXXVII

Soaking time	Tempering temperature				
1 hour.................	300°F.	325°F.	350°F.	375°F.	400°F.
2 hours................	280°	305°	330°	355°	375°
4 hours................	260°	285°	310°	335°	350°
8 hours................	240°	265°	290°	315°	325°

How fast does tool steel heat in a pack?

Effect of Packing Materials.—Pack hardening consists of packing the tool in a closed metal container with charcoal, clean cast iron chips, or some other suitable material, and then heating the entire pack to the hardening temperature. When thoroughly heated, the pack is opened and the tool is removed and quenched. The purpose of pack hardening is to avoid scale and surface decarburization (sometimes called "bark" or "soft skin").

For example, high-carbon, high-chromium tool steel is used extensively for intricate dies and tools that must maintain accuracy in hardening and long life in service. This steel is hardened from 1750° to 1800°F., at which temperature both scale and soft surface can easily become a problem. Concerning the heat treatment of high-carbon, high-chromium tool steel (OIL-WEAR), the following information was given on page 309:

"The best procedure is to pack in clean cast iron borings, heat uniformly to 1750° to 1800°F., soak thoroughly, then remove the tools from the pack and quench in oil."

While cast iron borings are preferred and are recommended over other packing materials such as charcoal, nevertheless where borings are not available, charcoal may be used on steels which are heated above 1700°F.

With the tool thus packed in a closed box, surrounded by one of these materials of relatively low heat conductivity, it is not at all easy to tell when the tool is up to the required heat. Obviously the container itself will come to heat fairly promptly but, unlike a solid piece of steel, the inside of the pack does not come up to heat nearly as fast. In fact, measurements show that the steel is only about *half way* up to heat when the outside of the box is *all the way* up. It would be worth knowing how long it takes the tool to heat under such circumstances. Questions such as these arise:

Will the steel heat faster in cast iron chips than in charcoal? Does the size of the charcoal lumps make any difference? Does "spent"[1] charcoal heat differently from new charcoal? Does the inside of the pack ever heat spontaneously, and get hotter than the furnace?

To investigate these questions, a test was run in which the conditions were as follows:

Steel Used.—High carbon, high chromium, 1″ round × 3″ long.

Thermocouple.—At center of the steel.

Box.—A length of 3″ pipe, capped with discs sealed in the ends.

Furnace.—Atmosphere-controlled electric furnace with variable atmospheres.

Tmax.—Furnace maintained constantly at 1780°F.

Packing Materials.—

(*a*) New charcoal—pea size and finer.

(*b*) New charcoal—larger than pea size.

(*c*) "Spent" charcoal—pea size and finer.

(*d*) New clean cast iron borings.

The heating curves for these four materials are shown in Fig. 321. Observe that much time is consumed in heating the steel through the last 20°F. The time values may therefore be listed as "practically up to heat" and "fully up to heat," as shown in Table XXXVIII.

TABLE XXXVIII.—TIME REQUIRED TO HEAT IN A 3″ DIAMETER PACK Containing 1″ round OIL-WEAR tool steel—thermocouple at center of steel Furnace temperature 1780°F.

Packing material	Practically up to heat	Fully up to heat
New charcoal—pea size and finer.......	1 hr., 30 mins.	2 hrs., 00 mins.
New charcoal—larger than pea size......	1 hr., 00 mins.	1 hr., 30 mins.
"Spent" charcoal—pea size and finer....	1 hr., 30 mins.	2 hrs., 00 mins.
New clean cast iron borings............	1 hr., 00 mins.	1 hr., 30 mins.

[1] This is a name frequently applied to charcoal that has been used in previous packs. It differs from "new" charcoal principally in the fact that the moisture has been driven out. Speaking literally, charcoal would not really be "spent" until it had been reduced to ashes.

It is obvious from this table that lump charcoal heats faster than fine charcoal. New and "spent" charcoal take about the same time to reach Tmax, but "spent" charcoal heats a little faster during the early part of the cycle.

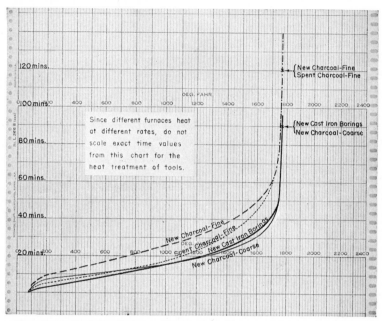

FIG. 321.—Pack hardening. Effect of packing material on heating rate. Heating OIL-WEAR Tool Steel, 1″ round—thermocouple at center of steel—packed in 3″ iron pipe with ends capped.

No "spontaneous heating" inside the pack was observed. An effort was made to *cause* spontaneous heating if possible. A charcoal pack was prepared, and two ⅜″ diameter holes were drilled in the covers at each end. The furnace atmosphere was run with 8% oxygen to assist the combustion of the charcoal—but nothing happened. In no case was it possible to cause the inside of the pack to become hotter than the furnace. We are not unmindful of the fact that such spontaneous heating has been reported, but must simply record the fact that we could not make it happen with these particular materials at this temperature. We are quite certain that the hardener need not fear spontaneous heating if he will not heat his furnace above 1800°F., and will use one of the two packing materials recommended.

As a helpful hint to the hardeners, cast iron chips can be

prevented from sticking to the tool by wrapping the tool in heavy brown paper before placing it in the pack. The paper will char and practically disappear when the heated tool is removed for quenching—but in the meantime, it will keep the cast iron chips from adhering to the surface of the tool.

Effect of Pack Size.—Any answer to the question of how the size of pack affects time required to heat must necessarily be approximate. The pipe used in Fig. 321 was 3″ in diameter. A similar run was made using a 6″ pipe, and the time values are given in Table XXXIX.

TABLE XXXIX.—TIME REQUIRED TO HEAT IN A 6″ DIAMETER PACK Containing 1″ round *high carbon, high chromium* tool steel—thermocouple at center of steel
Furnace temperature 1780°F.

Packing material	Practically up to heat	Fully up to heat
New charcoal—pea size and finer......	3 hrs., 40 mins.	4 hrs., 20 mins.
"Spent" charcoal—pea size and finer...	3 hrs., 40 mins.	4 hrs., 20 mins.
New clean cast iron borings..........	2 hrs., 30 mins.	2 hrs., 50 mins.

We have already seen that a *solid* piece of steel 6″ round requires exactly twice as long to heat as a solid piece 3″ round. In these packed pipes, we are not dealing with solid pieces of steel—but even so, a comparison of Tables XXXVIII and XXXIX shows that the 6″ pack comes *fully* up to heat in roughly twice the time required for the 3″ pipe. What seems even more surprising is the fact that the time required to heat the last 20°F. (that is, the difference between "practically up" and "fully up") is just about the same for *both* sizes of pipe, namely 30 minutes. It would therefore appear that these time values might serve some useful purpose in the hardening room as a rough guide to the heating time of packs. The following variables should be borne in mind:

Gas circulation (see Fig. 319).—These figures were secured in an atmosphere controlled electric muffle furnace. A gas-fired, or oil-fired furnace would be expected to bring the container up to heat somewhat faster, and a "dead" electric muffle somewhat slower. Bear in mind, however, that the circulating furnace gases cannot influence the time for "those last 20°"—because at this stage the container is fully up to heat, and the furnace gases cannot help the rate of heat transfer through the pack.

Shape of container (see Table XXXIV).—Presumably the *shape* of the box would have roughly the same effect as in solid pieces. It is also probable that a long *square* box (if raised off the furnace floor) would heat at about the same rate as a long *cylindrical* pipe. Short stubby boxes ought to heat more like *cubes* and *spheres*.

Chemical effect of packing materials.—Thus far, charcoal and cast iron chips have been compared only as to their relative heating rate—with the *time advantage* in favor of the cast iron. There is however still another difference between these two packing materials. Pack hardening at this high temperature has a **mild carburizing action.** If we take the four pieces of OIL-WEAR used to draw the curves in Fig. 321, and analyze the carbon in a layer .007″ deep turned from the surface of the pieces, we get the results shown in Table XL.

TABLE XL.—CARBURIZING EFFECT OF PACKING MATERIALS
By analyzing a layer .007″ deep turned from the surface

Packing material	Carbon analysis of the steel	Surface carbon after packing	Surface carbon gained in pack
New charcoal—pea size and finer......	2.02%	2.45%	.43%
New charcoal—larger than pea size....	2.02	2.41	.39
"Spent" charcoal—pea size and finer..	2.02	2.29	.27
New clean cast iron borings..........	2.02	2.14	.12

This carburizing effect is of course maximum at the surface of the tool, and gradually tapers off. Whether or not there is any virtue in an excessive carbon pick-up is something that each user must determine for himself. It is possible that it might be helpful on the smooth surface of a draw die, and harmful on the sharp corner of a blanking die. At any rate, it is one of the properties of a packing material that the hardener should be familiar with.

Does the analysis of a steel affect the rate at which it heats?

In answering this question, it is necessary to discuss specific steels with known analyses. The work to be reported was all done in the Carpenter Laboratory on Carpenter Tool Steels,

and as a matter of both accuracy and convenience, these steels
will be referred to by their brand names.

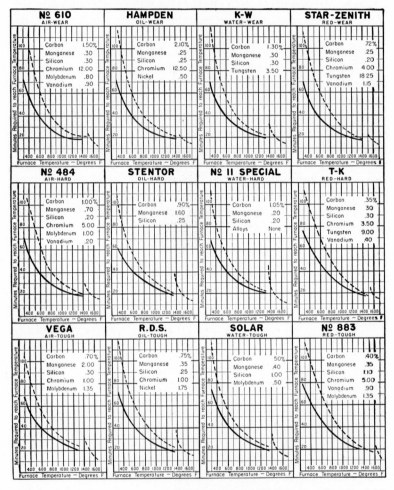

FIG. 322.—Tmax Curves for Carpenter Matched Tool Steels. Based on 1″
diameter cylinders—heated in electric furnace—with controlled atmosphere for
temperatures above the critical point. Solid line—dark surface on steel.
Broken line—machined surface. Do not scale these curves.

Since the heat conductivity of all tool steels is about the same,
there is no difference in the rate of heating under the critical.
In Fig. 322 are given the Tmax heating curves for the twelve
Carpenter Matched Tool Steels, including the effect of *surface*

for temperatures below the critical. These curves embrace the normal hardening temperature for every steel excepting *Star-Zenith* (RED-WEAR) and *T-K* (RED-HARD). These two are high tungsten steels requiring high hardening temperatures, and the curves cover only the "preheat" range. A careful examination of all the curves between 300°F. and 1300°F. will show them to be practically identical. This means that the analysis of the steel does *not* materially affect the rate at which it absorbs heat from the furnace.

On the other hand, because the steels have different analyses, their critical points fall at different temperatures—hence the "blind spot" occurs at a different Tmax on the curves. Therefore, if we were to compare the heating time of *No. 11 Special* (WATER-HARD) and *Star-Zenith* (RED-WEAR) in a furnace heated to 1375°F., the carbon steel would take more than twice as long to reach temperature as the high speed steel. If, however, the temperature selected were 1550°F., the carbon steel would then heat in considerably *less* time than the high speed steel. This apparent contradiction is due to the difference in the location of the critical points and, in this sense, analysis would be influencing the heating time. However, since the hardening temperatures recommended for the Matched Tool Steels carefully avoid the "blind spots," and in view of the evidence supplied by the curves, it is easy to see why the answer to the effect of analysis is "mostly none."

CHAPTER 20

QUENCHING AND TEMPERING

Quenching may be defined as a controlled cooling operation which causes steel to harden. The cooling may be conducted in various media, or "coolants," the most common being air, oil and water, the selection of the medium depending upon the analysis and hardenability of the steel. (See Chapter 4.) The water may be fresh, or it may contain appropriate percentages of ordinary salt or caustic soda, usually the former. For certain special purposes heated baths may be used, and these take the form of either molten salt, or molten metal. A more complete discussion of quenching baths will be found in Chapter 10, page 247. In the present chapter the word "quenching" will not be taken to include the slower forms of quenching such as air cooling, but rather will apply only to the faster types of quenching, which, on account of their drastic nature, present a problem to the hardener. This narrows our discussion down to oil and water quenching. Particular attention will be given the latter.

Quenching is one of the most important—and least understood steps in the heat treating operation. Anyone who has ever seen a piece of hot tool steel disappear into a quenching tank, and come out a few seconds later cold, can appreciate how difficult an operation it is to study. However, when he further considers that it is at this stage that the steel hardens—and further, that warpage, size change, cracking, internal strains, and soft spots are all products of this operation, he gains some idea of its importance.

There are possibilities in the quenching tank that the hardener does not realize—let alone apply. It is common knowledge that quenching produces *internal strains* in a piece of steel—forces that are sometimes powerful enough to smash a piece of hardened steel whose strength may measure close to 400,000 lbs. per sq. in. If forces of this magnitude can be developed in quenching, why not devote some effort to making them *useful* instead of destructive? This is exactly the same thought that went through Benjamin

Franklin's head when he tried to harness a bolt of lightning with a kite string. Practically, control of internal strains in tool steel is accomplished by two means, first by directing the coolant *where* it is wanted, *when* it is wanted, by such means as quenching fixtures; and second, by regulating the rate of cooling through the latter stages of the quench. In order to understand these statements thoroughly, let us take a brief look at the theory and principles of the hardening of tool steel.

Fig. 323 shows what happens to a piece of water-hardening tool steel as it is heated and cooled slowly, and heated and quenched. Following the solid line with the arrows pointing upward, as the steel is heated it expands up to a temperature of about 1350°F., where it suddenly contracts to a temperature of 1400°F., then continues to expand. The limited range through which the steel contracts is the *critical range on heating.* As the steel goes through this range, two things happen; first, most of the carbon goes into solution in the iron, and second, the iron becomes non-magnetic. For convenience this solution of carbon and iron has been given the name "austenite." There is nothing mysterious about this name, and it is used in exactly the same way as we use the word "brine" to describe a solution of salt and water.

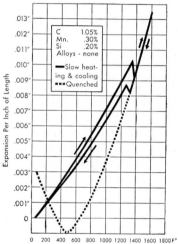

FIG. 323.—Dilation curve for WATER-HARD tool steel.

Following the arrows downward, if the steel is cooled slowly, as in a furnace, it follows the course of the solid line. It contracts down to 1300°F., where it suddenly expands until the temperature drops to about 1250°F., after which it continues to contract down to room temperature. The brief range of expansion is known as the "critical range on cooling," and through this range the steel regains its magnetism, carbon again drops out of solution in the form of small "carbide" particles, and regardless of how fast or slowly it may be cooled from about 1250°F. down to room temperature, the steel will be in the annealed condition.

If instead of being cooled slowly from above the critical range, the piece had been quenched in brine, it would follow the course of the dotted line. The steel in cooling speeds past the range of 1300°F. to 1100°F. so rapidly that the critical transformation has no chance to occur. It will be interesting at this point to recall the discussion of "gate speed" or "critical quenching" speed in Chapter 4, page 61. We said in that discussion that at about 1100°F. there is an imaginary gate through which the steel must be cooled rapidly in order to insure hardening. We said that this gate tends to snap shut and prevent the steel from hardening, and that the speed with which it tends to close is determined by the analysis of the steel, certain alloy additions tending to slow up the gate speed as in the case of the oil and air-hardening steels. We termed this speed the "critical quenching speed" of the steel, and said that in order to harden a piece of steel therefore, it is necessary to cool it past about 1100°/1300°F. faster than its critical quenching speed. We further said that having cooled past the gate temperature rapidly enough, the steel has "made up its mind" to harden, but actually does not begin to harden until it reaches about 450°F. Following the dotted line in Fig. 323 it will be seen that expansion starts at this point, and continues until hardening is complete. Through this expansion range the relatively soft solution "Austenite" is changing to a harder and less dense structure. This structure is always formed when tool steel is properly hardened, and is known for convenience as "Martensite."

Tool steel is in a very interesting "twilight" condition when its quench has been interrupted between 1100°F. and about 500°F. It has not yet hardened, so that it can be bent with a hammer. Since it has definitely made up its mind to harden it will do so, even though it might be held at 500°F. for a consider-able time and then cooled. For many years hardeners of files and other long tools took advantage of this fact, straightened these tools by interrupting the quench, performing the straight-ening operation above 500°F., then allowing the tool to cool and harden. On account of lack of exact information on the behavior of steel in this range, however, little further use was made of this principle until a paper published in 1928[1] started a series of

[1] "What Happens When High Speed Steel Is Quenched"—B. H. DeLong and F. R. Palmer (The Carpenter Steel Co.), A.S.M. Vol. 13, 1928, page 420.

researches which have added greatly to our knowledge of so-called "sub-critical" changes in quenching. The authors of this paper chose high speed steel for study, since on account of its slow critical quenching rate they could air cool and observe the changes below the "gate" temperature in "slow motion."

Fig. 324 was constructed by heating a piece of high speed steel to about 2300°F., rushing it to a Brinell hardness tester and making a series of Brinell hardness tests as the piece cooled.

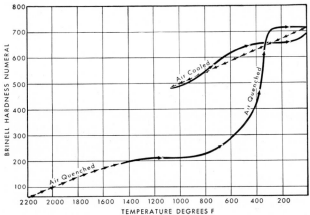

FIG. 324.—Brinell hardness of high speed steel during quenching and tempering.

The thermocouple of a pyrometer was embedded in the piece so that its temperature could be measured at the time of making each hardness determination. The progress of actual hardening can be followed by entering the diagram at the lower left corner along the dotted arrows. The first hardness determination was made at about 1600°F. and showed a Brinell of about 160. When the piece had cooled to 800°F., the hardness was about 220 (which is just about the hardness of annealed high speed steel). As it cooled below this temperature actual hardening commenced, and after passing about 450°F. the hardness increased rapidly until at 200°F. it reached 720 Brinell. Hardening was now complete and there was no further change as it cooled to room temperature.

It might be argued that the softness at 800°F. was due entirely to the fact that the steel was hot—and therefore easier to indent. This can be investigated by reheating the same piece to 1100°F., which is a normal drawing temperature for high speed steel.

This operation is indicated by the arrows on the upper curve. The piece was now removed from the drawing furnace and another series of Brinell hardness readings taken as it cooled back to room temperature. These values are shown on the solid line of the upper curve.

While it is true that in the heated condition the steel was somewhat softer (480 Brinell at 1100°F.—compared to 720 Brinell at room temperature), still if this 480 Brinell is compared with 210 Brinell, the hardness shown on the lower curve when the steel cooled to 1100°F., it must be apparent that the steel had not hardened at the time the lower curve was drawn. The upper curve also gives us a clue as to how much of the hardening shown by the lower curve, as the steel cooled below 1100°F., was due simply to lower temperature, and how much was due to an actual structural change. Examination of the two curves shows that they are roughly parallel down to about 450°F., indicating that actual structural hardening started at about 450°F. It is interesting to note that refined methods developed more recently have placed this point at 430°F.

Thus, in the case of high speed steel, it makes its "promise to harden" at about 1300°F. It actually starts to harden at about 450°F. In between these two temperatures there is quite a wide range where the steel is in the same "twilight" condition as the carbon steel was when its quench was interrupted at 500°F.—it has made up its mind to harden, but it has not yet actually done so. A more complete account of the behavior of high speed steel during hardening will be found in Chapter 13. While the method just described served for the study of high speed steel in this twilight or sub-critical zone, it of course could not be used on water and oil-hardening steels. Subsequent investigators hit on a suitable method however, that of quenching down quickly in a hot bath to some definite temperature, holding at this temperature until the austenite began to "break down," or change to another constituent, and noting the exact length of time required from the instant of quench to the instant breakdown began, then continuing at temperature and noting the time it took for breakdown to be complete. By quenching to a series of different temperatures all the way from above the critical range to room temperature, a curve could be plotted showing the time required for beginning and completion of break-down at each temperature.

Such a curve for carbon steel is shown in Fig. 325. On account of its shape it has been dubbed the "S" curve, but is often referred to also as the "TTT" curve, meaning "Time, Temperature, Transformation."

It will be noted in plotting this curve that the horizontal time scale increases very rapidly to the right. This is because the

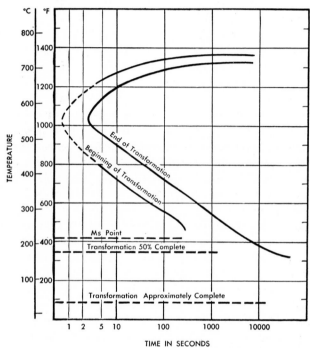

Fig. 325.—"S" curve of 1.10% carbon steel showing time required for transformation at various temperatures, after quenching from 1450°F. and holding at those temperatures.

times for transformation at some temperatures are so long that the scale has to be condensed to get the entire curve on one graph. The curve shows that if we quench and hold in a hot bath at about 1100°F., transformation will start almost immediately, and will be complete in about 3 seconds, carbide coming out of solution somewhat as it does in annealing. The steel consequently will have increased very little in hardness. If we quench and hold at 600°F., transformation will not start until about a minute has elapsed, and will not be complete for about 10 minutes. If it is allowed to complete itself, the steel will harden to some extent, but it will not reach its full possible hardness, since again carbide has come out of solution. If we quench to say 350°F., part of the transformation occurs immediately we cross the line at about 400°F., but if the steel were held constant at this temperature, the transformation would not complete itself for an extremely long time. The very important thing to note here is that the constituent which starts to form as the steel passes the line at about 400°F. is *martensite*, and this temperature is therefore often referred to as the "Ms point" of the particular steel, meaning the martensite starting point. If the reader will now turn to Fig. 323, he will see that this "Ms point" corresponds approximately to the point on the dotted line where expansion starts. If both this figure and Fig. 325 are kept in mind at the same time, it will be seen that as the steel cools from about 400°F. down to room temperature, more and more martensite forms, the steel at the same time expanding because martensite occupies more space then the austenite from which it formed. At room temperature approximately 100% of the steel structure is martensite, any remainder being retained austenite—and the steel has fully hardened. It is important here to note that the speed of cooling from about 400°F. does not affect the final hardness. Remember we said the steel had made up its mind to harden, so that the cooling from 400°F. to room temperature may be retarded, if desired, without diminishing final hardness.

While "S" curves of all steels are of the same general form, they differ in detail depending on composition. The one we have just described is for WATER-HARD. When alloys are added which increase hardenability, the curve moves toward the right, meaning that all the transformations require a longer time. In such steels it is particularly important to note that the "knee" of the curve at about 1100°F. moves farther away from the zero line, allowing longer holding, or slower cooling, at this temperature without transformation. This is another way of saying that these alloys have slowed the critical quenching speed. Alloys also affect the temperature at which the knee occurs, as well as the Ms temperature. As we have already seen the Ms temperature for high speed steel is 430°F.

Let us now take a general look at the "S" curve (Fig. 325). Note that the so-called "knee" of the curve at about 1100°F. corresponds to our "gate" temperature, the temperature through which we must cool very rapidly on the quench, and at which the steel "makes up its mind" to harden. After cooling below this temperature it is obvious from the curve that the steel may be cooled much more slowly, or even held at some constant temperature, without change. When we cool to the Ms point at about 400°F. and then continue cooling, hardening takes place through the transformation to martensite. We thus see clearly defined the two steps in quenching; first, the quick cooling through the range of 1300° to 1100°F., and second, the subsequent hardening from about 400°F. down. Now note that each of these steps introduces its own hazard. In a water-hardening steel the extremely quick cooling through 1100°F. sets up stresses due alone to bringing the piece of steel from 1450°F. down to 1000°F. —from red to black—in a matter of split seconds. Having passed through this stage, the steel next encounters the second stage of cooling from 400°F. to room temperature, in which rapid expansion takes place when the steel is quite rigid. Through the first stage, the stresses if not controlled, will cause warpage; through the second stage, under certain circumstances, if not controlled, they may cause cracking. These two stages should be kept clearly in mind during the following discussion.

First of all, there are four fundamental laws of quenching that must be known and understood. The laws, themselves, are quite simple.

Law No. 1.—*Steel is stronger cold than hot.*

Everyone knows that steel is easier to bend, shape or deform when it is hot. Therefore, when hot steel comes into conflict with cold steel, the cold steel always wins.

Law No. 2.—*Steel expands when heated and contracts when cooled.*

We have already seen this in Fig. 323. Starting at room temperature, the steel gradually expands up to about 1350°F. when it will be about .010″ longer per inch than it was when it started. Here, it reaches the critical point, and while going through the critical, it shrinks somewhat. Above the critical, it continues to expand at a more rapid rate.

On slow cooling, it shrinks until it reaches about 1310°F., expands while going through the critical and then shrinks back to its original size as it reaches room temperature.

Law. No. 3.—*Some tool steels increase in volume when hardened.*

This is particularly true of water-hardening tool steels. They actually increase in size all over—just as water expands when it freezes. The dotted line in Fig. 323 shows the approximate course through which this steel would travel if it were quenched instead of being cooled slowly. It would continue to shrink (without any critical point interruption) to some temperature in the neighborhood of 500°F. As it quenched below this temperature, it would expand until it would finally be about .003″ per inch longer than it was when it started in the annealed condition.

Law No. 4.—*All steels have the same elastic properties when stressed under the elastic limit—regardless of composition or heat treatment.*

This may seem impossible, but it is true nevertheless and can be demonstrated by a simple experiment. Fig. 326 illustrates a simple apparatus that will support a rod on one end and allow the free end to stick out like a fishing pole. When this photograph was taken, the rod on the right was a piece of high speed tool steel in the hardened condition. The piece on the left was a rod of exactly the same size, but made of soft bar iron. It would be hard to find two samples differing more in analysis and hardness.

On the free end of each rod is hung a bail for supporting weights. The light wooden wand across the top is simply placed there so that the observer can readily see any difference in deflection when the weights are added.

Fig. 327 shows the same apparatus after equal weights have been hung on both bails. It will be observed that both rods have deflected the same amount. They will continue to show the same deflection until sufficient load has been added so that one of them becomes permanently bent. Obviously this will happen first on the soft iron. Fig. 328 shows how the iron rod finally gives way when enough weights are added. This does not disprove the rule, because when all the weights are removed, as shown in Fig. 329, it will be seen that the soft iron rod has been permanently bent.

This fourth law has so many important engineering applications that it may well be discussed further. Consider, for example, a milling machine arbor that might measure $1\frac{1}{4}''$ diameter × 10″ long. Under heavy cuts, the operator notices that the cutter springs away from the work—and perhaps even chatters. To correct the trouble he asks for an alloy steel arbor heat treated

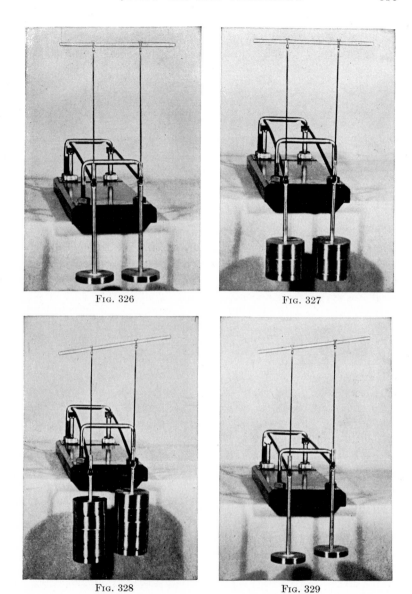

Fig. 326

Fig. 327

Fig. 328

Fig. 329

Figs. 326–329.—Demonstration of modulus of elasticity (see text).

to a high strength.   This will obviously do no good because the new arbor will have exactly the same elastic properties as the old one.   The only thing he can do to obtain greater stiffness is to increase the diameter of the arbor—or decrease its length.   If the arbor had permanently *bent* in service, he could, of course, correct this by using a stronger steel of the same size.

All metals have a property known as the **modulus of elasticity.** For steel, this value is approximately 30 million, for copper it is about 15 million and for lead it is only 2½ million.   If it is desired to think of this number as having some definite meaning, it would be the number of pounds per square inch necessary to stretch the material elastically to double its length.   Of course, no metal will stand these forces without breaking—but small fractions of the load will operate in exactly this ratio.   For example, 1/1,000th of this load would be 30,000 lbs. per sq. in., and if such a load were placed on a piece of steel one inch long, it would stretch it exactly 1/1,000th inch.   Copper, having half of the modulus of steel would stretch or deflect twice as much under any given load.

In connection with this discussion of quenching, it is important to repeat that all steels *regardless of their analysis or heat treatment* will stretch exactly .001″ per inch under a load of 30,000 lbs. per sq. inch.   The reason this is important is because there is no other means of measuring the internal strains in a piece of hardened tool steel.   The reader is asked to visualize a piece of hardened steel that measures exactly 1″ long.   It is now drawn for a long time at a temperature which is so low that the hardened structure is not disturbed.   Upon remeasurement, it is found to be only .999″ long.   There has obviously been relieved a strain approximating 30,000 lbs. per sq. in. over the cross section of the piece.

With this thought in mind, it will be interesting to follow some simple quenching experiments.   Consider a block of 30% nickel steel about 1″ square and 3″ long as illustrated at the top of Fig. 330.   The 30% nickel steel is used because this material will not harden, and hardening is a thing to be avoided in this experiment. This block is heated to say 1400°F. and it is then quenched sideways into water—being lowered through the surface of the water very slowly.   As the quenching starts, there appears the condition illustrated in sketch *B*.   The bottom edge which entered the water first has become black and is shrinking rapidly.   The upper edge is still red hot and, of course, does not want to shrink yet. Here is where quenching rule No. 1 begins to operate—hot metal comes into conflict with cold metal, the cold metal wants to shrink and the hot metal does not—but the cold metal has its way and proceeds to *hot upset* the upper portion of the block. Strictly speaking, each layer hot upsets the layer just above it.

After the block has become entirely cold all over, the upper edge has done some additional shrinking on its own account—but, due to the fact that it was upset while it was hot, it is now too short to fit the rest of the piece. Since the bottom edge is cold, the top edge cannot deform it, and as shown in sketch *C*, the piece is warped with the short edge on top.

This is one of the mechanisms by which steel warps during quenching. Even if the experiment were conducted on tool steel and it was actually hardening, this warping mechanism would go on just the same. Superimposed on it would be other changes which will presently be discussed.

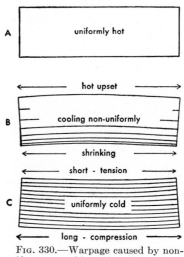

Fig. 330.—Warpage caused by non-uniform quenching of a 30% nickel steel block.

This explains why long slender tools should be quenched vertically—and should not be swished around in the bath. The object is to cool the entire cross section as uniformly as possible and thus avoid this upsetting action which can happen in the twinkling of an eye.

In order to measure the internal strain in the above piece of metal, it could be split in half lengthwise with a saw—thus separating the top half from the bottom half. The lower half of the piece would tend to lengthen, because the pull from the top piece had been removed. The top piece would tend to shorten—because the stretching effect of the bottom piece had been removed. Since this movement would be entirely elastic, it would not be a difficult job to figure out just how much load had been necessary to hold them in the shape where they did not want to be.

Consider another simple quenching experiment—this time on a cylinder 1″ round and 3″ long as illustrated in Fig. 331.   It is again made of a 30% nickel steel which has no critical point and does not harden, but is nevertheless controlled by quenching

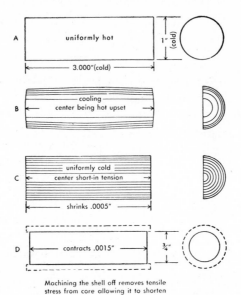

Fig. 331.—Effect of quenching on 30% nickel steel cylinder—water quenched from 1425°F.

law No. 4.   This piece is heated to 1425°F. and then quenched endwise so that it will warp as little as possible.   However, the surface will cool much faster than the interior of the piece and if examined while the center is still red hot, a condition would appear on the longitudinal section such as is illustrated in sketch B.   The surface has gotten black and is shrinking rapidly.   The center is still red hot but it has to go along with the surface and it is being hot upset.   The upset metal has to go *somewhere,* so it bulges the sides.   The third sketch shows the condition when the cylinder has completely cooled.   Measurement of the length shows that it is now .0005″ shorter.   The center metal has, of course, shrunk as it cooled and it is now too short to fit the outside of the piece.   The outside is trying to be 3″ long and the inside is trying to be considerably shorter. The average between them accounts for the new measurement.

To prove that this strain condition really exists, the quenched piece is now mounted in a lathe and the diameter reduced to ¾″ as shown in sketch *D*. This removes the surface metal that wants to be long and gives the interior a chance to contract to the size that it wants to be. No metal has been removed from the ends of the piece at all—but it now measures .0015″ shorter than 3″.

Fig. 332.—Fracture of specimen illustrated in Fig. 334.

Consider the condition that existed in sketch *C*. The core of the piece is being held .001″ longer than it naturally should be. Since this amount of stretch extends over a total length of 3″, the stretch per inch is ⅓ thousandths inch. Since a load of 30,000 lbs. per sq. in. would stretch the metal .001″ per in., the load in the third sketch must have been 10,000 lbs. per sq. in. The compression in the ⅛″ shell that was machined from the outside could be similarly figured.

Another experiment will show what happens in a piece of plain carbon water-hardening tool steel. When a piece ⅝″ diameter × 3″ long is quenched, it will harden only on the surface and will have a tough unhardened core. A typical fracture of such a piece is shown in Fig. 332. What does the hardened case "want to do," and what does the tough core "want to do" in the way of size change?

To study the behavior of the fully hard case, it is helpful to study a piece of this same steel only ¼″ diameter and 3″ long. This will harden clear through and will indicate what the hardened case "wants to do." Fig.

Volume changes produced by hardening (martensite)

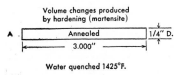

Water quenched 1425°F.

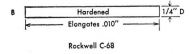

Rockwell C-68

Volume changes produced by toughening (troostite)

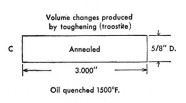

Oil quenched 1500°F.

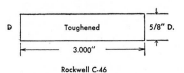

Rockwell C-46

Fig. 333.—Experiment to show size change tendencies of case and core in carbon tool steel.

333 shows such a ¼″ piece 3″ long and sketch B shows what happens when water quenched from 1425°F. The length has increased .010″. This does not represent internal strain. Quenching law No. 3 says that this steel will expand when hardened—and it is this expansion that has just been measured.

A larger sized piece would have an unhardened core, and the structure of this core is called "troostite." This troostite constituent can be produced by quenching a piece of the steel ⅝″ diameter into *oil* from 1500°F. This will yield a Rockwell hardness of about C-46 which is equivalent to the hardness of the core of a piece that has been quenched in water. Sketches *C* and *D* in Fig. 333 show the measurements on such a sample oil quenched from 1500°F. It has not changed length at all.

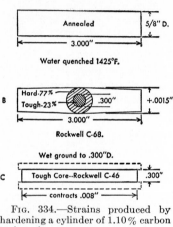

Fig. 334.—Strains produced by hardening a cylinder of 1.10% carbon tool steel.

These two preliminary experiments have shown that the hardened surface wants to expand and the core wants to "stay put."

The next step is to take a piece of water-hardening tool steel, ⅝″ diameter, heat it to 1425°F., and quench it in water or brine. The measurements are shown in Fig. 334. The second sketch shows that the length has not changed at all. The diameter has expanded .0015″ at the center and the piece is slightly barrel shaped. If this piece were cut in half, it would be found that the diameter of the core was about .300″ and the rest of the cross section was hardened case. In order to investigate the strains, all of the case is very carefully removed by grinding down to a diameter of .300″, but no metal at all is removed from the ends of the piece. Upon measurement, the length of the core is now found to have contracted elastically .008″. This means that, in the second sketch, the core was being stretched this amount and the strain involved was 80,000 lbs. per sq. in.

The reader must understand further that while this tool steel cylinder was being quenched, the same hot upsetting mechanism was operating that was earlier described in connection with the cylinder made of 30% nickel iron. The final result is a compromise between this and the hardening mechanism. However,

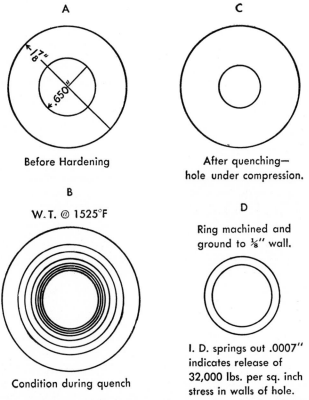

FIG. 335.—Effect of internal quenching on a 30% nickel steel ring.

the strains that were measured are "net"—regardless of where they came from.

The purpose of all the above experiments was to pave the way to harnessing these internal strains to some useful purpose, and it is now time to consider a very simple shape that might be used as a tool. Fig. 335 illustrates a ring made of 30% nickel steel which is to be quenched in a quenching fixture. The water will be squirted through the hole and the outside will be kept perfectly dry—thus cooling comparatively slowly. The ring is approximately ⅝″ thick in the direction vertical to the paper. Sketch A shows the dimensions before hardening. The ring is heated uniformly to 1525°F. and is flushed through the hole as described. Sketch B illustrates the condition after the walls of the hole have become black but while the outside of the ring is still red hot. The hole has shrunk to a smaller diameter while the rim has contracted very little. Here is another of those contests between hot and cold metal—and, since the inside cannot separate from the outside, it must pull the outside along with it by a hot upsetting action. Later on, the outside cools and shrinks on its own account, and since the I.D. is now rigid, these outer bands pinch down on it—just like shrinking a steel tire on a wheel. When the entire ring is cold, the I.D. is under compressions and the O.D. is in tension.

In order to measure the compression at the I.D., the ring is mounted in a lathe and the O.D. is completely removed by machining—leaving only a small ring as shown in Sketch D. Careful measurement of the I.D. before and after machining, shows that it has expanded .0007″ when the outside "hoops" were machined off. From the elastic formula it can readily be figured that the compressional strain on the I.D. had amounted to 32,000 lbs. per sq. in. Incidentally, this is just about equal to the elastic limit of this kind of material.

Now suppose that this ring were a portion of a rifle barrel. Explosion of the charge would, of course, tend to burst the barrel. If the barrel were simply machined as shown in Sketch A— and the elastic limit of the material were 32,000 lbs. per sq. in., a bursting stress in excess of this figure would stretch the I.D. and permanently deform it—or perhaps even burst the barrel. Now suppose the barrel is in the condition shown in Sketch C. A bursting stress of 32,000 lbs. per sq. in. will do nothing more than expand the I.D. up to the diameter that it "wants to be" anyway. This force will simply relieve the compression strain already present and will put the inner wall back into "neutral." It would take an additional stress of 32,000 lbs. per sq. in.—or a total of 64,000 lbs. per sq. in.—to permanently deform the metal. Thus, by introducing favorable quenching strains, the useful strength of the material has been doubled.

When this same experiment is conducted on a piece of plain

carbon water-hardening tool steel (Fig. 336)—and the outside metal is removed by grinding—it is found that the compressional stress on the hole is approximately 115,000 lbs. per sq. in. The reason the figure is so high is because the metal in the walls of the hole has hardened and has tried to expand in accordance with

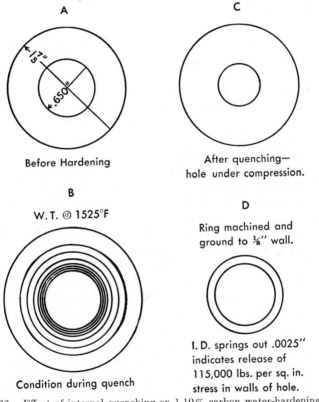

FIG. 336.—Effect of internal quenching on 1.10% carbon water-hardening tool steel ring.

quenching law No. 3. This expansion is resisted by the shrinking action of the outer metal and the final stress is the total of the hot upsetting action which was observed in the 30% nickel ring plus the expanding action of the hardened inside wall.

If this tool steel ring is to be used as a drawing die, the stresses of service will have a bursting action—just like the exploding gun powder. The first 115,000 lbs. pressure exerted "won't count" because it will simply be removing the compressional strains already in the walls of the hole. Beyond this, there will be the entire strength of the steel available before any damage can occur. A steel maker would not know where to find alloys to add to the analysis of plain carbon tool steel in order to increase its effective strength by 115,000 lbs. per sq. in.—but the hardener can do this by the use of a simple flushing fixture.

It has been earlier emphasized that the purpose of drawing (tempering) is to remove harmful, internal strains. Obviously, if the internal strains were favorable, there would be little desire to remove them. Consequently, a draw ring hardened as above would be a better and stronger tool if it were not tempered at all. This is borne out by practical experience. At this point, it will be worth while to say a word about the effect of drawing (tempering) in removing these internal strains set up by quenching. Strains set up by the mechanism of quenching law Nos. 1 and 2 (hot upsetting action) can be substantially removed by prolonged drawing within the range of 200° to 400°F. However, strains set up by the action of rule No. 3 (structural expansion) cannot be entirely eliminated as long as the enlarged structure remains. For example, when carbon tool steel is hardened and expands, it will remain in the expanded state however long it might be drawn at any temperature under about 400°F. If a hardened (and expanded) section is attached to an unhardened section, they will never "fit" until the drawing temperature is raised above 500°F. and the enlarged structure is broken down. However, the zone of concentrated stress between the two areas can be dissipated and relieved to a certain extent by prolonged drawing at a low temperature. O. V. Greene[1] gives some interesting figures along this line. For example, a carbon tool steel ring 1⅞" O.D., ⅝" I.D., and ¾" thick was flushed through the hole from 1450°F. The tangential compression on the walls of the hole "as quenched" was measured at 188,000 lbs. per sq. in. Upon drawing at various low temperatures for one hour, these strains decreased as shown in Table XLI.

Thus it will be seen that internal strains set up under Quenching Law No. 3 are not eliminated by any normal drawing pro-

[1] "Estimation of Internal Stress in Quenched Hollow Cylinder of Carbon Tool Steel." O. V. Greene (The Carpenter Steel Co.), Transactions A.S.S.T.—Vol. XVIII—page 369.

cedure as applied to tools—and this is true whether the initial
quenching strains are favorable or unfavorable.

TABLE XLI.—EFFECT OF DRAWING ON INTERNAL STRAINS

Drawn 1 Hr. at:	Compression at Hole, Lbs. per Sq. In.
As quenched	188,000
200°F.	180,000
300	167,000
400	151,000
425	145,000
450	123,000

It is interesting to consider what might have happened to the
30% nickel ring in Fig. 335, if it had simply been quenched all
over in a still quenching tank. The water would act much more
freely on the outside diameter than it would on the inside—
where vapor pockets would be likely to form. With the O.D.
cooling first it would shrink rapidly and would hot upset
the interior metal toward the hole. After the outside had
become rigid, the hot interior would continue shrinking and
would try to pull away from the rim. When the ring was
cold, the hole would be under *tension*—and if the outside
were removed by machining, the I.D. would close in as the
strains were removed. Thus, under a bursting action, the
available strength of such a ring would be considerably *less*
than its normal elastic limit. If the ring were made of tool
steel, the same thing would happen and the measured strains
at the I.D. would be in the neighborhood of 140,000 to
150,000 lbs. per sq. in.—in the *wrong direction*. A draw ring
quenched in this manner should be thoroughly and completely
tempered to decrease these internal strains—but the tool would
never come even close to being as strong as the one quenched in
the hole.

Fig. 337 shows a section through a solid cold heading die that
has been hardened by flushing the hole and allowing the outside
to cool slowly. The figures show the Rockwell hardness at a
number of places on the tool. Since cold heading dies are subject
to the same bursting action as a draw die or a rifle barrel, the
advantages of this procedure are evident. The reader may jump
to the conclusion that all tools that are flush quenched should
never be drawn. This is not true. Thus far there has been
considered only the strain that is developed in a *radial* direction.

Looking at Fig. 337, it is easily seen that the hardened "tube" in the center has not only expanded *radially* when it hardened, but it has expanded *lengthwise*. This lengthwise expansion is opposed by the unhardened portion of the die that wants to remain the same length as before. This puts the walls of the hole under compression in a longitudinal direction. In service, the heading hammer would come down on the end and further compress the hardened tube. Therefore, these longitudinal stresses are unfavorable and there is no known method of quenching that could prevent it. Fortunately, hard tool steel will withstand a much higher load in *compression* than it will in *tension*. Hence, it is quite permissible to rob Peter (compression) to pay Paul (tension). While straight header dies without countersunk ends (such as are used for heading rivets) can be used without drawing, most other types of header dies should be drawn in the neighborhood of 350/425°F. which will remove at least a part of the strain in both directions. It is worth repeating that this does not remove all of the strain because the walls of the hole will still be hard and will still "want" to be expanded. The balance of the tool will still remain soft and will "want" to hold its size. The effect of drawing is simply to allow a small amount of flow to take place so that these opposing desires will be somewhat reconciled.

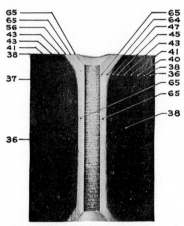

Fig. 337.—Etched section of solid cold header die quenched in fixture shown in Fig. 145. Figures denote Rockwell C hardness values.

Another simple shape, as illustrated in Fig. 338 will now be considered. When a 2″ cube is quenched, the corners and edges cool first. Looking at the sketch B, the reader can visualize how the twelve edges combine to form a sort of "cage" that is compressing the hot metal in the center. This metal cannot escape anywhere excepting through the six sides. Since the middle of each side is hotter than the corners and edges, a definite bulge appears as a result of this hot extruding action. Later on, when the center becomes cold and tries to shrink, it cannot pull the bulge out of the surfaces which have now become rigid. This puts the entire center of the cube under a sort of "vacuum" strain and there is a very definite tendency for all six of the flat faces to be pulled inward. If this were a coining die with an

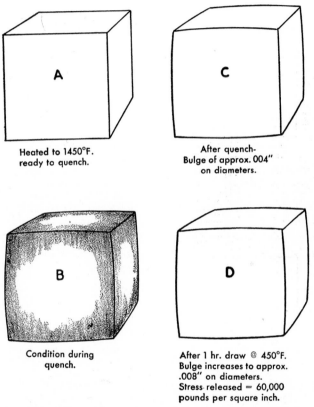

A

Heated to 1450°F.
ready to quench.

B

Condition during
quench.

C

After quench-
Bulge of approx. 004"
on diameters.

D

After 1 hr. draw @ 450°F.
Bulge increases to approx.
.008" on diameters.
Stress released = 60,000
pounds per square inch.

Fig. 338.—Effect of immersion quenching on a 2" tool steel cube.

impression on one of the faces, the stresses of service would also tend to crush in the center of the flat face—and the internal quenching strains would be helping this tendency along.

The third sketch in the figure shows that the bulge on the sides after quenching amounts to .004". Some idea of the amount of strain present can be had by tempering the block and measuring what happens to this bulge. Below sketch D the figures are given. Part of the strain tending to collapse the flat faces has been removed and they have now sprung out to a more normal position. The strain relieved by the draw amounted to 60,000 lbs. per sq. in. It is not difficult to see how a value like this would be sufficient to make the difference between the success and failure of a coining die.

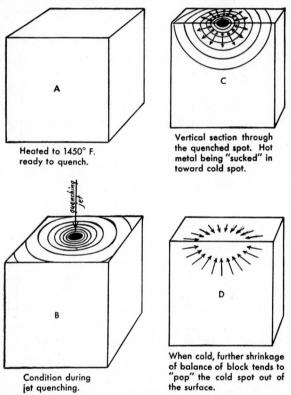

A

Heated to 1450° F.
ready to quench.

C

Vertical section through
the quenched spot. Hot
metal being "sucked" in
toward cold spot.

B

Condition during
jet quenching.

D

When cold, further shrinkage
of balance of block tends to
"pop" the cold spot out of
the surface.

Fig. 339.—Effect of flush quenching on tool steel cube.

It would be desirable to devise a means of quenching a cube that would reverse the above procedure. Can not internal strains be developed that will tend to push the flat faces *outward* instead of pulling them inward? This can be done by using a flush that will strike the center of the flat face first. If the quench is arranged so that the impression in the die is always colder than the metal which surrounds it—especially the corners and edges—favorable internal strains will be generated to resist the crushing action of actual service. The mechanism of this quench is illustrated in Fig. 339. The first thing to cool is a spot in the center of the flat face. As this spot shrinks, it "sucks" the surrounding hot metal toward it with a hot stretching action. Later on, when these outer jackets cool and shrink, the tendency will be to "pop" the original cold spot right out of the piece. Service stresses will tend to drive it back in, and thus will be built up a total strength greater than the actual strength of the surface.

This method of stress analysis can become quite complicated on tools which are of irregular shape. The reader will do well to figure out what happens in several other simple shapes with different kinds of quenching. He will gradually acquire a general understanding of the tendencies and will finally come to a sort of instinctive realization of how flushes should be applied in order to be most useful.

It will be well to emphasize individually some of the things that happen in the quenching bath.

INTERNAL STRAINS

Tremendous internal strains can be built up in a tool during hardening. These may be favorable or unfavorable to the utility of the tool. Unfortunately, the strains set up by quenching all over in a still bath are generally unfavorable. Even when quenching fixtures are used to get favorable strains in one direction, unfavorable strains may develop in another direction. In spite of this limitation, it is commercially practicable to tremendously increase the life of certain tools by the use of controlled flush quenching.

The purpose of drawing is to remove unfavorable strains and increase the strength and toughness of the tool. This is done by a combination of time and temperature. General experience shows that the best average results are secured by drawing the Matched Tool Steels at the toughness peak of the torsion impact curve. Even when the hardener believes that he has introduced favorable strains by his quenching method, he should go slow in eliminating the drawing operation. At best, drawing a water-hardening steel at the torsion impact peak cannot remove *all* the internal strains. If they are favorable, some percentage of them will be left, and the same will be true if they are unfavorable.

Thus far, nothing has been said about any other quenching

medium than water or brine. Since oil quenches much more slowly than water, the temperature differences throughout the piece are much less, hence the hot upsetting action is slight. Furthermore, oil-hardening steels do not change size (according to quenching law No. 3) as much as water-hardening steels. Therefore, strains set up from this source are also smaller. Air-hardening steels will keep internal stresses at an absolute minimum. Some people think that an oil-hardening "non-changeable" tool steel has no thermal coefficient of expansion— that is, does not expand in heating or contract in cooling. This is *not* true. These steels expand and contract thermally just like the water-hardening steels, and hence are subject to the action of quenching laws Nos. 1 and 2. It is however a fact that the "hot upsetting" action is minimized by an oil quench and further, since the bulk of the existing strain comes from this source (rather than from volume change), a prolonged draw will be effective in removing a much higher percentage of the strain—be it favorable or unfavorable.

WARPING

Warping in the quenching bath is generally produced by the mechanism described on page 511. It is due to a hot upsetting action resulting from the application of quenching laws Nos. 1 and 2. If a tool is not hardened all over—quenching law No. 3 may cause excessive warpage. For example, if a long thin piece of carbon tool steel were hardened only down one side, the expansion of this side would cause excessive warpage—with the hardened edge convex.

There are two other important sources of warpage which should be mentioned. If a tool maker were to purchase a bar of tool steel $1'' \times \frac{1}{4}''$ in order to make a keyway broach, the very act of notching one edge—and leaving the other edge solid would tend to set up machining strains. Even if this piece did not become crooked during machining, if it were heated in a hardening furnace, it would probably go crooked while it was being heated. Of course, this might not be noticed, and when it came out of the quench crooked, the tool maker would believe that it had warped in quenching. Maybe it did, but sometimes a lot of time is spent hunting for warpage in the quenching tank when it really happened in the furnace.

When tools go out of shape from machining strains as described, they should be rough machined to remove most of the metal, heated to just below the critical point and cooled slowly—thus permitting the strains to creep out—then finish machined. This is the strain relieving anneal described on page 211.

A second source of warping comes from long thin tools "sagging" while they are at the hardening heat. If the broach described above were laid horizontally on the hearth of a furnace that was not level, it might sag considerably while it was hot and soft. A furnace bottom can be levelled with sand to give uniform support to such tools and prevent sagging. Sometimes tools are suspended vertically in a furnace of the type illustrated in Fig. 142, page 241.

SIZE CHANGE

By the action of quenching law No. 3 some tool steels (mostly the water-hardening varieties) change size when they harden. If only the surface hardens, this is the only portion that will *tend* to enlarge. Although, theoretically, the core might tend to hold exact size, it will actually shrink through the application of laws Nos. 1 and 2. Thus, small sizes of water-hardening steel that harden practically throughout will expand. Very large sizes that are composed principally of core will shrink; and certain critical intermediate sizes will be exactly balanced and will do neither. The final result depends upon the percentage of hard case and tough core in the cross section. Deep hardening steels will therefore tend to expand more than shallow hardening steels (or they will shrink less if the size is large). If the timbre of the steel has been carefully controlled, the amount of size change can frequently be forecast with considerable accuracy—and some allowance made for it in machining. Absolute dependability in this respect, however, is secured by using the oil-hardening steels of the Oil-Hardening Matched Set or the air-hardening steels of the Air-Hardening Matched Set.

SOFT SPOTS

Soft spots and their causes were discussed on page 78. They are mentioned here only because of their effect on internal strains in the tool. Imagine a soft spot the size of a dime in the center of a flat surface that is otherwise hard. All of the hard surface is tending to expand (under law No. 3) while the soft spot wants to retain its original size. This puts the soft spot under tension in every direction like a drumhead. Theoretically, the strain between the soft spot and its hard surroundings will be about 90,000 lbs. per sq. in. If such a surface is ground on a surface grinder under rather unfavorable conditions, the additional strain of grinding will sometimes produce a crack that will entirely outline the soft spot and thus permit it to separate from the metal which was trying to stretch it.

SPECIAL QUENCHING METHODS

The foregoing discussion has concerned itself not so much with the martensite expansion, as with the *first stage* of the quench, its effects on warpage and size change, and its control. Let us look more closely now at the second stage, that of cooling through the lower range of about 400°F. to room temperature.

First, it must be obvious that since the expansion through this range results from a drop in temperature, if that temperature drop differs in different parts of the piece, the expansion will also differ—and the result will be very high stresses. The ideal conditions in quenching therefore would seem to be quick cooling to about 450°F., allowing the tool to equalize its temperature there, and then cooling slowly through the hardening range. While this procedure is perfectly sound in theory, there are still many practical difficulties in its actual application which are beyond the equipment found in the average hardening room. There was a time when it was considered good practice to snatch a water-hardening tool steel from the quenching bath when it got down to 400°/600°F. and transfer it to oil to complete the quench. Practical experience, however, has shown that this is difficult to accomplish successfully unless the tool is very small and of uniform shape. It is difficult to remove the average tool from the quench when *all* the sections of the tool are within this narrow temperature range, and if the hardener misses this range, he does the steel more harm than good. In the average hardening room handling a great variety of tools, therefore, the safest average practice is to quench the tool right down to a temperature below 200°F. before removing it from the water or brine. It is preferable, however, not to cool it "stone cold."

In recent years through the use of special quenching baths and very careful timing, several highly successful methods of controlled cooling through these ranges have been developed. These involve careful control of time cycles for each size and type of tool, and they are therefore best adapted to production hardening of a large number of similar tools. It is still too early to predict their value in the hardening of miscellaneous tools. These methods were mentioned in Chapter 4, and will now be described briefly.

Martempering.—This method as commonly practiced consists in quenching into a salt bath held at just above the Ms point of the steel, which will be 400° to 600°F. depending upon the type of steel being treated. The tool is held in this bath until the temperature is uniform throughout its section, and is then air cooled. One of the important requirements is that the cooling power of the hot bath be sufficient to quench the steel fast enough to exceed its critical quenching speed. It is not possible at the present time to obtain salts which will quench the shallow hardening steels fast enough, their speed when properly agitated being about equal to that of oil. Consequently martempering in salt baths is confined to the deeper hardening steels, such as the oil-hardening types. For the shallow hardening steels, such as water-hardening tool steel, modifications of the martempering procedure are being used in which the tools or parts are being quenched in water or brine, the time in the quench being controlled very accurately by stop watch or automatic timing, and then transferred to oil or air above the Ms temperature, and allowed to cool. Obviously timing must be on a split second basis.

Still another modification of martempering recently developed consists in quenching in a special oil, heated to 300°F. to 400°F. While the full advantages of martempering are not obtained by quenching in this lower temperature range, it is claimed that the practice nevertheless results in less cracking and warpage than a quench in oil at the usual temperature, that is, about 100°F.

Austempering and **Isothermal quenching** are two methods of interrupted quenching, which though adapted primarily to the treating of parts rather than tools, are worthy of mention. In austempering the parts are quenched in a hot bath held at some temperature between 500°F. and 1000°F., and allowed to soak at temperature until the steel transforms by crossing the line in Fig. 325 marked "End of Transformation." On high carbon steels the resulting hardness will be C-48 to C-55 Rockwell. The advantage of the method is in securing additional toughness over that possible by quenching and drawing to an equivalent hardness. Isothermal quenching is like martempering but is conducted at a lower temperature, usually slightly above the Ms point of the steel. Fig. 340 shows at a glance the

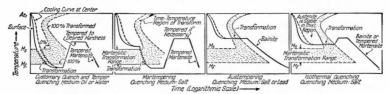

Fig. 340.—Diagram of four important quenching methods. (*Courtesy of E. F. Houghton & Co. and Metal Progress, October* 1944.)

four types of quenching, (1) direct quenching, (2) martempering, (3) austempering, and (4) isothermal quenching, as they are related to the "S" curve.

TEMPERING

No chapter on quenching would be complete without including also a mention of that "guardian angel" of successful hardening —namely tempering.

Tempering (or drawing) is a heating operation applied to a tool after hardening in order to relieve the strains and increase the toughness. Incidentally, it usually causes the tool to lose some of its hardness—but this is not the purpose of tempering, since the tool maker would rather leave his tools fully hard if he were sure they would not break. Tempering is conducted at relatively low temperatures as compared to those used in quenching.

It is well known that enormous internal strains may be built up in a tool during hardening. Sometimes these strains are greater than the strength of the hardened steel and it cracks in the quench. At other times they may approach 98% of the strength of the steel—in which case the tool does not crack immediately, but may break later upon the slightest provocation. The average strains are doubtless much below this figure, but the tool maker should always remember that the useful strength of a tool is equal to the total strength of the steel minus the internal strains. (See page 522.)

This conception must be crystal clear in order to fully appreciate the importance of the tempering operation. For example, assume that a fully hardened piece of tool steel has a total strength of 400,000 p.s.i. Suppose the unfavorable internal strains are 90% of this figure, or 360,000 p.s.i. Then the strength remaining to do useful work is only 40,000 p.s.i. If, by proper tempering, these internal strains can be reduced to 200,000 p.s.i., the useful strength will be boosted to 200,000 pounds—or a gain of 400%.

Tempering is the Cinderella of tool making operations. When you machine a fine tool from a block of steel, you can see what you get for your money. When, by the magic of a red-heat and a sizzling quench, the tool is hardened, you feel well repaid for the time and money spent. But in the low-heat tempering operation, nothing important seems to happen. The only visible change (loss of hardness) is something that is unwanted. Under the circumstances, it is but human to begrudge any time or money spent on the operation. It is not until the "golden slipper" of production is fitted to the foot of this unpopular

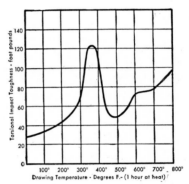

Fig. 341.—How various tempering heats affect the toughness of WATER-HARD Tool Steel.

stepchild that we begin to see the sense behind it all. When records become available showing how insufficiently tempered tools collapse prematurely in service, and how properly tempered tools continue to serve under the most trying conditions, it becomes easier to exchange Cinderella's pumpkins and mouse traps for some real tempering equipment.

Let's take a good look at this tempering operation. Tempering accomplishes its purpose through a combination of temperature and time. It is not sufficient to merely heat a hardened tool steel to some definite temperature—it must be soaked at that temperature for a definite length of time.

Temperature.—Torsion impact toughness curves (see page 274) show that there are narrow temperature ranges for each tool steel where maximum toughness can be had without too great sacrifice of hardness.　Fig. 341 shows the torsion impact curve for WATER-HARD tool steel.　It will be observed that the toughness increases as the drawing temperature is raised up to 350°/375°F., but that at higher temperatures the toughness falls off again. Thus (for a soaking time of one hour) 350°/375°F. is the best temperature on this steel to secure the maximum combination of hardness and toughness.　Similarly, each of the other Matched Tool Steels has a definite drawing temperature where best results are most likely to be secured.

Time.—The total time required is the heating time, plus the soaking time.　Chapter 19 discusses heating time in great detail, but it is advisable to repeat here some of the information given in that chapter.　Few people realize how long it takes to heat a piece of steel to the low temperatures used in tempering. It takes three or four times as long to heat a piece of steel to 400°F. as it does to heat it to 1500°F.　The following table is reproduced here merely for the purpose of driving home the importance of having enough tempering apparatus (of the proper type, and with proper controls) to do a good job.

TABLE XLII.—APPROXIMATE TIME NEEDED TO HEAT VARIOUS SIZES
OF TOOL STEEL TO 400°F.

(Based on holding the furnace *at heat* all the time)

Size of piece	Time required to heat	
	In a quiet hot air oven	In a hot oil bath
$\frac{3}{4}''$ rd. × 2″ lg.	At least ½ hour	At least ¼ hour
$1\frac{1}{2}''$ rd. × 3″ lg.	" " 1 "	" " ½ "
3″ rd. × 6″ lg.	" " 2 "	" " 1 "
6″ rd. × 12″ lg.	" " 5 "	" " 2½ "

The time figures in the above table are minimum.　For example, the surface on these pieces was in best condition for most rapid absorption of heat.　Also, the time consumed in going through the last 10°F. (from 390° to 400°F.) wasn't counted.　If it had been, it would have been necessary to add another 50% to the time.　For example, in an oven the 6″

round would take five hours to reach 390°, and about $2\frac{1}{2}$ hours more to cover those last 10°, or a total of $7\frac{1}{2}$ hours.

Just to show how important the time factor is, suppose we were going to temper a hardened die measuring $1'' \times 4'' \times 6''$ made of WATER-HARD. We look at the torsion impact data and decide to draw at 350°F. for one hour—but make no particular allowance for heating time. The tool is placed in an electric oven heated to 350°F., left there for 1 hour and then removed. Although by this time the die would have attained a temperature of about 340°F., it has had no soak and therefore structurally it approximates the condition shown on the torsion impact curve (Fig. 341) for a drawing temperature of about 275°F. In other words, it has developed scarcely 50% of its peak toughness. These facts about tempering have been emphasized so that the reader may consider his tempering equipment more accurately in the light of his own individual needs. It is obviously not enough to merely say, "Oh yes, we have a tempering furnace," but rather a matter of studying how much work goes through daily, how many different temperatures must be used for various kinds of tools, and how long a time is needed to do a good job on each tool.

Many first-class hardening rooms get along with a minimum of tempering equipment by having automatic temperature control on the units, and then doing some of the longer drawing jobs at night. Frequently a hardener can load a unit before he goes home, set the controls, and then simply leave a note for one of the night men to pull certain switches or unload certain units at a given time.

There is another way to economize on tempering equipment. Suppose your tempering furnace is now busy running at 350°F., and a tool is hardened that requires a 425°F. draw. You don't want the newly hardened tool to lie around indefinitely without drawing—and still there is no furnace available at 425°F. to use. There is no harm in putting the tool in with the others at 350°F. for an hour or two; then it will be safe to let it lie around until it can be properly drawn at its own temperature. (You could not, of course, reverse this procedure, that is, draw first at 425°, if only 350°F. was really wanted.)

In concluding this discussion of tempering the opportunity must not pass to again emphasize two important rules:

1. Never draw or temper any Matched Tool Steel until it has cooled after hardening to a point where it can be handled in the bare hands.
2. Never let a tool get stone cold and lie around indefinitely without drawing. (A good place to "store" them for an hour or two is in a warm bath of quenching oil.)

CHAPTER 21

"TROUBLE SHOOTING"

The term "trouble shooting" has been aptly applied to the business of trying to find out why something went wrong. A good trouble shooter must be open minded and unprejudiced. He cannot first make up his mind what he "hopes" the trouble is—and then set out to prove he is right. Furthermore, he must be well informed on his subject. Possession of the knowledge contained in the earlier chapters of this book would automatically make a tool maker a reasonably good trouble shooter. The purpose of the present chapter is to focus on this particular phase of the work. The Matched Set method of selecting tool steels depends for its success upon the ability of a tool maker to know what is wrong with an unsatisfactory tool—and what extra property he wants, to correct it. Thus, trouble shooting is an inseparable part of using this method.

THE CAUSES AND EFFECTS OF STRAIN

The Critical Strain Theory was presented at the beginning of Chapter 14 on Design. It will be repeated here in somewhat different words for the present purpose.

A piece of hardened tool steel has just so much strength—depending upon the analysis of the steel—the quality of the steel—and the way it has been heat treated.

When the total forces brought to bear on the piece of steel exceed its strength, it cracks or fails.

There are two kinds of forces that combine to break a tool:

1. The internal strains set up during the manufacture of the tool.
2. The external strains of service.

When the total of these forces exceeds the strength of the tool, it fails.

The above seems almost too simple to warrant repeating— exactly the same rule could be applied to a pane of glass or a concrete building. It is, however, because an investigator so

533

often overlooks the obvious that he becomes mired knee-deep in troubles that really ought not to confuse him at all.

The internal strains in a finished tool can be great or small. One of the authors once held in his hands a finished ground tool and while he was examining it, a piece suddenly cracked loose from the tool and it was ruined. This tool must have been 99.99% broken when it was picked up. The slight warmth of the body was sufficient to cause it to expand a little—and this brought the strain over the 100% mark. Obviously, such a tool would have been useless in service. The internal strains in a finished tool probably never approach zero. A file hard piece of tool steel should have a tensile strength approaching 400,000 lbs. per sq. inch. Practical experience, however, shows that tools will fail as a rule well under 200,000 lbs. per sq. inch. It is therefore likely that there is seldom available more than 50% of the strength, even under good conditions. However, even 50% is a long way from destruction. There is little point in discussing the external strains of service—they are quite obvious and there is not much that can be said about them. There is, however, much to be said about the internal strains. A great deal of this has been discussed in earlier chapters but it may be summarized here. Internal strains are affected by practically every step in the manufacture of the tool.

Design.—This was fully discussed in Chapter 14. Tools can be designed so poorly that they cannot possibly be gotten through the hardening room in one piece—or they can be so well balanced that they can absorb a lot of abuse and still live to a ripe old age.

Forging.—This is the first mention of this important subject, other than the specific instructions given in Chapter 12. Such apparent neglect is justified only by the fact that few tool makers forge their tools—and those who do would want a specific type of discussion which is outside the scope of this book. From a "trouble shooting" angle, however the reader should know that forging can introduce damage of many kinds. Invisible, internal bursts may originate from a non-uniform "wash heat"—or from eccentric hammering. Surface seams, laps or folds may be introduced. Internal checks or "flakes" (or even outright cracking of the forging) may arise from improper cooling after forging. Structurally the steel may be damaged by overheat, or by too high a finishing temperature. The latter may be corrected by normalizing, while the former frequently can not. It would require a greater knowledge of metallurgy than a tool maker could be expected to have in order to "take a forging apart" and definitely diagnose its condition. However, when a forging operation is involved in the manufacture of a tool, it cannot be ignored by the trouble shooter.

Machining.—Mention has already been made of the strains produced by removing a large percentage of the metal from a block of tool steel. A rough machining cut also distorts the metal at the surface and leaves it in a strained condition. Any cold hobbing operation that deforms the metal will likewise strain it and these strains carry along to be added to the hardening strains. Deep stamp marks deform and strain the metal—and also introduce sharp notches from which cracks can readily start. Prick punch marks used in laying out a die will do the same thing. Even though the punch mark itself may have been removed by machining, the deformed and strained metal in the walls of the mark may still remain. If this occurs in a sharp corner, it may be the straw that will ultimately break the camel's back.

All machining strains and cold working strains can be completely removed by a strain relieving anneal below the critical before hardening (see page 211).

Hardening.—The many ways of straining a tool in the hardening room are too numerous to recount. Improper heating, improper quenching and insufficient drawing can all contribute their share.

Drawing (Tempering).—This is a strain relieving operation (providing the quench has been properly completed). A tool might leave the quenching tank 99% cracked—but if thoroughly and properly drawn, enough strain can be removed to restore the usefulness of the tool. This operation is the worst possible place to try to save time or money.

Grinding.—The effect of grinding in producing strains was discussed on page 75. Grinding sets up in the surface instantaneous strains that may or may not cause it to crack. Obviously, all grinding checks are not the fault of the grinder. If he receives a poorly hardened and poorly drawn tool that is almost ready to fall apart when he gets it, he cannot grind it successfully, no matter how careful he may be. On the other hand, many perfectly good tools are ruined in grinding; it is so easy to hog into the work on the roughing cuts—and then remove all *apparent* damage by a fine finishing cut.   However, as we shall see later, the damage is not removed.

THE POSSIBLE SOURCES OF TROUBLE

With the above picture clearly in mind, there will now be listed some of the headings under which trouble may be sought:

The Tool Steel.—It may be the wrong analysis.   This can be checked in some cases by means of a spark test while at other times a chemical analysis must be made.

Is the steel sound?   When this question arises in connection

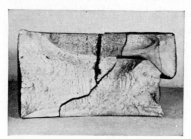

with a tool failure, the tool in question can be annealed and a disc can be sawed off at right angles to the length of the orig-inal bar.   This can be etched in accordance with instructions contained in Chapter 15.   Fig. 342 illustrates a rather gross case of failure due to unsound steel.   Here an acid test was

Fig. 342.—Failed tool containing pipe.

not needed; an open pipe may be seen on the fracture projecting like a ragged worm hole into the center of the steel.

NOTE: In trouble shooting, never anneal a failed tool for hot acid inspection or any other purpose until all necessary investigations have been made in the hardened condition.   Much valuable evidence may be lost in the anneal.   If possible, it is well to break the tool in half (or cut it in half with a thin abrasive wheel) and anneal only one half. This leaves part of the steel in its original hardened condition to be used as needed.

How is the timbre?   If the tool is large enough it can be annealed and a $\frac{3}{4}''$ round timbre test can be machined.   This can be tested as described in either Chapter 4 or 16.   If the pieces are too small to cut a timbre test, it is still possible to find out whether it is tough timbre or brittle timbre.   An interesting application of this will be illustrated.

A manufacturer making a large quantity of cutters like those illustrated in Figure 343 from plain carbon tool steel, found that certain batches went through with practically no cracking, while others showed a high percentage of loss in hardening.   He took a few cutters from a good lot and a few cracked ones from a bad lot. He annealed these and then quenched them from 1550°F.—and broke them to examine the fracture. The fractures from the

Fig. 343.—Carbon tools which gave trouble due to cracking.

good tools came from this test as shown in Figure 344. The grain is fine and silky and the timbre is obviously tough. The cracked ones of course cracked even worse at this high temperature and their fractures appeared as in Figure 345—coarse grained and

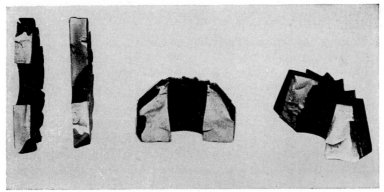

Fig. 344.—Good tools after rehardening at 1550°F.

brittle timbre. This is a very simple and inexpensive test, well within the reach of any tool maker or hardener.

Design.—Look for sharp corners and badly unbalanced sections. Could holes have been drilled through the heavy section so that they would balance up more nearly with the light sections? (See high speed form tool page 392, Figs. 232 and 233.) If sharp corners and unbalanced sections cannot be eliminated, an oil-hardening steel may be needed.

Machining.—Be suspicious of tools from which large amounts of metal have been cut. Avoid deep, sharp stamp marks. In case of doubt, it is better to err on the safe side and give such tools a strain relieving anneal before hardening them. Fig. 346 shows a pneumatic chisel that failed in service from fatigue that started in a deep stamp mark.

Fig. 345.—Cracked tools after rehardening at 1550°F.

Hardening Cracks.—If the tool cracks in hardening, and there is nothing suspicious about the steel or the design, look at the nature of the cracks.

If the crack penetrates deeply, and does not parallel the length of the original bar, or if the crack shatters the piece, it may be due to one of two causes: too high a hardening heat, or placing a hard tool in a hot furnace. In connection with this last cause, sometimes a tool does not come from the hardening just as the hardener wants it. He decides to reharden the job and throws it back into a hot furnace. This is a terrible strain on the hard tool and it is likely to cause a shattered type of cracking. Since these tools cracked while still in the hardening furnace, the faces of the fracture will contain furnace scale. This definitely indicates that the tool either cracked on the first hardening, or cracked when placed in the furnace for the second hardening. Fig. 347 shows the pieces of a tool that cracked in the furnace when an attempt was made to reharden it.

Hardening cracks that might be described as "spalling" or

shelling off of corners and edges, are generally due to too low a hardening heat, non-uniform hardening heat, or removing the tool from the quench and drawing it before it is fully hard.

The first cause can usually be distinguished from the third by the fact that there are likely to be soft areas on the underheated portions of the tool—whereas a tool removed from the quench too soon is likely to be hard all over. A tool that has been non-uniformly heated may come out hard all over or it may contain soft spots. Fig. 348 illustrates a carbon steel reamer that was hardened from a lead pot and the extreme end spalled off in quenching. This tool was not in the lead long enough for the entire tool to become uniformly heated and only the end actually got through the critical far enough to

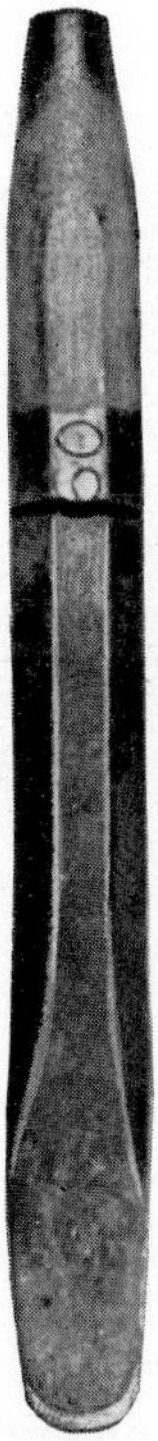

FIG. 346.—Pneumatic chipping chisel failed through stamp mark.

FIG. 347.—Pieces of tool cracked by placing in hot furnace to reharden.

properly harden. In order to demonstrate the lack of hardness on the body of the reamer, it was sawed part way through with a hack saw and then broken the rest of the way. The *spalled end*, the "*bald headed fracture*," and the *soft body*—all point to non-uniform underheating.

Figs. 349 and 350 illustrate two more examples of "spalled" fractures from non-uniform heating. Fig. 350 is an oil-hardening tool steel. One corner has spalled off and the other has cracked.

While the holes appear to have played a part in the failure, they are not the prime cause. This tool was soft on the flat faces which had not been hot enough, and was file hard on the spalled corners—a clear case of non-uniform underheating.

Sometimes cracks of very shallow depth and having somewhat the appearance of grinding checks occur on unground surfaces. Often they follow tool marks. When such cracks are encountered, look for a decarburized surface, either some original bark

Fig. 348.—¾″ carbon steel reamer cracked by non-uniform underheating.

Fig. 349.—Tool spalled by quenching from within the critical range.

from the bar not properly removed in machining, or decarburization occurring in hardening. They develop because of the difference in expansion of the skin and the underlying metal. In quenching, the metal underneath expands, while the surface metal, being soft, continues to contract. The skin is thus put under tension and tends to crack, particularly in any surface notches such as tool marks, stamp marks, etc. The cracks are usually confined to the decarburized layer.

Soft Spots.—These are most likely to occur in the water-hardening steels, and are sometimes indicated by the appearance of the tool after hardening. A surface that hardens will usually throw the scale cleaner than a surface which does not harden. It is well to investigate the scaled surfaces with a file; it does not necessarily follow that they will be soft, but the matter is worth looking into. Characteristic soft spots are illustrated in Fig. 66, page 78.

Soft spots may originate from using fresh water instead of brine for quenching. They may be due to dross from a lead pot sticking to a tool and interfering with the quench. There is nearly always a soft spot where the hardener grabs a tool with his tongs for quenching. Sometimes a quenching bath becomes dirty with oil or soap. Thoughtless mechanics will sometimes wash their hands in a quenching tank with soap, and soapy water is a very

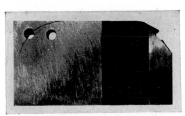

Fig. 350.—Oil-hardening tool steel cracked by non-uniform underheating.

Fig. 351.—Trimmer die for drop forging.

poor quenching medium. So is water with oil floating on the surface.

It should be pointed out that soft spots are not necessarily trouble makers—sometimes they cause trouble, but more often they do not. For example, if the trimming die in Fig. 351 were made of water-hardening tool steel—or even oil-hardening tool steel—some of the flat faces might contain soft spots. If the cutting edge is fully hard, the tool will undoubtedly do its work satisfactorily. If the reader will refer back to Fig. 337 on page 520, he will see a tool on which soft areas were deliberately encouraged to *strengthen* the tool. It is safe to say that most large tools coming from the hardening room contain some spots that are not fully hard—under the tong hold, if nowhere else—and their discovery is no warrant for rehardening the tool. Accidental soft spots are not desirable and the hardener should do his best to avoid them; but he will die of a broken heart if he refuses to pass all tools that are not 100% hard all over.

On the other hand, after a tool has failed, the trouble can sometimes be traced to accidental soft spots that occurred in the *wrong place*. This is the time to investigate them and take steps to either eliminate them—or chase them back where they will do no harm.

A prolific cause for "thumb nail" checks in chipping chisels (Fig. 352) is a soft spot occurring on the bit a short distance back from the cutting edge. The crack encloses the soft spot. The cure for this trouble is to switch to a brine quench, whereupon the soft spot will disappear—and with it, the thumb nail check.

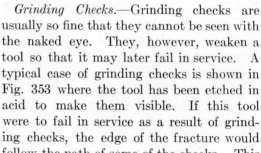

Grinding Checks.—Grinding checks are usually so fine that they cannot be seen with the naked eye. They, however, weaken a tool so that it may later fail in service. A typical case of grinding checks is shown in Fig. 353 where the tool has been etched in acid to make them visible. If this tool were to fail in service as a result of grinding checks, the edge of the fracture would follow the path of some of the checks. This makes a characteristic jagged edge to the fracture which should immediately suggest heating the tool in acid to investigate grinding checks.

Fig. 352.—Sketches showing typical appearance of thumb nail checks on chisels.

Fig. 353.—Typical grinding checks revealed by acid etching.

Size Change.—Some size change is to be expected in a water-hardening steel. If the tool changes much more than expected, the timbre may be different from usual—or the hardening temperature may have gotten out of control.

An oil-hardening non-changing tool steel will come out close to the original size providing it has received a strain relieving anneal (when this is necessary) and providing it was properly hardened and drawn at the correct temperature. Excessive size change in such a steel is nearly always caused by one of the three things just mentioned. It should be observed that either *overheat* or *underheat* in hardening will cause an oil-hardening steel to change size. As we have already noted on pages 307 and 318, the high carbon, high chromium steels when overheated shrink badly, and become partially non-magnetic.

Learn to be suspicious of tools that are off-size badly in only one dimension. Sometimes the tool maker makes a mistake in machining on some dimension and the measurement was not correct when the tool went to the hardening room. It would be practically impossible for a piece of tool steel to change size radically in only one dimension during hardening. For example, the I.D. of a ring will not open up while the O.D. and thickness stay put.

Warpage and Shape Change.—Excessive warpage may be due to the absence of a strain relieving anneal. It may come from over heat in hardening, or from careless quenching, or from sagging in the hardening furnace. Of course, the design of the tool also affects the manner in which it will probably warp.

NOTE: Many people confuse *size change* and *shape change*. They are not the same thing and arise from different causes. A tool made of water-hardening tool steel may expand or shrink in *size*, with practically no warping or shape change. This is due to the action of quenching law No. 3 (page 508). On the other hand, an oil-hardening, non-shrinkable tool steel can go out of shape by warping and still not change size (no change of volume). Of course both size and shape can change at the same time, but this is no reason to confuse them—or their causes.

Lack of Hardness or Wear Resistance.—Somtimes the entire tool is soft. This can be due to only three things—the wrong steel has been used, or the hardening heat was too low—or the drawing heat was much too high.

If only the surface is soft—as can be readily determined by digging in with a file—this may arise from three causes. It may be that all of the decarburized surface (bark) was not completely machined from the original bar of steel. Compare the hardness on the surfaces which are at right angles to the length of the original bar with the hardness on the longitudinal surface. Obviously, there can be no *bar* decarburization on the saw-cut ends. Therefore if the ends are hard and the sides are decarburized, it certainly did not come from the hardening furnace and must result from the original bar. This condition often exists on only one side of the tool as a result of eccentric machining.

Decarburization can, of course, occur in the hardening furnace—in which case it will be on all surfaces of the tool. It can originate in improper furnace atmosphere and particularly if it has been rehardened several times in an improper atmosphere. Sometimes the surface decarburization reduces the carbon only a few points so that the surface is still fairly hard to a file, but not sufficiently hard to prevent burrs and scratches in service. In using a file to detect decarburization it is important to "get the feel" of a properly hardened piece of the same steel which you know has *not* been decarburized, before testing the unknown surface.

Finally a soft surface is sometimes produced by badly overheating the surface of the tool in the grinding. This can be investigated with a file by comparing the hardness of a ground surface with an unground surface.

Wear Resistance.—If a tool that is properly hardened fails to wear long enough in service, it is time to move north on the Matched Diagram—providing there is toughness to spare.

Lack of Toughness in Service.—When a tool breaks in service, the entire Critical Strain Theory is involved. It is necessary to review the manufacture of the tool from beginning to end and try to find the difficulty. If the fault is in the steel not being tough enough, move south on the Matched Diagram. If the trouble is in design, heat treatment or something else in the manufacture of the tool, correct this first and thereby save the wear resistance that will have to be sacrificed by moving south on the Diagram.

A rather obscure cause for breaking is sometimes found in "acid brittleness." If the tool has been immersed in acid at any time after hardening, this will make it quite brittle. Chromium plated tools will become brittle from this cause. A tool that might have been etched to inspect for grinding checks would also be brittle. Every trace of acid brittleness may be removed from a tool by drawing it at 250/300°F. for an hour—or longer if the tool is very large—and this precaution should *always* be employed if the hardened tool has been in contact with any acid.

Spalling in Service.—This is a different condition from "breaking in service" and arises from a different cause. Tools like header dies, coining dies, striking dies, and embossing dies which are under heavy pressure must usually be made from a surface hardening tool steel. If they are made from a tool steel that hardens clear through, they are likely to split—they need the reenforcement of a tough core in order to hold together. If the hardened case is too shallow for the pressures involved, it will cave in like thin ice. This sinking action frequently progresses slowly; but eventually a chip will come loose and this is known as spalling. A typical example is shown in Fig. 354.

Fig. 354.—Cold header die spalled in service.

Fig. 355.—Hot drawing mandrel heat checked.

The remedy for this is to use a higher hardening heat, or a flush quench, or both, to drive the hardness penetration deeper. Failing in this, use a steel having slightly deeper hardening characteristics. If the problem must be solved by using a deeper hardening steel of the surface hardening type, it is sometimes necessary to resort to a "prima donna" (see page 109).

Heat Checks.—In the red-hard tool steels used for hot forming operations, the working surface of the tool will frequently become crazed with a pattern that is suggestive of grinding checks. When the tool is in contact with the heated work, it is suddenly heated. If a liquid coolant is used, the minute the hot forging is removed the surface is rapidly chilled. This process is repeated many times and finally the surface starts to heat check. A hot drawing mandrel, badly heat checked, is illustrated in Fig. 355.

The susceptibility of a steel to heat checking depends to a considerable extent upon the analysis. On the Matched Diagram, the likelihood of heat checking increases as the tool maker travels north; it is almost never seen in RED-TOUGH—seldom seen in RED-HARD and quite likely to be encountered in RED-WEAR. Heat checking can be greatly helped by not employing so violent a coolant. A stream of water can be replaced by an air blast. In fact, anything that will decrease the severity of the temperature changes in the tools will help to prevent heat checking. Also, a tool that has been drawn back far enough to have some ductility will resist heat checking better than a harder tool.

In this connection it should be mentioned that hot working tools should be preheated before they are put to work. If the tools are stone cold, the first few pieces forged will set up terrific strains. It is a pity to be compelled to select a steel and a heat treatment that will withstand this kind of abuse, because in so doing, there is always thrown away a certain amount of red-hardness and wear resistance that will be badly needed when the tools finally reach their maximum temperature.

———— · · ————

In concluding this final chapter, a word of general caution may not be amiss. The information contained in these pages should expand the horizon of any tool maker who will take the time to study them. He will leave far behind him the erroneous ideas that there is nothing in steel beyond its analysis, and nothing to heat treating but fire and water. And yet, in more capable hands, each chapter could have been expanded into a book, and the entire story of tool steel into a complete library without exhausting the subject. And what is more—beyond the combined knowledge of the entire tool steel industry, there lie vast realms of possibilities as yet untouched. Indeed there is little room for conceit in any of us. Knowledge, like a powerful telescope, expands the sphere of our awareness—only to correspondingly enlarge the frontiers of our ignorance. The only man who "knows it all" is he who has lost his telescope.

PART V

TABLES

TABLE XLIII.—FAHRENHEIT-CENTIGRADE CONVERSION

Fahrenheit	Centigrade	Fahrenheit	Centigrade	Fahrenheit	Centigrade
32°	0°	640°	338°	1080°	582°
212	100	650	343	1090	588
220	104	660	349	1100	593
230	110	670	354	1110	599
240	116	680	360	1120	604
250	121	690	366	1130	610
260	127	700	371	1140	616
270	132	710	377	1150	621
280	138	720	382	1160	627
290	143	730	388	1170	632
300	149	740	393	1180	638
310	154	750	399	1190	643
320	160	760	404	1200	649
330	166	770	410	1210	654
340	171	780	416	1220	660
350	177	790	421	1230	666
360	182	800	427	1240	671
370	188	810	432	1250	677
380	193	820	438	1260	682
390	199	830	443	1270	688
400	204	840	449	1280	693
410	210	850	454	1290	699
420	216	860	460	1300	704
430	221	870	466	1310	710
440	227	880	471	1320	716
450	232	890	477	1330	721
460	238	900	482	1340	727
470	243	910	488	1350	732
480	249	920	493	1360	738
490	254	930	499	1370	743
500	260	940	504	1380	749
510	266	950	510	1390	754
520	271	960	516	1400	760
530	277	970	521	1410	766
540	282	980	527	1420	771
550	288	990	532	1430	777
560	293	1000	538	1440	782
570	299	1010	543	1450	788
580	304	1020	549	1460	793
590	310	1030	554	1470	799
600	316	1040	560	1480	804
610	321	1050	566	1490	810
620	327	1060	571	1500	816
630	332	1070	577	1510	821

TABLE XLIII.—FAHRENHEIT-CENTIGRADE CONVERSION.—(*Continued*)

Fahrenheit	Centigrade	Fahrenheit	Centigrade	Fahrenheit	Centigrade
1520°	827°	2000°	1093°	2480°	1360°
1530	832	2010	1099	2490	1366
1540	838	2020	1104	2500	1371
1550	843	2030	1110	2510	1377
1560	849	2040	1116	2520	1382
1570	854	2050	1121	2530	1388
1580	860	2060	1127	2540	1393
1590	866	2070	1132	2550	1399
1600	871	2080	1138	2560	1404
1610	877	2090	1143	2570	1410
1620	882	2100	1149	2580	1416
1630	888	2110	1154	2590	1421
1640	893	2120	1160	2600	1427
1650	899	2130	1166	2610	1432
1660	904	2140	1171	2620	1438
1670	910	2150	1177	2630	1443
1680	916	2160	1182	2640	1449
1690	921	2170	1188	2650	1454
1700	927	2180	1193	2660	1460
1710	932	2190	1199	2670	1466
1720	938	2200	1204	2680	1471
1730	943	2210	1210	2690	1477
1740	949	2220	1216	2700	1482
1750	954	2230	1221	2710	1488
1760	960	2240	1227	2720	1493
1770	966	2250	1232	2730	1499
1780	971	2260	1238	2740	1504
1790	977	2270	1243	2750	1510
1800	982	2280	1249	2760	1516
1810	988	2290	1254	2770	1521
1820	993	2300	1260	2780	1527
1830	999	2310	1266	2790	1532
1840	1004	2320	1271	2800	1538
1850	1010	2330	1277	2810	1543
1860	1016	2340	1282	2820	1549
1870	1021	2350	1288	2830	1554
1880	1027	2360	1293	2840	1560
1890	1032	2370	1299	2850	1566
1900	1038	2380	1304	2860	1571
1910	1043	2390	1310	2870	1577
1920	1049	2400	1316	2880	1582
1930	1054	2410	1321	2890	1588
1940	1060	2420	1327	2900	1593
1950	1066	2430	1332	2910	1599
1960	1071	2440	1338	2920	1604
1970	1077	2450	1343	2930	1610
1980	1082	2460	1349	2940	1616
1990	1088	2470	1354	2950	1621

TABLE XLIV.—BRINELL-ROCKWELL-SCLEROSCOPE CONVERSION TABLE

The hardness conversion table given below is that developed by The Iron and Steel Division of the Society of Automotive Engineers. It applies only to annealed or heat treated steels which have not been cold worked, containing a total alloy content of not over approximately 4.00 %. It is therefore less accurate in highly alloyed Tool Steels or Stainless Steels.

Brinell		Rockwell		Shore	Brinell		Rockwell		Shore
Dia. in mm. 3,000 kg. load, 10 mm. ball	Hardness number	C scale, 150 kg. load, 120 deg. diamond cone	B scale, 100 kg. load, $\frac{1}{16}$ in. diam. ball	Sclero-scope number	Dia. in mm. 3,000 kg. load, 10 mm. ball	Hardness number	C scale, 150 kg. load, 120 deg. diamond cone	B scale, 100 kg. load, $\frac{1}{16}$ in. diam. ball	Sclero-scope number
2.20	780	70	...	106	4.20	207	..	95	30
2.25	745	68	...	100	4.25	202	..	94	30
2.30	712	66	...	95	4.30	197	..	93	29
2.35	682	64	...	91	4.35	192	..	92	28
2.40	653	62	...	87	4.40	187	..	91	28
2.45	627	60	...	84	4.45	183	..	90	27
2.50	601	58	...	81	4.50	179	..	89	27
2.55	578	57	...	78	4.55	174	..	88	26
2.60	555	55	...	75	4.60	170	..	87	26
2.65	534	53	...	72	4.65	166	..	86	25
2.70	514	52	...	70	4.70	163	..	85	25
2.75	495	50	...	67	4.75	159	..	84	24
2.80	477	49	...	65	4.80	156	..	83	24
2.85	461	47	...	63	4.85	153	..	82	23
2.90	444	46	...	61	4.90	149	..	81	23
2.95	429	45	...	59	4.95	146	..	80	22
3.00	415	44	...	57	5.00	143	..	79	22
3.05	401	42	...	55	5.05	140	..	78	21
3.10	388	41	...	54	5.10	137	..	77	21
3.15	375	40	...	52	5.15	134	..	76	21
3.20	363	38	...	51	5.20	131	..	74	20
3.25	352	37	...	49	5.25	128	..	73	20
3.30	341	36	...	48	5.30	126	..	72	..
3.35	331	35	...	46	5.35	124	..	71	..
3.40	321	34	...	45	5.40	121	..	70	..
3.45	311	33	...	44	5.45	118	..	69	..
3.50	302	32	...	43	5.50	116	..	68	..
3.55	293	31	...	42	5.55	114	..	67	..
3.60	285	30	...	40	5.60	112	..	66	..
3.65	277	29	...	39	5.65	109	..	65	..
3.70	269	28	...	38	5.70	107	..	64	..
3.75	262	26	...	37	5.75	105	..	62	..
3.80	255	25	...	37	5.80	103	..	61	..
3.85	248	24	...	36	5.85	101	..	60	..
3.90	241	23	100	35	5.90	99	..	59	..
3.95	235	22	99	34	5.95	97	..	57	..
4.00	229	21	98	33	6.00	95	..	56	..
4.05	223	20	97	32	....	...	..	..	..
4.10	217	..	96	31	....	...	..	..	..
4.15	212	..	96	31	....	...	..	..	..

TABLE XLV.—WEIGHT OF ROUND, SQUARE, HEXAGON AND OCTAGON STEEL BARS PER LINEAL FOOT[1]

Size in inches	Round	Square	Hexagon	Octagon	Size in inches	Round	Square	Hexagon	Octagon
1/32	.0026	.0033	.0029	.0028	3	24.03	30.60	26.50	25.35
1/16	.0104	.0133	.0115	.0110	3 1/16	25.04	31.89	27.62	26.42
1/8	.0417	.0531	.0460	.0440	3 1/8	26.08	33.20	28.75	27.51
3/16	.0938	.1195	.1035	.0990	3 3/16	27.13	34.55	29.92	28.62
1/4	.1669	.2123	.1840	.1760	3 1/4	28.20	35.92	31.10	29.75
5/16	.2608	.3333	.2875	.2751	3 5/16	29.30	37.31	32.31	30.91
3/8	.3756	.4782	.4141	.3961	3 3/8	30.42	38.73	33.54	32.08
7/16	.5111	.6508	.5636	.5391	3 7/16	31.56	40.18	34.79	33.28
1/2	.6676	.8500	.7361	.7042	3 1/2	32.71	41.65	36.07	34.50
9/16	.8449	.9317	...	...	3 9/16	33.90	43.14	37.37	35.75
5/8	1.043	1.328	1.150	1.100	3 5/8	35.09	44.68	38.69	37.01
11/16	1.262	1.608	1.392	1.331	3 11/16	36.31	46.24	40.04	38.30
3/4	1.502	1.913	1.656	1.584	3 3/4	37.56	47.82	41.41	39.61
13/16	1.763	2.245	1.944	1.859	3 13/16	38.81	49.42	42.80	40.94
7/8	2.044	2.603	2.254	2.157	3 7/8	40.10	51.05	44.21	42.29
15/16	2.347	2.989	2.588	2.476	3 15/16	41.40	52.71	45.65	43.67
1	2.670	3.400	2.945	2.817	4	42.73	54.40	47.11	45.07
1 1/16	3.014	3.838	3.324	3.180	4 1/16	44.07	56.11	48.65	46.45
1 1/8	3.379	4.303	3.727	3.565	4 1/8	45.44	57.85	50.10	47.93
1 3/16	3.766	4.795	4.152	3.972	4 3/16	46.83	59.62	51.60	49.38
1 1/4	4.173	5.312	4.601	4.401	4 1/4	48.24	61.41	53.16	50.88
1 5/16	4.600	5.857	5.072	4.852	4 5/16	49.66	63.23	54.70	52.34
1 3/8	5.019	6.428	5.567	5.325	4 3/8	51.11	65.08	56.36	53.91
1 7/16	5.518	7.026	6.085	5.820	4 7/16	52.58	66.95	58.05	55.45
1 1/2	6.008	7.650	6.625	6.338	4 1/2	54.07	68.85	59.63	57.04
1 9/16	6.520	8.301	7.189	6.877	4 9/16	55.59	70.78	61.29	58.62
1 5/8	7.051	8.978	7.775	7.438	4 5/8	57.12	72.73	62.98	60.25
1 11/16	7.604	9.682	8.385	8.021	4 11/16	58.67	74.70	64.70	61.83
1 3/4	8.178	10.41	9.018	8.626	4 3/4	60.25	76.71	66.44	63.55
1 13/16	8.773	11.17	9.673	9.253	4 13/16	61.84	78.74	68.25	65.19
1 7/8	9.388	11.95	10.35	9.902	4 7/8	63.46	80.81	70.05	66.92
1 15/16	10.02	12.76	11.05	10.57	4 15/16	65.10	82.89	71.81	68.64
2	10.68	13.60	11.78	11.27	5	66.76	85.00	73.61	70.42
2 1/16	11.36	14.46	12.53	11.98	5 1/16	68.44	87.14	75.53	72.20
2 1/8	12.06	15.35	13.30	12.72	5 1/8	70.14	89.30	77.37	73.93
2 3/16	12.78	16.27	14.09	13.48	5 3/16	71.86	91.49	79.35	75.79
2 1/4	13.52	17.22	14.91	14.26	5 1/4	73.60	93.72	81.16	77.63
2 5/16	14.28	18.19	15.75	15.06	5 5/16	75.37	95.96	83.15	79.45
2 3/8	15.07	19.18	16.61	15.89	5 3/8	77.15	98.23	85.13	81.40
2 7/16	15.86	20.20	17.49	16.73	5 7/16	78.95	100.5	87.14	83.28
2 1/2	16.69	21.25	18.40	17.60	5 1/2	80.77	102.8	89.07	85.20
2 9/16	17.53	22.33	19.33	18.50	5 9/16	82.62	105.2	91.18	87.15
2 5/8	18.40	23.43	20.29	19.41	5 5/8	84.49	107.6	93.24	89.10
2 11/16	19.29	24.56	21.27	20.34	5 11/16	86.38	110.0	95.35	91.08
2 3/4	20.20	25.00	22.27	21.30	5 3/4	88.29	112.4	97.35	93.13
2 13/16	21.12	26.90	23.29	22.28	5 13/16	90.22	114.9	99.58	95.17
2 7/8	22.07	28.10	24.34	23.28	5 7/8	92.17	117.4	101.7	96.20
2 15/16	23.04	29.34	25.41	24.30	5 15/16	94.14	119.9	103.9	99.26

[1] Weights are based on 489.6 lbs. per cubic foot of steel.   18-4-1 high speed steel will run about 11% heavier.   6-6-2 high speed steel will run about 3% heavier.

TABLE XLV.—WEIGHT OF ROUND, SQUARE, HEXAGON AND OCTAGON STEEL BARS PER LINEAL FOOT.[1]—(*Continued*)

Size in inches	Round	Square	Hexagon	Octagon	Size in inches	Round	Square	Hexagon	Octagon
6	96.14	122.4	106.0	101.4	9	216.3	275.4	238.5	228.1
6 1/16	98.14	125.0	108.2	103.4	9 1/16	219.3	279.3	241.9	231.2
6 1/8	100.2	127.6	110.4	105.7	9 1/8	222.4	283.2	245.4	234.6
6 3/16	102.2	130.2	112.7	107.7	9 3/16	225.4	287.0	248.6	237.5
6 1/4	104.3	132.8	115.1	109.9	9 1/4	228.5	290.9	252.2	240.8
6 5/16	106.4	135.5	117.3	112.2	9 5/16	231.5	294.9	255.4	244.0
6 3/8	108.5	138.2	119.6	114.3	9 3/8	234.7	298.9	259.0	247.5
6 7/16	110.7	140.9	122.0	116.7	9 7/16	237.9	302.8	262.4	250.8
6 1/2	112.8	143.6	124.4	118.9	9 1/2	241.0	306.8	265.7	254.2
6 9/16	114.9	146.5	126.7	121.2	9 9/16	244.2	310.9	269.4	257.4
6 5/8	117.2	149.2	129.3	123.5	9 5/8	247.4	315.0	273.8	260.8
6 11/16	119.4	152.1	131.8	125.9	9 11/16	250.6	319.1	276.6	264.2
6 3/4	121.7	154.9	134.0	128.4	9 3/4	253.9	323.2	280.1	267.6
6 13/16	123.9	157.8	136.7	130.6	9 13/16	257.1	327.4	283.6	271.0
6 7/8	126.2	160.8	139.1	133.0	9 7/8	260.4	331.6	287.4	274.6
6 15/16	128.5	163.6	141.7	135.4	9 15/16	263.7	335.8	290.8	278.0
7	130.9	166.6	144.3	138.0	10	267.0	340.0	294.4	281.7
7 1/16	133.2	169.6	146.8	140.4	10 1/16	270.4	344.3	298.4	285.3
7 1/8	135.6	172.6	149.4	142.8	10 1/8	273.8	348.5	302.2	288.8
7 3/16	137.9	175.6	152.1	145.4	10 3/16	277.1	352.9	305.6	292.1
7 1/4	140.4	178.7	154.8	148.0	10 1/4	280.6	357.2	309.6	296.9
7 5/16	142.8	181.8	157.5	150.6	10 5/16	284.0	361.6	313.4	299.4
7 3/8	145.3	184.9	160.3	153.2	10 3/8	287.4	366.0	317.0	303.0
7 7/16	147.7	188.1	162.8	156.7	10 7/16	290.9	370.4	320.8	306.8
7 1/2	150.2	191.3	165.6	158.4	10 1/2	294.4	374.9	325.0	310.5
7 9/16	152.7	194.4	168.3	160.8	10 9/16	297.9	379.4	328.6	314.1
7 5/8	155.2	197.7	171.2	163.0	10 5/8	301.4	383.8	332.5	316.8
7 11/16	157.8	200.9	174.1	166.3	10 11/16	305.0	388.3	336.5	321.6
7 3/4	160.3	204.2	176.7	168.9	10 3/4	308.6	392.9	340.5	325.4
7 13/16	163.0	207.6	179.7	171.8	10 13/16	312.2	397.5	344.3	329.2
7 7/8	165.6	210.8	182.6	174.5	10 7/8	315.8	402.1	348.4	333.0
7 15/16	168.2	214.2	185.5	177.3	10 15/16	319.5	406.8	353.5	337.0
8	171.0	217.6	188.4	180.3	11	323.1	411.4	356.3	340.8
8 1/16	173.6	221.0	191.4	182.9	11 1/16	326.8	416.1	360.7	344.7
8 1/8	176.3	224.5	194.5	185.8	11 1/8	330.5	420.9	364.7	348.5
8 3/16	179.0	228.0	197.4	188.7	11 3/16	334.3	425.5	368.8	352.4
8 1/4	181.8	231.4	200.6	191.7	11 1/4	337.9	430.3	372.6	356.3
8 5/16	184.5	234.9	203.5	194.5	11 5/16	341.7	435.1	376.7	360.2
8 3/8	187.3	238.5	206.7	197.4	11 3/8	345.5	439.9	381.2	364.3
8 7/16	190.1	242.0	209.7	200.5	11 7/16	349.4	444.8	385.6	368.3
8 1/2	193.0	245.6	212.7	203.5	11 1/2	353.1	449.6	389.5	372.2
8 9/16	195.7	249.3	215.7	206.3	11 9/16	357.0	454.5	392.8	376.5
8 5/8	198.7	252.9	219.6	209.4	11 5/8	360.9	459.5	398.2	380.6
8 11/16	201.6	256.6	222.3	212.4	11 11/16	364.8	464.4	402.7	384.7
8 3/4	204.4	260.3	225.5	215.5	11 3/4	368.6	469.4	406.6	388.6
8 13/16	207.4	264.1	228.7	218.7	11 13/16	372.6	474.4	411.1	392.8
8 7/8	210.3	267.9	232.0	221.7	11 7/8	376.6	479.5	415.7	397.2
8 15/16	213.3	271.6	235.2	224.8	11 15/16	380.6	484.5	419.5	401.4
					12	384.3	489.6	424.0	405.6

[1] Weights are based on 489.6 lbs. per cubic foot of steel.   18-4-1 high speed steel will run about 11% heavier.   6-6-2 high speed steel will run about 3% heavier.

TABLE XLVI.—WEIGHT OF FLAT STEEL BARS PER LINEAL FOOT[1]

Thickness inches	Width—inches										
	½	⅝	¾	⅞	1	1⅛	1¼	1⅜	1½	1⅝	1¾
1⁄16	.1060	.1381	.1594	.1859	.212	.2391	.2656	.292	.319	.346	.372
⅛	.2125	.2656	.3188	.3720	.4250	.4782	.5312	.585	.638	.692	.744
3⁄16	.319	.399	.478	.558	.638	.717	.797	.875	.957	1.04	1.15
¼	.425	.531	.636	.743	.850	.957	1.06	1.17	1.28	1.38	1.49
5⁄16	.531	.664	.797	.929	1.06	1.20	1.33	1.46	1.59	1.73	1.86
⅜	.638	.797	.957	1.116	1.28	1.43	1.59	1.76	1.92	2.08	2.23
7⁄16	.744	.929	1.116	1.302	1.49	1.68	1.86	2.05	2.23	2.42	2.60
½	.850	1.06	1.275	1.487	1.70	1.92	2.12	2.34	2.55	2.72	2.98
9⁄16	.957	1.20	1.434	1.674	1.92	2.15	2.39	2.63	2.87	3.11	3.35
⅝	1.06	1.33	1.594	1.859	2.12	2.39	2.65	2.92	3.19	3.46	3.72
11⁄16	1.17	1.46	1.753	2.045	2.34	2.63	2.92	3.22	3.51	3.80	4.09
¾	1.28	1.60	1.913	2.232	2.55	2.87	3.19	3.51	3.83	4.15	4.47
13⁄16	1.38	1.73	2.072	2.417	2.76	3.11	3.45	3.80	4.14	4.49	4.84
⅞	1.49	1.86	2.232	2.604	2.98	3.35	3.72	4.09	4.47	4.84	5.20
15⁄16	1.60	1.99	2.391	2.789	3.19	3.59	3.99	4.39	4.78	5.18	5.58
1	1.70	2.13	2.55	2.98	3.40	3.83	4.25	4.68	5.10	5.53	5.95
1 ⅛	1.91	2.39	2.87	3.35	3.83	4.30	4.78	5.26	5.74	6.22	6.70
1 ¼	2.12	2.66	3.19	3.72	4.25	4.79	5.31	5.85	6.38	6.91	7.44
1 ⅜	2.34	2.92	3.51	4.09	4.67	5.26	5.84	6.43	7.02	7.60	8.18
1 ½	2.55	3.19	3.83	4.47	5.10	5.74	6.38	7.02	7.65	8.29	8.93
1 ⅝	2.76	3.45	4.15	4.84	5.52	6.22	6.90	7.60	8.29	8.98	9.67
1 ¾	2.98	3.72	4.45	5.21	5.95	6.70	7.44	8.19	8.92	9.67	10.42
1 ⅞	3.19	3.99	4.79	5.58	6.38	7.17	7.97	8.77	9.57	10.36	11.15
2	3.40	4.25	5.10	5.95	6.80	7.65	8.50	9.35	10.20	11.05	11.90

Thickness inches	Width—inches										
	2	2¼	2½	2¾	3	3¼	3½	3¾	4	4¼	4½
1⁄16	.425	.478	.531	.584	.638	.691	.744	.797	.850	.904	.956
⅛	.850	.962	1.06	1.17	1.28	1.38	1.49	1.59	1.70	1.81	1.91
3⁄16	1.28	1.44	1.59	1.75	1.91	2.07	2.23	2.39	2.55	2.71	2.87
¼	1.70	1.92	2.12	2.34	2.55	2.76	2.98	3.19	3.40	3.61	3.83
5⁄16	2.12	2.39	2.65	2.92	3.19	3.45	3.72	3.99	4.25	4.52	4.78
⅜	2.55	2.87	3.19	3.51	3.83	4.15	4.47	4.78	5.10	5.42	5.74
7⁄16	2.98	3.35	3.72	4.09	4.46	4.83	5.20	5.58	5.95	6.32	6.70
½	3.40	3.83	4.25	4.67	5.10	5.53	5.95	6.38	6.80	7.22	7.65
9⁄16	3.83	4.30	4.78	5.26	5.74	6.22	6.70	7.17	7.65	8.13	8.61
⅝	4.25	4.78	5.31	5.84	6.38	6.91	7.44	7.97	8.50	9.03	9.57
11⁄16	4.67	5.26	5.84	6.43	7.02	7.60	8.18	8.76	9.35	9.93	10.52
¾	5.10	5.75	6.38	7.02	7.65	8.29	8.93	9.57	10.20	10.84	11.48
13⁄16	5.50	6.21	6.90	7.60	8.29	8.98	9.67	10.36	11.05	11.74	12.43
⅞	5.95	6.67	7.44	8.18	8.93	9.67	10.41	11.16	11.90	12.65	13.39
15⁄16	6.38	7.18	7.97	8.77	9.57	10.36	11.16	11.95	12.75	13.55	14.34
1	6.80	7.65	8.50	9.35	10.20	11.05	11.90	12.75	13.60	14.45	15.30
1 ⅛	7.65	8.61	9.57	10.52	11.48	12.43	13.39	14.34	15.30	16.26	17.22
1 ¼	8.50	9.57	10.63	11.69	12.75	13.81	14.87	15.94	17.00	18.06	19.13
1 ⅜	9.35	10.52	11.69	12.85	14.03	15.20	16.36	17.53	18.70	19.87	21.04
1 ½	10.20	11.48	12.75	14.03	15.30	16.58	17.85	19.13	20.40	21.68	22.95
1 ⅝	11.05	12.43	13.81	15.19	16.58	17.96	19.34	20.72	22.10	23.48	24.87
1 ¾	11.90	13.40	14.88	16.37	17.85	19.34	20.83	22.32	23.80	25.29	26.78
1 ⅞	12.75	14.34	15.94	17.53	19.13	20.72	22.31	23.91	25.50	27.10	28.69
2	13.60	15.30	17.00	18.70	20.40	22.10	23.80	25.50	27.20	28.90	30.60

[1] Weights are based on 489.6 lbs. per cubic foot of steel. 18-4-1 high speed steel will run about 11% heavier. 6-6-2 high speed steel will run about 3% heavier.

TABLE XLVI.—WEIGHT OF FLAT STEEL BARS PER LINEAL FOOT.[1]—
(*Continued*)

Thick-ness inches	Width—inches										
	4¾	5	5¼	5½	5¾	6	6¼	6½	6¾	7	7¼
1/16	1.01	1.06	1.116	1.169	1.222	1.275	1.328	1.381	1.434	1.487	1.540
1/8	2.02	2.13	2.232	2.338	2.444	2.550	2.656	2.762	2.869	2.975	3.081
3/16	3.03	3.19	3.35	3.51	3.67	3.83	3.99	4.14	4.30	4.46	4.62
1/4	4.04	4.25	4.46	4.67	4.89	5.10	5.31	5.53	5.74	5.95	6.16
5/16	5.05	5.31	5.58	5.84	6.11	6.38	6.64	6.90	7.17	7.44	7.70
3/8	6.06	6.38	6.69	7.02	7.34	7.65	7.97	8.29	8.61	8.93	9.25
7/16	7.07	7.44	7.81	8.18	8.56	8.93	9.29	9.67	10.04	10.41	10.78
1/2	8.08	8.50	8.93	9.35	9.77	10.20	10.63	11.05	11.48	11.90	12.32
9/16	9.09	9.57	10.04	10.52	11.00	11.48	11.95	12.43	12.91	13.39	13.86
5/8	10.10	10.63	11.16	11.69	12.22	12.75	13.28	13.81	14.34	14.87	15.40
11/16	11.11	11.69	12.27	12.85	13.44	14.03	14.61	15.20	15.78	16.36	16.94
3/4	12.12	12.75	13.39	14.03	14.67	15.30	15.94	16.58	17.22	17.85	18.49
13/16	13.12	13.81	14.50	15.19	15.88	16.58	17.27	17.95	18.65	19.34	20.03
7/8	14.13	14.87	15.62	16.36	17.10	17.85	18.60	19.34	20.08	20.83	21.57
15/16	15.14	15.94	16.74	17.53	18.33	19.13	19.92	20.72	21.51	22.32	23.11
1	16.15	17.00	17.85	18.70	19.55	20.40	21.25	22.10	22.95	23.80	24.65
1 1/8	18.17	19.13	20.08	21.04	21.99	22.95	23.91	24.87	25.82	26.78	27.73
1 1/4	20.19	21.25	22.32	23.38	24.44	25.50	26.56	27.62	28.69	29.75	30.81
1 3/8	22.21	23.38	24.54	25.71	26.88	28.05	29.22	30.39	31.56	32.72	33.89
1 1/2	24.23	25.50	26.78	28.05	29.33	30.60	31.88	33.15	34.43	35.70	36.98
1 5/8	26.25	27.63	29.01	30.39	31.77	33.15	34.53	35.91	37.99	38.67	40.05
1 3/4	28.27	29.75	31.24	32.73	34.22	35.70	37.19	38.68	40.17	41.65	43.14
1 7/8	30.28	31.87	33.47	35.06	36.65	38.25	38.85	41.44	43.03	44.63	46.22
2	32.30	34.00	35.70	37.40	39.10	40.80	42.50	44.20	45.90	47.60	49.30

Thick-ness inches	Width—inches										
	7½	7¾	8	8¼	8½	8¾	9	9½	10	10½	11
1/16	1.594	1.647	1.70	1.753	1.806	1.859	1.913	2.019	2.135	2.232	2.338
1/8	3.188	3.294	3.40	3.506	3.612	3.720	3.826	4.037	4.250	4.463	4.876
3/16	4.78	4.94	5.10	5.26	5.42	5.58	5.74	6.06	6.38	6.70	7.02
1/4	6.36	6.58	6.80	7.01	7.22	7.43	7.65	8.08	8.50	8.92	9.34
5/16	7.97	8.23	8.50	8.76	9.03	9.29	9.56	10.10	10.62	11.16	11.68
3/8	9.57	9.88	10.20	10.52	10.84	11.16	11.48	12.12	12.75	13.39	14.03
7/16	11.16	11.53	11.90	12.27	12.64	13.02	13.40	14.14	14.88	15.62	16.36
1/2	12.75	13.18	13.60	14.03	14.44	14.87	15.30	16.16	17.00	17.85	18.70
9/16	14.34	14.82	15.30	15.78	16.26	16.74	17.22	18.18	19.14	20.08	21.02
5/8	15.94	16.47	17.00	17.53	18.06	18.59	19.13	20.19	21.35	22.32	23.38
11/16	17.53	18.12	18.70	19.28	19.86	20.45	21.04	22.21	23.38	24.54	25.70
3/4	19.13	19.77	20.40	21.04	21.68	22.32	22.96	24.23	25.50	26.78	28.05
13/16	20.72	21.41	22.10	22.79	23.48	24.17	24.86	26.24	27.62	29.00	30.40
7/8	22.32	23.05	23.80	24.55	25.30	26.04	26.78	28.26	29.75	31.34	32.72
15/16	23.91	24.70	25.50	26.30	27.10	27.89	28.69	30.28	31.88	33.48	35.06
1	25.50	26.35	27.20	28.05	28.90	29.75	30.60	32.20	34.00	35.70	37.40
1 1/8	28.68	29.64	30.60	31.56	32.52	33.47	34.43	36.34	38.25	40.17	42.08
1 1/4	31.88	32.94	34.00	35.06	36.12	37.20	38.26	40.37	42.50	44.63	46.76
1 3/8	35.06	36.23	37.40	38.57	39.74	40.91	42.08	44.41	46.75	49.08	51.42
1 1/2	38.26	39.53	40.80	42.08	43.35	44.63	45.90	48.45	51.00	53.55	56.10
1 5/8	41.44	42.82	44.20	45.58	46.96	48.34	49.73	52.49	55.25	58.02	60.78
1 3/4	44.63	46.12	47.60	49.09	50.58	52.07	53.56	56.53	59.50	62.48	65.45
1 7/8	47.82	49.40	51.00	52.60	54.20	55.79	57.38	60.56	63.75	66.94	70.12
2	51.00	52.70	54.40	56.10	57.80	59.50	61.20	64.60	68.00	71.40	74.80

[1] Weights are based on 489.6 lbs. per cubic foot of steel. 18-4-1 high speed steel will run about 11% heavier. 6-6-2 high speed steel will run about 3% heavier.

INDEX